Advanced Electricity and Magnetism
for Undergraduates

Consulting Editor
Professor J. M. Cassels, M.A., Ph.D., F.R.S.
Lyon Jones Professor of Physics
University of Liverpool

Other titles in the European Physics Series
Adkins: Equilibrium Thermodynamics
Braddick: Vibrations, Waves, and Diffraction
Duffin: Electricity and Magnetism
Kamal: Problems in Particle Physics
Kibble: Classical Mechanics
Matthews: Introduction to Quantum Mechanics 2/E
Mattuck: A Guide to Feynman Diagrams in the Many-Body Problem
Squires: Practical Physics

Advanced Electricity and Magnetism
for Undergraduates

W. J. Duffin
Senior Lecturer in Physics
University of Hull

McGRAW-HILL · LONDON
New York · Sydney · Toronto · Mexico · Johannesburg · Panama

Published by
McGRAW-HILL Publishing Company Limited
MAIDENHEAD · BERKSHIRE · ENGLAND

94069

PRINTED AND BOUND IN GREAT BRITAIN

Plan of Book

Preface

With the inclusion of ever more material in the final year of undergraduate physics courses, there is a continual need to reassess the place of a classical subject like electromagnetism. On the one hand, there is no longer the time for a leisurely stroll through electrostatics and magnetostatics, nor is it proper nowadays to relegate wave aspects to a hurried treatment at the end of a long course. On the other hand, electromagnetism in general has plenty of relevance to present-day physics and for this to be exhibited, the complete Maxwell's equations and the wave equation should be developed early.

This book has been planned with these points in mind and with the hope that it will meet the requirements of the later stages of modern honours degree courses, particularly the final year. Part 1 covers as concisely as possible the basic electromagnetism from steady fields to propagation and generation of electromagnetic waves in free space. The first three chapters of this part, on steady and quasi-steady fields, are usually dealt with amply in more elementary courses, but are included here for completeness, so that the student can more easily obtain an overall picture of the whole subject growing from its initial experiments to its final generalization. By the end of Part 1, the complete Maxwell's equations and wave properties are available for dealing in more detail with more specialized topics. This part thus provides a core which can be used either as a short course in itself or as a basis for any number of extensions.

Parts 2 to 5 are important extensions of this type. Part 2 shows how we begin to tackle more complicated actual problems than the very simple cases of Part 1: chapter 5 deals with specified distributions of charge and current such as occur in atomic and nuclear models, and chapter 6 with boundary problems. Part 3 relates the electromagnetic theory to optics and then extends to cover the classical view of the interaction generally of radiation with matter. Part 4 deals with matters of more practical interest and much of this would now lie within the province of the electrical or electronic engineer. No apology is made, however, for including the material here, partly for reasons made clear in the text and partly because it is my view that too much emphasis on purely theoretical matters is as bad as too little. Part 5 is an attempt to relate classical electromagnetism to the two great modern theories of special relativity and quantum mechanics. These are not easy topics and the reader will find here that a fair amount of knowledge outside the field of electricity and magnetism is assumed.

Indeed, throughout the book the assumption is made that the reader has reached a stage of some maturity in his study of physics, and this must be my excuse for having the temerity to use the word 'advanced' in the title. Certainly, it has been taken for granted that some more elementary course in electricity and magnetism has been already pursued and that, in this, the experimental foundations have been properly laid.

It has also been my aim to make the whole treatment as direct and concise as possible so as to give the student a more homogeneous view of the subject than can be obtained from an exhaustive treatise. To achieve this, some extensions to the text are left to problems, and so the answers provided have been made more explicit than is usual.

The choice of topics in the later parts and the depth to which they are taken is a compromise between the desirable and the practicable. In many cases, it would have been pleasant to have pursued a matter more deeply, but to do so would have bordered on the province of the specialized treatise. Whether it is better to omit a topic entirely rather than deal with it somewhat superficially is always arguable. The latter course has at least the merit of making the undergraduate aware of what is going on, and in cases where I am conscious that a treatment only touches the fringes of a subject I have provided references for the reader who wishes to read more deeply.

Acknowledgements

Any author writing a book at this level is deeply indebted to many articles and texts which he has read and absorbed, and to many colleagues with whom he has discussed problems of presentation and understanding. It is not possible to do more than acknowledge a general debt to all such sources.

The later stages of the writing were carried out in the School of

Physics at the University of Sydney, and here I am specifically indebted to many people: first, to Reckitt and Colman Ltd., who, through Mr B. Reckitt, sponsored the exchange which made my visit possible; second, to my colleagues at Hull who took on extra duties during my absence; and finally to Professor Harry Messel and all those at Sydney who made my stay so enjoyable and provided me with a refuge in which I could write undisturbed.

W. J. Duffin

Hull, March, 1967
Sydney, October, 1967

Contents

Glossary of Symbols

The symbols used in this book conform generally with those recommended by the International Organization for Standardization and by the Symbols, Units, and Nomenclature Commission of the International Union of Pure and Applied Physics. The important changes made are the use of τ for volume (instead of V), $\mathbf{N}$ for the Poynting vector (instead of $\mathbf{S}$), and γ for electric conductivity (instead of σ) to avoid confusion within one equation. Vectors with circumflexes are always unit vectors, e.g., $\hat{\mathbf{x}}$. The normal and tangential components of a vector quantity are indicated respectively by the subscripts n and t or tan. A zero subscript on a field quantity indicates either an applied field due to external sources, or the amplitude of a periodically varying field.

The following list does not include symbols used temporarily in one section only; nor does it include symbols for units which are given in appendix D.

A	Area, particularly of plates and cross-sections
$\mathbf{A}$, A	Vector potential
$\mathbf{a}$, a	Acceleration
$\mathbf{a}$	4-Potential
a	Length, particularly of radii
$\mathbf{B}$, B	Magnetic flux density or induction
B	Susceptance
b	Damping constant
C	Capacitance
c	Velocity of light *in vacuo*
$\mathbf{D}$, D	Electric displacement
D	Coefficient of diffusion
d	Distance, e.g., between parallel wires

$\mathbf{E}$, E	Electric field strength; $\mathbf{E}_Q$ Electrostatic field; $\mathbf{E}_M$ Non-electrostatic field; $\mathbf{E}_P$ Electric field of polarization charges
E	Total energy
$\mathscr{E}$	Electromotive force
e	Electronic charge
$\mathbf{F}$, F	Force; local electric field
$\mathbf{G}$, G	Electromagnetic momentum density
G	Conductance
$\mathbf{H}$, H	Magnetic field strength
H	Hamiltonian
$\mathscr{H}$	Magnetomotive force
h	Planck's constant; $\hbar = h/2\pi$
h	Height
$\mathbf{I}$, I	Electric current
i	Imaginary operator, $i^2 = -1$
$\mathbf{J}$, J	Volume current density
$\mathbf{J}_s$, J_s	Surface current density
$\mathbf{j}$	4-Current density
j	Imaginary operator $= -i$
K	Kinetic energy
$\mathbf{k}$, k	Wave vector
k	Boltzmann's constant
$\mathbf{L}$, L	Angular momentum
L	Self-inductance
L	Lagrangian
L	Lorentz transformation matrix
$\mathbf{l}$, l	Length, particularly of wire or line
$\mathbf{M}$, M	Magnetization
M	Mutual inductance
M	Inversion operator
$\mathbf{m}$, m	Magnetic moment
m	Mass
$\mathbf{N}$, N	Poynting vector
N	Number of turns, conductors, etc.
N_A	Avogadro's number
$\mathbf{n}$, n	Normal to surface
n, n	Refractive index
n	Number per unit volume, length or time
$\mathbf{P}$, P	Electric polarization
P	Power

$\mathbf{p}$, p	Electric dipole moment; linear momentum
p	Operator d/dt
Q	Electric charge
$\mathbf{q}$, q	Quadrupole moment
q	Generalized co-ordinate
R	Reflecting power; resistance
$\mathscr{R}$	Magnetic reluctance
$\mathbf{R}$	Rotation operator
$\mathbf{r}$, r	Polar co-ordinate
$\mathbf{S}$, S	Surface area
$\mathbf{s}$, s	General displacement or direction in space
$\mathbf{T}$, T_θ	Torque or couple
T	Absolute temperature
t	Time
U	Potential energy; U_E Electric energy; U_M Magnetic energy; U_{EM} Electromagnetic energy
u_E, u_M, u_{EM}	Energy densities corresponding to U_E, U_M, U_{EM}
$\mathbf{V}$, V	Electric potential
V_m	Magnetic scalar potential
$\mathbf{v}$, v	Velocity; v_p Phase velocity; v_g Group velocity; v_e Energy or signal velocity
W	Work
X	Reactance
x	Cartesian co-ordinate
$\mathbf{Y}$, Y, y	Admittance
y	Cartesian co-ordinate
$\mathbf{Z}$, Z, z	Impedance
z	Cartesian co-ordinate
α	Penetration depth; polarizability
β	Ratio of velocity to c
γ	Electric conductivity; $1/(1 - \beta^2)^{1/2}$
δ	Finite difference in
ε_0	Electric constant
$\boldsymbol{\varepsilon}_r$, $\boldsymbol{\varepsilon}_r$, ε_r	Relative permittivity
θ	Polar co-ordinate; general angle
κ	Imaginary part of refractive index
λ	Wave-length; linear charge density
μ	Mobility
μ_0	Magnetic constant
μ_r	Relative permeability
ν	Frequency

ρ	Volume charge density
σ	Surface charge density; scattering cross-section
τ	Volume; relaxation time; *ict* in relativistic expressions
Φ	Magnetic flux
ϕ	Polar co-ordinate
χ_e	Electric susceptibility; χ_m Magnetic susceptibility
Ω	Solid angle
ω	Angular or circular frequency

Part 1

Basic Electromagnetism

In these first four chapters, the basic equations of classical electromagnetism are developed *ab initio*. Starting from fundamental laws, whose experimental foundations are described at length in more elementary texts, we deal first with steady electric and magnetic fields produced by charges and currents, and proceed with increasing generality to the laws governing the whole of electromagnetism with stationary media, summarized in Maxwell's equations. We end in chapter 4 by looking at some important consequences of these equations: the properties and production of electromagnetic radiation *in vacuo*, topics dealt with at some greater length than others because elementary courses are apt to omit them.

Our aim in Part 1 is to obtain a comprehensive view of electromagnetism, so that certain aspects of importance in present-day physics can be examined in more detail in succeeding parts. For this reason, the text is as direct as possible and the student is expected to tackle the problems at the ends of the chapters to gain greater familiarity with the concepts and methods. *The reader is assumed to have studied the subject to an intermediate level* and so, to avoid repetition of more elementary work, references to the author's *Electricity and Magnetism* are given where appropriate.

1

Steady electric fields

Electric field strength is defined at any point *in vacuo* as the force per unit stationary charge at the point, i.e.,

$$\mathbf{E} = \lim_{Q \to 0} \frac{\mathbf{F}}{Q} \tag{1.1}$$

and it is implicit in this definition that the sources of **E** are unaffected by the test charge Q. In this chapter, we shall be concerned with electric fields which do not vary with time or whose variation is so slow that at any instant the same laws may be assumed to apply as to a steady field (quasi-steadiness). Where necessary, we shall distinguish between electric fields that arise from charges (electrostatic fields) and those that arise from other sources, denoting the former by $\mathbf{E}_Q$ and the latter by $\mathbf{E}_M$.

1.1 Electric charges *in vacuo*

The basic law of electrostatics is formulated in terms of point charges between any two of which the force is given by Coulomb's law:

$$\mathbf{F} = \frac{QQ'}{4\pi\varepsilon_0 r^2}\,\hat{\mathbf{r}} \tag{1.2}$$

where Q and Q' are the magnitudes of the charges separated by a displacement $\mathbf{r}$, $\hat{\mathbf{r}}$ being a unit vector along $\mathbf{r}$. The universal constant ε_0 has a value depending on the units chosen for **F**, **r**, and Q, and it is assumed that the reader is familiar with either the CGS e.s.u. system in which $4\pi\varepsilon_0 = 1$ or the rationalized MKSA system in which $\varepsilon_0 = 8{\cdot}854 \times 10^{-12}$ F/m. In this book, we shall use the Sommerfeld version of the MKSA system (see *Electricity and Magnetism*, section

16.7), and for numerical examples we shall use the sufficiently accurate value $4\pi\varepsilon_0 \approx 10^{-9}/9$ F/m.

The experimental facts supporting equation (1.2) make it one of the most well-established laws of physics. It applies to interactions between atomic particles down to 10^{-12} cm and to electrons and muons down to 10^{-14} cm with no known discrepancies. It also applies to interactions between slowly moving particles although there will now, in addition, be a magnetic force (see *Electricity and Magnetism*, section 2.5 for more details of these matters).

The *principle of superposition* is also found to apply to forces given by (1.2) so that they add like vector quantities when more than two charges interact.

From (1.1) and (1.2), the electric field strength at any point a distance **r** from a charge Q is

$$\mathbf{E} = \frac{Q}{4\pi\varepsilon_0 r^2}\hat{\mathbf{r}} = \frac{Q}{4\pi\varepsilon_0 r^3}\mathbf{r} \tag{1.3}$$

and, by superposition, the resultant electric field due to *any* system of charges can be concisely expressed as

$$\mathbf{E} = \sum_i \frac{Q_i}{4\pi\varepsilon_0 r_i^{\,2}}\hat{\mathbf{r}}_i. \tag{1.4}$$

For values of r much greater than interatomic distances, the charges can usually be regarded as continuously distributed over a region and the summation in (1.4) is then carried out by splitting the distribution into elements each containing dQ and finding the contribution of a typical element to **E**. The resultant, as with point charges, would be obtained by resolving and summing, the latter process becoming an integration. The elements of charge, dQ, may be expressed as $\rho\,\mathrm{d}\tau$, $\sigma\,\mathrm{d}S$, or $\lambda\,\mathrm{d}l$, where ρ, σ, and λ are volume, surface, and line densities of charge respectively.

E as a vector field. The electric field of a system of static charges has a value at every point over certain regions of space and thus forms a vector field which can be represented pictorially by lines of force. We wish to establish those properties of **E** as a vector field that arise from its origin in Coulomb's law.

In the first place, equation (1.3) can be re-written as

$$\mathbf{E} = -\frac{Q}{4\pi\varepsilon_0}\,\mathbf{grad}\left(\frac{1}{r}\right) \tag{1.5}$$

and, therefore, since **curl grad** is always zero (equation (A.31)),

curl E = 0. By superposition, this applies to any system of charges and so

$$\mathbf{curl}\ \mathbf{E}_Q = 0 \tag{1.6}$$

where we use the symbol $\mathbf{E}_Q$ because we shall encounter steady electric fields whose **curl** is not zero. To obtain the integral form of (1.6), we consider a surface S bounded by a closed path C. The flux of **curl E** over S is zero by (1.6), and by Stokes's theorem (A.37), this is equal to the line integral of **E** along C. Thus

$$\oint_C \mathbf{E}_Q \cdot \mathrm{d}\mathbf{l} = 0 \tag{1.7}$$

round any path C *in vacuo*. This means that the work done against $\mathbf{E}_Q$ in taking a charge round a closed path is zero; or, the work done in taking a charge from one point to another in $\mathbf{E}_Q$ is independent of the path. A vector field with the properties (1.6) and (1.7) is said to be *irrotational*, since no lines of force can close on themselves in such a field. All central fields of force have these properties.

Secondly, the flux of $\mathbf{E}_Q$ over any *closed* surface S from a point charge Q inside it is, using (1.3),

$$\oint_S \mathbf{E}_Q \cdot \mathrm{d}\mathbf{S} = \oint_S \frac{Q}{4\pi\varepsilon_0} \frac{\mathbf{r} \cdot \mathrm{d}\mathbf{S}}{r^3}.$$

Since $\mathbf{r} \cdot \mathrm{d}\mathbf{S}/r^3$ is the solid angle subtended at Q by $\mathrm{d}\mathbf{S}$ (equation (A.20)), its integral over S has the value 4π and the right-hand side is therefore simply Q/ε_0. By superposition, this applies to any system of charges within S so that the total outward flux of $\mathbf{E}_Q$ over S is equal to $\sum Q/\varepsilon_0$ where $\sum Q$ is the algebraic sum of the enclosed charges. No sources *originating* lines of **E** are known other than charges and the subscript Q on **E** can therefore be dropped, giving

$$\oint_S \mathbf{E} \cdot \mathrm{d}\mathbf{S} = \sum Q/\varepsilon_0. \tag{1.8}$$

This equation is known as *Gauss's electrostatic theorem* and S as a *Gaussian surface*.

Using the divergence theorem (A.35), the surface integral is converted to the volume integral of div **E** over the region enclosed by S. At the same time, $\sum Q$ is expressed as a volume integral of charge density, giving

$$\int_\tau (\mathrm{div}\,\mathbf{E} - \rho/\varepsilon_0)\,\mathrm{d}\tau = 0.$$

The integrand must be zero since this is true for any τ, and so

$$\operatorname{div} \mathbf{E} = \frac{\rho}{\varepsilon_0} \tag{1.9}$$

known as the differential form of Gauss's theorem.

The properties of the electric fields due to charges are summarized by equations (1.6) and (1.9), namely:

$$\boxed{\mathbf{curl\ E} = 0; \qquad \operatorname{div} \mathbf{E} = \rho/\varepsilon_0.} \tag{1.10}$$

1.2 Electric potential

Because $\mathbf{E}_Q$ is irrotational, it can always be expressed as the gradient of a scalar known as the potential. It is conventional to define electric potential V so that

$$\mathbf{E}_Q = -\mathbf{grad}\ V \tag{1.11}$$

from which it follows that the component of $\mathbf{E}_Q$ in any direction $\mathbf{s}$ is given by

$$E_s = -\frac{\partial V}{\partial s} \tag{1.12}$$

and that the *potential difference* between two points is given by

$$V_B - V_A = \int_A^B -\mathbf{E}_Q \cdot \mathbf{ds}. \tag{1.13}$$

The potential V forms a scalar field determined by (1.11) except for an added constant. This constant must be fixed by choosing a zero which can conveniently be located at infinity for a finite system of charges. Thus, from (1.11) and (1.5), the potential due to a single point charge at a distance r from it is

$$V = \frac{Q}{4\pi\varepsilon_0 r} \quad \text{(zero at } \infty) \tag{1.14}$$

while the potential due to a collection of discrete charges or to a continuous distribution of charge is given by one of the following (so long as the distribution is finite):

$$V = \sum \frac{Q}{4\pi\varepsilon_0 r}; \qquad V = \int_\tau \frac{\rho\, d\tau}{4\pi\varepsilon_0 r}; \qquad V = \int_S \frac{\sigma\, dS}{4\pi\varepsilon_0 r};$$

$$V = \int_C \frac{\lambda\, dl}{4\pi\varepsilon_0 r}. \tag{1.15}$$

It should be particularly noted that the integrations are performed over the *sources* of the fields which cannot all be at the origin (see note in appendix A).

In all the expressions (1.15), V and the potential difference between any two points are single-valued because of (1.7). The potential defined above is identical with that of elementary electrostatics which is usually defined from (1.13). It is clear that V has the dimensions of work per unit charge and that its MKSA unit will be the joule/coulomb or volt: the unit of **E** from (1.12) is thus the volt/metre.

Potential due to an ideal dipole. In Fig. 1.1a, the potential at P due to the $+Q$ alone is $Q/4\pi\varepsilon_0 r$, which we shall call for the moment V_1. The potential at P due to $-Q$ is the negative of that at P′ due to $+Q$ and for a dipole small compared with **r** is thus $-(V_1 + \mathbf{ds}\,.\,\mathbf{grad}\,V_1)$—see equation (A.19). The resultant potential at P due to the dipole

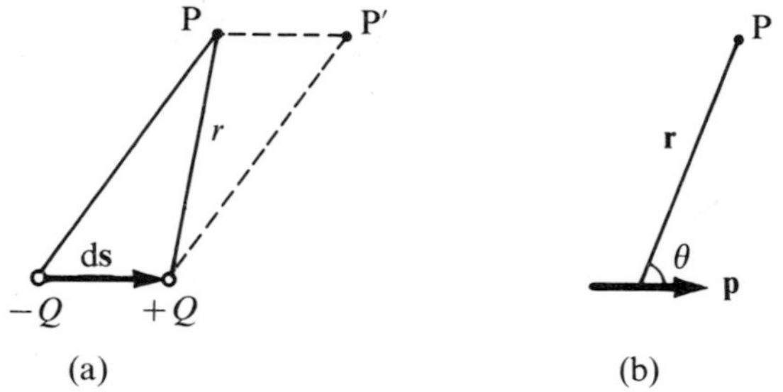

Fig. 1.1 (a) An electric dipole formed from equal and opposite charges; (b) geometry for an ideal dipole

is therefore $-\mathbf{ds}\,.\,\mathbf{grad}\,V_1$. In the limiting case of an ideal dipole, Q tends to infinity and **ds** to zero in such a way that $Q\,\mathbf{ds} = \mathbf{p}$, the dipole moment, and, since $\mathbf{grad}\,(1/r) = -\mathbf{r}/r^3$, we have

$$V_{\text{dipole}} = -\frac{\mathbf{p}\,.\,\mathbf{grad}\,(1/r)}{4\pi\varepsilon_0} = \frac{\mathbf{p}\,.\,\mathbf{r}}{4\pi\varepsilon_0 r^3} = \frac{p\cos\theta}{4\pi\varepsilon_0 r^2} \qquad (1.16)$$

using the notation of Fig. 1.1b in the last form. For an alternative method, see problem 1.9.

Poisson's and Laplace's equations. By substituting (1.11) into the general relation (1.9), we obtain div $\mathbf{grad}\,V = -\rho/\varepsilon_0$ or

$$\nabla^2 V = -\frac{\rho}{\varepsilon_0} \quad \text{Poisson's equation.} \qquad (1.17)$$

In regions where $\rho = 0$,

$$\nabla^2 V = 0 \qquad \text{Laplace's equation.} \tag{1.18}$$

These are general differential equations which must be satisfied by V due to any system of charges. Because similar equations arise in other parts of the subject we leave methods for solving them until part 2, noting only for the moment that the geometry of a problem usually determines which co-ordinate system is best used to express (1.17) or (1.18) in a form suitable for solution. Solutions of Laplace's equation are known as *harmonic functions*.

Electrostatic problems are usually best solved in terms of V, a scalar, and then using (1.11) if $\mathbf{E}_Q$ is needed. The field $\mathbf{E}_Q$ can sometimes be obtained directly, for instance by using (1.8), but usually only where a high degree of symmetry exists.

1.3 Electric currents

In section 1.4, we shall include conductors in the treatment of steady electric fields, but a few general relations must first be established concerning the movement and conservation of charge.

Consider an electric current consisting of n discrete charges per unit volume each of magnitude Q moving with a velocity $\mathbf{v}$. The current I across an area $\mathbf{S}$ is the rate of passage of charge across it so that $I = nQ\mathbf{v} \cdot \mathbf{S}$ (see *Electricity and Magnetism*, section 1.7). If ρ is the volume density of charge nQ, then $I = \rho\mathbf{v} \cdot \mathbf{S}$. When, in general, $\mathbf{v}$ and ρ are not the same at all points on $\mathbf{S}$, we must write

$$I = \int_S \rho\mathbf{v} \cdot \mathrm{d}\mathbf{S}. \tag{1.19}$$

More useful for our purpose is the current density $\mathbf{J}$ whose flux across S gives the total current so that

$$I = \int_S \mathbf{J} \cdot \mathrm{d}\mathbf{S} \tag{1.20}$$

and it therefore follows that

$$\mathbf{J} = nQ\mathbf{v} = \rho\mathbf{v}. \tag{1.21}$$

This equation may have to be generalized to $\mathbf{J} = \sum nQ\mathbf{v}$ if more than one type of particle contributes to the current: it should be made clear, in any case, that $\mathbf{v}$ is the mean drift velocity of the particles and is independent of any random velocities due to collisions.

Equation of continuity. Whether currents occur in free space or in conductors, *conservation of charge* always applies. This is a further fundamental law to add to Coulomb's law and the principle of superposition. It ensures that any decrease in total charge within a volume must be accompanied by an equal outflow across the bounding surface. It follows that the rate of decrease of charge within the volume is equal to the total current flowing outwards over the bounding surface, or, using (1.20):

$$-\frac{\mathrm{d}}{\mathrm{d}t}\int_{\tau} \rho \, \mathrm{d}\tau = \oint_{S} \mathbf{J} \cdot \mathrm{d}\mathbf{S}.$$

Hence

$$\int_{\tau} -\frac{\partial \rho}{\partial t} \, \mathrm{d}\tau = \int_{\tau} (\operatorname{div} \mathbf{J}) \, \mathrm{d}\tau$$

using Gauss's divergence theorem and changing $\mathrm{d}/\mathrm{d}t$ to $\partial/\partial t$ since ρ may depend on position as well as time and we are only concerned with time variations. Since this relation applies to any τ, we have

$$\operatorname{div} \mathbf{J} = -\frac{\partial \rho}{\partial t} \qquad (1.22)$$

known as the *equation of continuity* and expressing in a formal way the conservation of charge. (Compare the hydrodynamic equation for a moving fluid of mass density ρ: $\operatorname{div}(\rho \mathbf{v}) + \partial \rho/\partial t = 0$. This follows from the conservation of mass.)

In this chapter, we are concerned only with steady conditions for which

$$\operatorname{div} \mathbf{J} = 0 \quad \text{or} \quad \oint_{S} \mathbf{J} \cdot \mathrm{d}\mathbf{S} = 0 \quad \text{steady currents} \qquad (1.23)$$

unless there are sources of current known as *electrodes*, when $\oint \mathbf{J} \cdot \mathrm{d}\mathbf{S}$ has a non-zero value I, the strength of the electrode. (This is strictly a device for excluding from a problem the ultimate source of the current, for in practice an electrode delivering a steady current must itself be supplied from elsewhere.)

Work done by an electric field. When a current is produced by an electric field $\mathbf{E}$, the force on each moving element of charge $\mathrm{d}Q$ is $\mathbf{E}\,\mathrm{d}Q$ or $\rho\mathbf{E}\,\mathrm{d}\tau$. Now the rate of working of a force $\mathbf{F}$ whose point of application moves with a velocity $\mathbf{v}$ is $\mathbf{F} \cdot \mathbf{v}$ and so the rate at which work is done by $\mathbf{E}$ in moving the element of charge is $\rho\mathbf{E} \cdot \mathbf{v}\,\mathrm{d}\tau$ or

$\mathbf{J} \cdot \mathbf{E}\, d\tau$. In producing a finite current, the total rate of working is thus

$$P = \int_\tau \mathbf{J} \cdot \mathbf{E}\, d\tau \tag{1.24}$$

and the sources of **E** do work at the rate of $\mathbf{J} \cdot \mathbf{E}$ per unit volume in maintaining the current. *In vacuo*, this represents a transfer of energy from the sources of **E** to the charges in the form of kinetic energy: in conductors, it is a transfer to the medium as heat provided the current is steady.

1.4 Conducting media

When we come to consider media, whether conducting or insulating, we are faced sharply with the problem of *models*. If we attempt from the start to represent a medium by a collection of atoms or molecules whose structure is given by quantum-mechanical calculations, we have a problem much too complex and one in which essential features may be obscured by detail. We therefore represent media initially by smoothed-out models in which the known graininess of matter is ignored. By doing this we give up for the moment any chance of finding out in detail what is happening inside the media but, if the models are good ones, we get an accurate picture of what happens outside together with a smoothed-out picture of conditions inside.

A conducting medium will be taken simply as one in which there are charges free to move as far as its boundaries under the influence of an electric field. Two distinct steady states are considered: first when no currents flow and then when steady currents occur.

Conductors carrying static charges only. Under static conditions with no currents flowing, it is clear that at all points in and on a conductor

$$\mathbf{E} = 0; \qquad V = \text{constant} \tag{1.25}$$

and application of Gauss's theorem (1.8) then shows that any unbalanced charge can only reside on the surface. The theorem also shows that if the surface density of charge at any point is σ, the electric field strength just outside the surface has a normal component given by

$$E_n = -\partial V/\partial n = \sigma/\varepsilon_0 \tag{1.26}$$

while $\mathbf{curl}\ \mathbf{E}_Q = 0$ ensures that the tangential component outside the surface is zero, as it is inside. These are special cases of general conditions for **E** at a boundary between two media (see equation (1.46)).

The general relations (1.10) are not affected by the presence of conductors carrying no currents.

Conductors carrying steady currents. When an electric field **E** is *maintained* in a conductor, a current density **J** exists and the relation between **J** and **E** at any point takes the form

$$\mathbf{J} = \gamma\mathbf{E}. \tag{1.27}$$

This equation defines γ, the electric conductivity of the medium at the point. For many conductors γ is a scalar quantity (**J** and **E** in the same direction) and these are therefore *isotropic*. Strained materials and single crystals of substances with crystalline symmetry lower than cubic are often *anisotropic* and for these γ is a tensor of rank 2. Equation (1.27) then stands for

$$J_x = \gamma_{xx}E_x + \gamma_{xy}E_y + \gamma_{xz}E_z; \qquad J_y = \gamma_{yx}E_x + \gamma_{yy}E_y + \text{etc.} \tag{1.28}$$

In this case, (1.27) becomes a relation between column vectors (J_x, J_y, J_z) and (E_x, E_y, E_z) with γ the matrix (see appendix B):

$$\begin{pmatrix} \gamma_{xx} & \gamma_{xy} & \gamma_{xz} \\ \gamma_{yx} & \gamma_{yy} & \gamma_{yz} \\ \gamma_{zx} & \gamma_{zy} & \gamma_{zz} \end{pmatrix}.$$

Metals are *linear* or ohmic provided the temperature is held constant and γ is then independent of **E**, but this is not true of other materials. The conductivity may also be a function of position in *non-homogeneous* conductors so that (1.27) is not necessarily as innocent as it appears. We shall adopt the terminology of *Electricity and Magnetism* and refer to the common special case of linear isotropic homogeneous materials by the initials LIH.

Sources of e.m.f. produce electric fields for which **curl E** is not zero. Such fields, denoted by $\mathbf{E}_\mathrm{M}$, may exist in certain regions of conductors in addition to the $\mathbf{E}_\mathrm{Q}$ produced by charges so that (1.27) becomes, in general,

$$\mathbf{J} = \gamma(\mathbf{E}_\mathrm{M} + \mathbf{E}_\mathrm{Q}). \tag{1.29}$$

In regions where no e.m.f.s occur, $\mathbf{E}^{\mathrm{M}}$ is zero and

$$\mathbf{J} = \gamma \mathbf{E}_{\mathrm{Q}} \quad \text{(no e.m.f.s).} \tag{1.30}$$

In homogeneous conductors carrying steady currents, it is the $\mathbf{E}_{\mathrm{Q}}$ produced by charges at the electrodes of localized sources of e.m.f. which forms the electric field producing the current (see *Electricity and Magnetism*, section 6.1). Thus in such conductors the general equations for $\mathbf{E}$ are

$$\boxed{\mathbf{curl}\ \mathbf{E} = 0; \qquad \mathrm{div}\ \gamma\mathbf{E} = \mathrm{div}\ \mathbf{J} = 0} \quad \text{(steady currents)} \tag{1.31}$$

for regions from which e.m.f.s are excluded.

The first equation in (1.31) means that an electric potential function V exists and we again choose $\mathbf{E} = -\mathbf{grad}\ V$. A potential difference between two points of the conductor is then given once again by (1.13) and for a cylindrical element of LIH conductor with its length l in the direction of current flow, the potential difference between the ends is

$$V_1 - V_2 = El = Jl/\gamma = Il/\gamma A = RI \tag{1.32}$$

where R is the *resistance* $(l/\gamma A)$ of the element whose cross-section is A. Note that the conductor is not now an equipotential region so that the conditions (1.25) and (1.26) do not apply.

The second equation of (1.31) reduces for LIH media to div $\mathbf{E} = 0$. It must be emphasized that this is not a *consequence* of (1.9) but it is in agreement with (1.9) since, as problem 1.11 shows, any volume charge density dissipates very rapidly in a good conductor and we may put $\rho = 0$. Thus in LIH conductors carrying steady currents and in regions where no e.m.f.s occur we have

$$\mathbf{curl}\ \mathbf{E} = 0; \qquad \mathrm{div}\ \mathbf{E} = 0 \quad \text{and hence} \quad \nabla^2 V = 0. \tag{1.33}$$

These are precisely the same equations as those applying to a region of space containing only electric fields produced by charges outside the region (see (1.18)), and the same methods for the solutions of problems are available, as we shall see in section 6.2.

Finally, equations (1.31) imply the following boundary conditions according to appendix A (A.43) and (A.45):

$$J_{\mathrm{n}} \text{ is continuous;} \qquad E_{\mathrm{t}} \text{ is continuous.} \tag{1.34}$$

Electromotive force. In general, the e.m.f. round a closed path C is defined by

$$\mathscr{E} = \oint_C \mathbf{E} \,.\, d\mathbf{s} \tag{1.35}$$

and, by virtue of (1.7), $\mathbf{E}_Q$ gives rise to no such e.m.f. Thus the sources of $\mathbf{E}_M$ are the only non-zero sources of $\mathscr{E}$ and are designated, in general, as *sources of e.m.f.* They are non-electrostatic in origin and, in fact, represent the external sources of energy for a system. We have seen, for instance, that $\mathbf{J} \,.\, \mathbf{E}$ gives the rate of energy input per unit volume by (1.24) so that now

$$P = \int_\tau \mathbf{J} \,.\, (\mathbf{E}_M + \mathbf{E}_Q) \, d\tau.$$

The integral may be extended to cover regions where $\mathbf{J} = 0$ without changing its value, and for a finite system of currents it may extend to infinity. Problem 1.14 shows that the contribution of $\mathbf{J} \,.\, \mathbf{E}_Q$ to the integral is then zero so that

$$P = \int_{\text{space}} \mathbf{J} \,.\, \mathbf{E}_M \, d\tau \quad \text{steady currents.} \tag{1.36}$$

In a conductor, this energy is all dissipated so that the rate of production of heat per unit volume is $\mathbf{J} \,.\, \mathbf{E}$ or, using (1.27),

$$\gamma E^2 \quad \text{or} \quad J^2/\gamma. \tag{1.37}$$

Diffusion currents. In addition to currents produced by electric fields, variations in the concentration of charged particles from one point to another will produce diffusion currents of density $-De$ **grad** n, where D is the coefficient of diffusion, e the charge, and n the carrier concentration. The total current density is then given by

$$\mathbf{J} = \gamma \mathbf{E} - De \,\mathbf{grad}\, n \tag{1.38}$$

and the diffusion current may predominate in some circumstances (see problem 1.16).

1.5 Dielectric media

Our smoothed-out model of a dielectric consists of a material in which each volume element polarizes under the influence of an applied electric field. The polarization $\mathbf{P}$ at any point is defined as the dipole moment per unit volume, so that for an element $d\tau$, the dipole moment is given by

$$\mathbf{p} = \mathbf{P}\, d\tau. \tag{1.39}$$

This model is consistent with observations made with all kinds of insulating materials except that, in some instances (electrets, ferro-electrics), **P** may exist independently of any applied field.

To find the effect of such a dielectric occupying a volume τ and bounded by a surface S (Fig. 1.2), we first write the potential at the point P due to an element as follows, using (1.16):

$$dV_P = +\frac{\mathbf{p} \cdot \mathbf{grad}\,(1/r)}{4\pi\varepsilon_0} = \frac{\mathbf{P} \cdot \mathbf{grad}\,(1/r)}{4\pi\varepsilon_0}\, d\tau.$$

The change of sign from (1.16) has occurred because we now wish to integrate over the sources of the field and need the *source gradient*

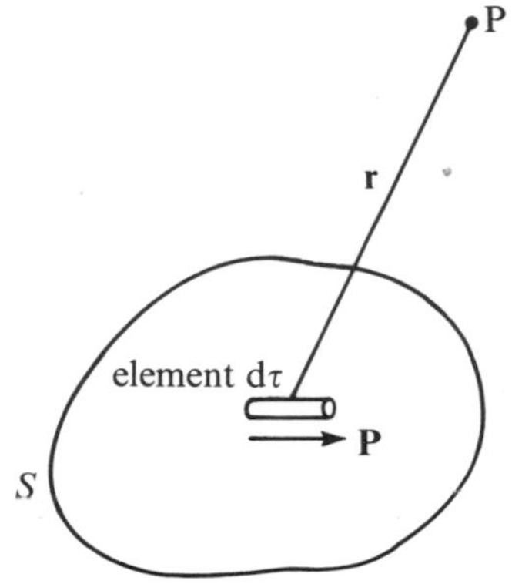

Fig. 1.2 Calculation of the potential due to a polarized dielectric

(see appendix A, equation (A.41)). Integrating over the volume τ and transforming the integrand using (A.24), we obtain

$$V_P = \frac{1}{4\pi\varepsilon_0}\left[\int_\tau \frac{-\operatorname{div}\mathbf{P}}{r}\, d\tau + \int_\tau \operatorname{div}\left(\frac{\mathbf{P}}{r}\right) d\tau\right].$$

Transforming the second term by Gauss's divergence theorem (A.35):

$$V_P = \int_\tau \frac{-\operatorname{div}\mathbf{P}}{4\pi\varepsilon_0 r}\, d\tau + \oint_S \frac{\mathbf{P} \cdot d\mathbf{S}}{4\pi\varepsilon_0 r}. \tag{1.40}$$

Comparison of (1.40) with (1.15) shows that the dielectric produces the same potential at P as a volume distribution of density $\rho_P = -\text{div}\,\mathbf{P}$ together with a surface distribution over S of surface density $\sigma_P = P_n$ or $\mathbf{P}\,.\,\hat{\mathbf{n}}$, the component of $\mathbf{P}$ normal to the surface. Together these are known as *Poisson's equivalent distribution.*

The electric field strength at P due to the dielectric will be given by the negative gradient of (1.40) and we denote this by $\mathbf{E}_P$. The total field will be the sum of any external or applied field $\mathbf{E}_0$ and $\mathbf{E}_P$:

$$\mathbf{E} = \mathbf{E}_0 + \mathbf{E}_P. \tag{1.41}$$

It is important to grasp the point that the applied field is a pre-existing field produced by some system of charges (such as those on a pair of condenser plates) and it is assumed that this system and thus $\mathbf{E}_0$ is held constant during any changes which take place in the dielectric.

The equivalent distribution can also be used for points *inside* the surface S, and we define a macroscopic field $\mathbf{E}$ within the dielectric by (1.41) where $\mathbf{E}_P$ is again the effect of ρ_P and σ_P. **Curl E** is then still zero everywhere and $\mathbf{E}$ irrotational, but since we are using a smoothed-out model the electric field so defined does not necessarily give the force on any actual charge within a real dielectric (the definition (1.1) specifically refers to a point *in vacuo*). The macroscopic $\mathbf{E}$ we have defined can be shown to be equal to the space and time average of the microscopic field (see Panofsky and Phillips, (1962), section 2.3) or to the force per unit charge in a small tubular cavity in the direction of $\mathbf{P}$ cut within the dielectric (see *Electricity and Magnetism*, section 13.8). Molecular fields are discussed further in chapter 8.

The divergence equation. It is useful to distinguish the above polarization charges of density ρ_P from conduction charges (which include those on conductors and free charges *in vacuo*) of density ρ_c. Equation (1.9) then becomes

$$\text{div}\,\mathbf{E} = \frac{\rho_c + \rho_P}{\varepsilon_0} = \frac{\rho_c - \text{div}\,\mathbf{P}}{\varepsilon_0}$$

or

$$\text{div}\,(\varepsilon_0\mathbf{E} + \mathbf{P}) = \rho_c. \tag{1.42}$$

We define the *electric displacement* $\mathbf{D}$ by

$$\mathbf{D} = \varepsilon_0\mathbf{E} + \mathbf{P} \tag{1.43}$$

and hence

$$\operatorname{div} \mathbf{D} = \rho_c \tag{1.44}$$

—only conduction charges are sources of **D**. Gauss's theorem (1.8) now becomes, on integrating (1.44) over a volume τ bounded by a surface S:

$$\oint_S \mathbf{D} \,.\, d\mathbf{S} = \sum_\tau Q_c. \tag{1.45}$$

The general laws governing fields in insulating media are thus

$$\boxed{\textbf{curl}\ \mathbf{E} = 0; \qquad \operatorname{div} \mathbf{D} = \rho_c} \tag{1.46}$$

which, by (A.43) and (A.45), imply that at any boundary

$$E_t \text{ is continuous;} \qquad D_n \text{ is discontinuous by } \sigma_c \tag{1.47}$$

where σ_c is the surface density of conduction charge at the boundary.

Electric susceptibility and permittivity. The dielectric properties of materials are determined by experiment and expressed as a relation between **P** and **E** just as those of conductors are expressed as a relation between **J** and **E**. *Electric susceptibility* χ_e is defined by putting

$$\mathbf{P} = \varepsilon_0 \chi_e \mathbf{E} \tag{1.48}$$

where χ_e is a scalar constant only for LIH materials. In electrets (permanently polarized materials), χ_e does not exist, and ferroelectrics are non-linear. Otherwise, χ_e is independent of **E**.

Substituting (1.48) in (1.43) gives

$$\mathbf{D} = \varepsilon_0(1 + \chi_e)\mathbf{E}$$

and the quantity $(1 + \chi_e)$ defines the *relative permittivity* ε_r at the point:

$$\varepsilon_r = 1 + \chi_e \tag{1.49}$$

so that

$$\mathbf{D} = \varepsilon_r \varepsilon_0 \mathbf{E}. \tag{1.50}$$

Like χ_e, ε_r is only a scalar constant for LIH materials. Some authors prefer to write ε for $\varepsilon_r\varepsilon_0$: ε is then the *permittivity* of the material.

The boundary conditions (1.47) can, in view of (1.50), be written

$$E_t \text{ is continuous;} \qquad \varepsilon_r E_n \text{ is discontinuous by } \sigma_c/\varepsilon_0 \tag{1.51}$$

or, using (1.12),

$$V \text{ is continuous}; \qquad \varepsilon_r\, \partial V/\partial n \text{ is discontinuous by } \sigma_c/\varepsilon_0. \quad (1.52)$$

It should be noted that Poisson's and Laplace's equations (1.17) and (1.18) do not retain their simple form in non-LIH media (see problem 1.17).

1.6 Electric energy and forces

Electric energy is energy possessed by a system of charges due to their relative positions and the electrostatic force (1.2). It is thus equal to their potential energy, and to evaluate this the work done in building up the system from some initial state must be found. First, however, we must agree that the charges themselves or certain elements thereof are given so that we can neglect any self-energy. We take as our system a finite collection of conduction charge distributed both as volume distributions of density ρ occupying a volume τ_c and as surface distributions on conductors with density σ: the conducting surfaces will be denoted by S_c (Fig. 1.3).

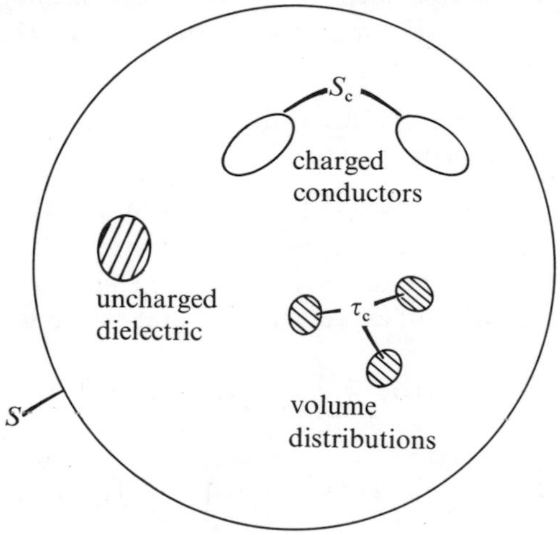

Fig. 1.3 General system for the calculation of electric energy

First, we shall assume that any dielectrics present are linear and later see the effect of non-linearity. The charges will be assembled by bringing them up in infinitesimal amounts in such a way that the volume and surface distributions increase in proportion at all times.

This can be expressed by letting the densities be $f\rho$ and $f\sigma$, where f increases from 0 to 1 as the charges grow. If the final potential at any point is V, it will be fV at an intermediate stage because of linearity. When f increases to $f + \mathrm{d}f$, the extra charges brought up are $\rho\, \mathrm{d}f\, \mathrm{d}\tau$ and $\sigma\, \mathrm{d}f\, \mathrm{d}S$ to typical elements of volume and surface, and the work done is $fV\rho\, \mathrm{d}f\, \mathrm{d}\tau$ and $fV\sigma\, \mathrm{d}f\, \mathrm{d}S$. For the whole system therefore

$$\mathrm{d}W\Big|_{f}^{f+\mathrm{d}f} = \int_{\tau_c} fV\rho\, \mathrm{d}f\, \mathrm{d}\tau + \oint_{S_c} fV\sigma\, \mathrm{d}f\, \mathrm{d}S. \tag{1.53}$$

Hence, as f increases from 0 to 1,

$$W = \int_{\tau_c} \rho V\left[\int_0^1 f\,\mathrm{d}f\right]\mathrm{d}\tau + \oint_{S_c} \sigma V\left[\int_0^1 f\,\mathrm{d}f\right]\mathrm{d}S \tag{1.54}$$

$$= \int_{\tau_c} \tfrac{1}{2}\rho V\, \mathrm{d}\tau + \oint_{S_c} \tfrac{1}{2}\sigma V\, \mathrm{d}S. \tag{1.55}$$

This expression is equivalent to the $\frac{1}{2}QV$ of elementary work. We now convert this to field quantities by using $\rho = \operatorname{div} \mathbf{D}$ and $\sigma = D_n$:

$$W = \int_{\tau_c} \tfrac{1}{2}V \operatorname{div} \mathbf{D}\, \mathrm{d}\tau + \oint_{S_c} \tfrac{1}{2}V\mathbf{D} \cdot \mathrm{d}\mathbf{S}. \tag{1.56}$$

Let the finite system be enclosed completely by a surface S (Fig. 1.3). The first integral of (1.56) may be extended to include the volume τ_0 between S and S_c without altering its value since $\rho = 0$ outside τ_c. Using identity (A.24) to express this integral as two terms:

$$W = \int_{\tau_c+\tau_0} \tfrac{1}{2} \operatorname{div}(V\mathbf{D})\, \mathrm{d}\tau - \int_{\tau_c+\tau_0} \tfrac{1}{2}\mathbf{D} \cdot \mathbf{grad}\, V\, \mathrm{d}\tau + \oint_{S_c} \tfrac{1}{2}V\mathbf{D} \cdot \mathrm{d}\mathbf{S}$$

$$= \oint_{S} \tfrac{1}{2}V\mathbf{D} \cdot \mathrm{d}\mathbf{S} - \oint_{S_c} \tfrac{1}{2}V\mathbf{D} \cdot \mathrm{d}\mathbf{S} + \int_{\tau_c+\tau_0} \tfrac{1}{2}\mathbf{D} \cdot \mathbf{E}\, \mathrm{d}\tau + \oint_{S_c} \tfrac{1}{2}V\mathbf{D} \cdot \mathrm{d}\mathbf{S}$$

using Gauss's divergence theorem to transform the volume integral to a surface integral outwards over S and *inwards* over S_c. The second and fourth terms cancel while the first tends to zero as S recedes to infinity because V decreases as $1/r$, $\mathbf{D}$ as $1/r^2$, and $\mathrm{d}\mathbf{S}$ increases as r^2:

the whole integrand thus decreases as $1/r$ and tends to zero as r tends to infinity. Thus the electric energy

$$U_E = W = \int \tfrac{1}{2}\mathbf{D} \cdot \mathbf{E}\, d\tau \tag{1.57}$$

in which the integration may now extend over the whole of space including the interior of conductors where $\mathbf{E} = 0$. It is useful to define an energy density u_E by

$$u_E = \tfrac{1}{2}\mathbf{D} \cdot \mathbf{E} = \tfrac{1}{2}\varepsilon_0 E^2 + \tfrac{1}{2}\mathbf{P} \cdot \mathbf{E}. \tag{1.58}$$

If any dielectric materials are non-linear, V will not increase linearly with ρ and σ. We can then only say, instead of (1.55), that if ρ and σ increase by $\delta\rho$ and $\delta\sigma$, the work done is

$$\delta W = \int_{\tau_c} V\, \delta\rho\, d\tau + \oint_{S_c} V\, \delta\sigma\, dS. \tag{1.59}$$

Using the same transformations to field quantities as before, we arrive at

$$\delta U_E = \delta W = \int (\mathbf{E} \cdot \delta\mathbf{D})\, d\tau \tag{1.60}$$

$$\delta u_E = \mathbf{E} \cdot \delta\mathbf{D} = \varepsilon_0 \mathbf{E} \cdot \delta\mathbf{E} + \mathbf{E} \cdot \delta\mathbf{P} \tag{1.61}$$

instead of (1.57) and (1.58). The second term of (1.61) represents the input of energy needed to increase the polarization and for a linear dielectric this would yield $\frac{1}{2}\mathbf{P} \cdot \mathbf{E}$ per unit volume after integration.

Forces and couples are often best found from the energy of a system but care must be taken to use the correct form.

Forces on conductors. The force on one of a system of conductors is easily shown to be

$$F_s = -\left(\frac{\partial U_E}{\partial s}\right)_Q = +\left(\frac{\partial U_E}{\partial s}\right)_V \tag{1.62}$$

in which U_E is best expressed in terms of coefficients of capacitance (see section 6.2 and *Electricity and Magnetism*, section 5.7). Both forms of (1.62) are consistent with $\mathbf{F} = -\mathbf{grad}\ U_E$, so that U_E plays the part of a potential energy. The outward force on the conduction charges in the surface of a conductor *in vacuo* is $\sigma^2/2\varepsilon_0$ per unit area, where σ is the surface density of charge.

Forces on dipoles. The force on an ideal dipole in a non-uniform applied electric field $\mathbf{E}_0$ is most easily obtained by considering the components p_x, p_y, p_z of its moment **p** as each consisting of two charges separated by small displacements. The expressions obtained are

$$F_x = p_x \frac{\partial E_x}{\partial x} + p_y \frac{\partial E_x}{\partial y} + p_z \frac{\partial E_x}{\partial z}; \text{ etc.} \tag{1.63}$$

which may be written as

$$\mathbf{F} = (\mathbf{p} \cdot \mathbf{grad})\mathbf{E}_0 \quad \text{or} \quad (\mathbf{p} \cdot \nabla)\mathbf{E}_0. \tag{1.64}$$

For a *permanent* dipole, **p** is constant and by (A.29) with **curl** $\mathbf{E}_0 = 0$, the force may be written

$$\mathbf{F} = \mathbf{grad}\ (\mathbf{p} \cdot \mathbf{E}_0) \quad \text{permanent dipole} \tag{1.65}$$

showing that an acceptable potential energy for such a dipole is

$$U = -\mathbf{p} \cdot \mathbf{E}_0 \quad \text{permanent dipole} \tag{1.66}$$

as given by elementary methods.

For an *induced* dipole, on the other hand, **p** is variable and (1.65) is incorrect. In that case, if the polarizability α (problem 1.24) is constant, we can write $\mathbf{p} = \alpha \mathbf{E}_0$ and (1.64) then becomes

$$\mathbf{F} = \alpha(\mathbf{E}_0 \cdot \mathbf{grad})\mathbf{E}_0 = \tfrac{1}{2}\alpha\, \mathbf{grad}\ (\mathbf{E}_0)^2 \quad \text{linear dipole} \tag{1.67}$$

so that an appropriate potential energy function would now be

$$U = -\tfrac{1}{2}\mathbf{p} \cdot \mathbf{E}_0 \quad \text{linear induced dipole.} \tag{1.68}$$

The appearance of the $\frac{1}{2}$ in (1.68) as opposed to (1.66) is characteristic of linear dependence (cf. the potential energy of a set of charges in an external field $= \sum QV$; the potential energy of a set of charges, each charge in the field of the others $= \sum \frac{1}{2}QV$).

The torque on a dipole in an electric field, whether uniform or not, is given by

$$\mathbf{T} = \mathbf{p} \times \mathbf{E}. \tag{1.69}$$

Forces on dielectrics. Each element of a polarized dielectric has a moment $\mathbf{p} = \mathbf{P}\, d\tau$ so that the force on a complete dielectric body in an external electric field $\mathbf{E}_0$ is, from (1.64),

$$\mathbf{F} = \int (\mathbf{P} \cdot \mathbf{grad})\mathbf{E}_0\, d\tau. \tag{1.70}$$

It might seem that **E** defined by (1.41) should be used here instead of

$\mathbf{E}_0$ since it is the resultant field, but we should remember the warning that it does not necessarily yield the microscopic field. In any case, however, a difference between the microscopic field and $\mathbf{E}_0$ is due to the dielectric itself and cannot contribute to the total force when integrated over the whole body. (This is not true when internal stresses in the dielectric are required, for these can arise from the effect of one part on another: this is a complex problem which we shall not consider and the reader is referred to Stratton (1941) for a general discussion.)

For an electret composed of permanent dipoles, (1.70) can be shown to result from a potential energy akin to (1.66):

$$U = -\int \mathbf{P} \cdot \mathbf{E}_0 \, d\tau \quad \text{electret.} \tag{1.71}$$

Where the dielectric is linear, however, the proportionality of $\mathbf{P}$ and $\mathbf{E}$ leads to

$$U = \int -\tfrac{1}{2}\mathbf{P} \cdot \mathbf{E}_0 \, d\tau \quad \text{linear dielectric} \tag{1.72}$$

which is akin to (1.68). One derivation of this is given in problem 1.26, but a more revealing one is as follows. The total energy of a dielectric in an external field $\mathbf{E}_0$ is the sum of three parts. The first is the mutual energy of interaction between $\mathbf{E}_0$ and the already polarized dielectric: this is $-\mathbf{P} \cdot \mathbf{E}_0$ per unit volume by (1.71). The second is the mutual energy of interaction between the individual elements of the dielectric: this is $-\frac{1}{2}\mathbf{P} \cdot \mathbf{E}_P$, where $\mathbf{E}_P$ is the field of ρ_P and σ_P and the $\frac{1}{2}$ occurs so that interactions are not counted twice. The third is the energy input needed to polarize the individual elements: this is $\frac{1}{2}\mathbf{P} \cdot \mathbf{E}$ per unit volume from (1.58). The sum of these, using (1.41), is $-\frac{1}{2}\mathbf{P} \cdot \mathbf{E}_0$ per unit volume.

The force (1.70) is also given by considering the external field to act on the equivalent distributions ρ_P and σ_P after suitable vector transformations.

PROBLEMS

1.1 Can you devise a law of electrostatic force which would be indistinguishable from the inverse square law over the range say from 10^{-13} cm to 10^{13} cm but might deviate outside the range?

1.2 Revise the calculation of $\mathbf{E}$ by the method of integrating over a source using the following example: a thin rod of length $2a$ lies along the x-axis with its mid-point at the origin and with a uniform charge of λ per unit length. Find **E** at a point a distance r along the y-axis. Why is the calculation unrealistic? For what values of r would the result be approximately correct?

1.3 Show that the equations of lines of force are given by $\mathrm{d}x/E_x = \mathrm{d}y/E_y = \mathrm{d}z/E_z$ with corresponding expressions in other co-ordinate systems. Find the equation of the lines of force of an ideal dipole.

1.4 A useful set of equipotential surfaces is yielded by two infinite parallel lines of charge densities $+\lambda$ and $-\lambda$ per unit length with negligible cross-section. If the distance between the lines is d, find the equations for the equipotentials in a plane perpendicular to the lines. Show that they form a set of circles.

1.5 Revise the use of Gauss's theorem in electrostatics by showing that **E** inside a spherical region of radius a filled with a uniform density of charge ρ is $Q\mathbf{r}/4\pi\varepsilon_0 a^3$ at **r** from its centre. Obtain the same result using Poisson's equation in spherical polars. Then show that the potential at the point is $Q(3 - r^2/a^2)/8\pi\varepsilon_0 a$ using infinity as a zero, and that the electric energy of such a sphere is $3Q^2/20\pi\varepsilon_0 a$. In all cases, Q is the total charge in the sphere. If this were a suitable model for the proton what would the electric energy in MeV be?

1.6 In the absence of charge, the field equations (1.10) for **E** reduce to **curl E** $= 0$, div **E** $= 0$. Some simple general properties of lines of force follow from these: for instance, suppose that in a region of space τ containing no charges all the lines of **E** are straight and parallel. Show that **E** must then be uniform over τ.

A straight **E** line does not necessarily mean that **E** is uniform along it. For instance, where axial symmetry exists, as in the field of a charged circular disc or loop, **E** decreases along the straight axial line of force as the distance from the charge increases. However, show that the lines of **E** in the immediate vicinity of the axis cannot also be straight.

1.7 Show that the force on a symmetrically charged sphere in any external electric field is the same as if all the charge were concentrated at the centre.

1.8 A theorem of interest in considering any system of charged particles is *Earnshaw's theorem*: a charged particle in an electrostatic field cannot rest in stable equilibrium under the action of the electrical forces alone. First, attempt to construct some simple system which might violate the theorem to convince yourself that it is plausible. Then prove it by way of an important intermediate step: show that if a spherical region of space contains no charge, the mean potential over the surface ($\bar{V} = \int V\,\mathrm{d}S/4\pi r^2 = \int V \sin\theta\,\mathrm{d}\theta\,\mathrm{d}\phi/4\pi$) is the same as that at the centre. Then show that this is violated if V is a maximum or minimum at any point not occupied by charge. Earnshaw's theorem will follow since stable equilibrium of Q in V means QV is a minimum.

1.9 The potential due to an ideal dipole can be derived in a slightly more elegant way than in section 1.2 using the idea of a source gradient (see appendix A, equation (A.41)). The dipole of Fig. 1.1a is formed by a displacement of $+Q$ by $-\mathbf{ds}$ and a reversal of sign. The potential at P is then the sum of V_{+Q} and $-(V_{+Q} - \mathbf{ds} \,.\, \mathbf{grad}_s\, V_{+Q})$, i.e., is $-\mathbf{ds} \,.\, \mathbf{grad}_f\, V_{+Q}$ as before. Use this method to find the potential due to ideal quadrupoles, etc. In particular, a linear quadrupole consists of charges $+Q$, $-2Q$, $+Q$ at the points $(-a, 0, 0)$, the origin, and $(+a, 0, 0)$ respectively. Show that the potential for $r \gg a$ is $q(3 \cos^2 \theta - 1)/4\pi\varepsilon_0 r^3$ in polar co-ordinates, where $q = Qa^2$. Find the components of $\mathbf{E}$ at (r, θ).

1.10 Compare the mean drift velocities of the electrons forming the current in a conducting wire and in a cathode-ray tube. Use typical laboratory values and look up any physical constants you need.

1.11 For poor conductors it is possible to measure both a conductivity γ and a relative permittivity ε_r. If a volume density of charge ρ_0 exists at some point in a material at time $t = 0$, show that the density at time t is given by $\rho = \rho_0 \exp(-t/\tau)$ where $\tau = \varepsilon_r\varepsilon_0/\gamma$. (Use div $\mathbf{J} = -\partial\rho/\partial t$ since currents are not steady.) τ is the *relaxation time* and determines how quickly any charge dissipates—an important matter for instance when storing inflammable liquids. Calculate relaxation times for some liquids using data from handbooks. For good conductors, τ will be much smaller. Calculate its value for copper assuming $\varepsilon_r = 1$ and see why the assumption that $\rho = 0$ is a good one under nearly steady conditions.

1.12 A copper rod of 1 mm^2 cross-section has equal and opposite charges induced at its ends by being placed in a uniform electric field. When the field is removed, the charges dissipate in a time comparable with τ in problem 1.11. If the rod is a few cm long, how is this possible in view of the answer to the first part of problem 1.10?

1.13 Current flows from one LIH conductor to another across a plane boundary. If the conductivities are γ_1 and γ_2 and the lines of current flow make angles θ_1 and θ_2 respectively with the normal to the boundary, show that $\tan \theta_1/\tan \theta_2 = \gamma_1/\gamma_2$. If γ_1 is much larger than γ_2 (the ratio can easily be 10^6 for a metal and an electrolyte), what can you say about the directions of the current flow in the two media? Show that for a metal electrode in an electrolyte the electrode possesses an almost equipotential surface.

1.14 Show that for a finite system of steady currents in LIH conductors the volume integral of $\mathbf{J} \,.\, \mathbf{E}_Q$ over all space is zero.

1.15 In solid state physics, electrochemistry and plasma physics the particulate nature of current is of more interest so that the expression (1.21) in the form $\mathbf{J} = \sum ne\mathbf{v}$ is most appropriate, n being the concentration of the carriers of the current and e their charge. The *mobility* μ of a carrier is its velocity per unit electric field. Show that the conductivity $\gamma = \sum ne\mu$ and, thus, that the conduction current in the common case of two carriers of opposite sign can be written as $\mathbf{J} = (n_+e_+\mu_+ + n_-e_-\mu_-)\mathbf{E}$.

1.16 If the concentration n of carriers in a conductor varies in the x-direction, show that the current density due to diffusion is given by $J_x = -De\,\partial n/\partial x$ where D is the coefficient of diffusion, assumed constant. D is defined as the flux of particles per unit concentration gradient. The total current in a conductor is then given by $\mathbf{J} = \gamma\mathbf{E} - De\,\mathbf{grad}\,n$. Under what conditions is diffusion likely to predominate over conduction as a migration process? Show that in a concentration cell the effective e.m.f. field is given by $\mathbf{E}_\mathrm{M} = (D/e\mu)\,\mathbf{grad}\,(\log_e n)$ where μ is the mobility.

1.17 What does Poisson's equation become for non-LIH dielectrics?

1.18 A LIH dielectric sphere of radius a and relative permittivity ε_r has electric charge of volume density ρ distributed uniformly throughout it. Find the electric potential and polarization as functions of the distance from the centre and show that the volume density of polarization charge is $\rho(1/\varepsilon_r - 1)$.

1.19 Show that an infinite slab of electret with parallel faces and with polarization everywhere perpendicular to the faces produces a zero **D** field over all space.

1.20 The simplest model of an ionic crystal is one in which the ions are regarded as point charges at their centres. It is then possible to calculate the electric or Coulomb interaction energy per unit cell of the crystal in the form $\alpha_\mathrm{M} e_1 e_2/4\pi\varepsilon_0 r_0$ where e_1 and e_2 are the charges on the ions and r_0 is the basic interionic distance. The coefficient α_M is called the *Madelung constant*, and is characteristic of the crystal structure. Although actual crystals are three-dimensional, a one-dimensional model consisting of alternate positive and negative ions of equal charge spaced at r_0 and extending to infinity is sufficient to obtain an order of magnitude. Find the Madelung constant for such a model, then see how you would tackle a three-dimensional crystal like NaCl.

1.21 A 'minimum energy' principle of some interest to applied mathematicians in the past is *Thomson's theorem*: that charges distribute themselves over conductors in such a way that the electric energy of the system is a minimum. Prove this by letting the electric field at any point with the true distribution (making the conducting surfaces equipotentials) be **E** and any other distribution be $\mathbf{E} + \mathbf{E}'$. Show that div $\mathbf{E}' = 0$ and that $\oint \mathbf{E}' \cdot \mathrm{d}\mathbf{S}$ over each conducting surface is also zero. Then show that $W' = \int \frac{1}{2}\varepsilon_0(\mathbf{E} + \mathbf{E}')^2\,\mathrm{d}\tau$ is always greater than $W = \int \frac{1}{2}\varepsilon_0 E^2\,\mathrm{d}\tau$.

1.22 By the principle of superposition two electric fields $\mathbf{E}_1$ and $\mathbf{E}_2$ at a point combine to produce a resultant field $\mathbf{E}_1 + \mathbf{E}_2$. Is the total energy density $\frac{1}{2}\varepsilon_0 E_1{}^2 + \frac{1}{2}\varepsilon_0 E_2{}^2$ or $\frac{1}{2}\varepsilon_0(\mathbf{E}_1 + \mathbf{E}_2)^2$?

1.23 Show that the electric field of an ideal dipole can be written as

$$\mathbf{E} = \frac{3(\mathbf{p}\cdot\mathbf{r})\mathbf{r}}{4\pi\varepsilon_0 r^5} - \frac{\mathbf{p}}{4\pi\varepsilon_0 r^3}$$

and hence that the mutual potential energy of two dipoles of moments $\mathbf{p}_1$ and $\mathbf{p}_2$ separated by $\mathbf{r}$ is

$$U = \frac{\mathbf{p}_1 \cdot \mathbf{p}_2}{4\pi\varepsilon_0 r^3} - \frac{3(\mathbf{p}_1 \cdot \mathbf{r})(\mathbf{p}_2 \cdot \mathbf{r})}{4\pi\varepsilon_0 r^5}.$$

What is U for coplanar dipoles making angles θ_1 and θ_2 with $\mathbf{r}$? Use the expression to find forces and couples between the dipoles and show that the system always has a resultant internal force and couple equal to zero.

1.24 Show that a particle of polarizability α (dipole moment per unit field) in an external electric field experiences a force tending to impel it towards regions of greater field strength.

1.25 Van der Waals forces in materials are short range interactions between electrically neutral parts caused by temporary or permanent polarization. For instance, take two molecules a distance r apart and suppose at some instant one of them has a dipole moment p_0. If the other has a polarizability α, show that an attractive force proportional to $\alpha p_0{}^2/r^7$ is exerted between them. If p_0 is due to oscillations within the molecule, the mean value $\bar{p}_0$ over a period of time will be zero, but $\overline{p_0{}^2}$ will not be zero so that there will be a mean attractive force. Van der Waals forces of this sort can occur in non-polar gases.

1.26 The change in energy when a dielectric is introduced into a pre-existing field is given by $-\frac{1}{2}\mathbf{P} \cdot \mathbf{E}_0$ per unit volume according to (1.72). Show that this is so by letting the original displacement and electric field be $\mathbf{D}_0$ and $\mathbf{E}_0$, and the new values $\mathbf{D}$ and $\mathbf{E}$. Then find the volume integral of $\frac{1}{2}\mathbf{D} \cdot \mathbf{E} - \frac{1}{2}\mathbf{D}_0 \cdot \mathbf{E}_0$. (Show first that the volume integrals of $\mathbf{E} \cdot (\mathbf{D} - \mathbf{D}_0)$ and $\mathbf{E}_0 \cdot (\mathbf{D} - \mathbf{D}_0)$ over all space are both zero and thus transform the change in U_E to $\int \frac{1}{2}(\mathbf{D}_0 \cdot \mathbf{E} - \mathbf{D} \cdot \mathbf{E}_0)\,\mathrm{d}\tau$.)

1.27 Show that when an infinite LIH dielectric of relative permittivity ε_r fills the whole of space between a number of isolated charged conductors the electric fields, forces, and electric energy all fall by a factor $1/\varepsilon_\mathrm{r}$. If the conductors are maintained at constant potentials, show that the forces and electric energy increase ε_r times instead, and account for the source of the energy.

1.28 Show that the energy loss per cycle per unit volume due to hysteresis in a ferroelectric is equal to the area of the **P–E** loop.

1.29 Show that if a current of density $\mathbf{J}$ flows in a poor non-homogeneous conductor, a volume density of charge accumulates given by $\rho = \varepsilon_0 \mathbf{J} \cdot \mathbf{grad}\,(\varepsilon_\mathrm{r}/\gamma)$ where ε_r is the relative permittivity and γ the conductivity. Show further that when the steady current flows across the boundary between two poor conductors, a surface density of charges accumulates given by $\varepsilon_0(\varepsilon_2/\gamma_2 - \varepsilon_1/\gamma_1)\mathbf{J} \cdot \hat{\mathbf{n}}$, where $\hat{\mathbf{n}}$ is the unit vector normal to the boundary. Explain these phenomena physically.

1.30 A horizontal electric field is applied to one arm of a vertical U-tube containing a liquid dielectric. Will the level rise or fall in this arm?

2

Steady magnetic fields

The laws governing magnetic forces between electric currents may be expressed in terms either of current elements or of small current-loop dipoles. With the first alternative we use a linear element $I\,\mathrm{d}\mathbf{l}$, where I is the current and $\mathrm{d}\mathbf{l}$ the length, or an equivalent volume element $\mathbf{J}\,\mathrm{d}\tau$, where $\mathbf{J}$ is the current density and $\mathrm{d}\tau$ the element of volume. The magnetic flux density or magnetic induction $\mathbf{B}$ at a point *in vacuo* has a direction defined by that of an element in stable equilibrium (zero force) at the point; and a magnitude defined as the force per unit element oriented perpendicular to the direction of $\mathbf{B}$. Thus $B = F/I\,\mathrm{d}l_{\perp}$ would define $\mathbf{B}$ in magnitude in a manner comparable to that for $\mathbf{E}$ in (1.1), but the following relations embody the complete definition:

$$\mathbf{F} = I\,\mathrm{d}\mathbf{l} \times \mathbf{B} = \mathbf{J} \times \mathbf{B}\,\mathrm{d}\tau. \tag{2.1}$$

If, instead, current-loop dipoles are used (as in *Electricity and Magnetism*, chapter 7), we start with a dipole of magnetic moment defined by

$$\mathbf{m} = I\,\mathrm{d}\mathbf{S} \tag{2.2}$$

where $\mathrm{d}\mathbf{S}$ is the area of the loop with a direction along the right-handed sense of the axis as determined by the current I. The direction of $\mathbf{B}$ is that of $\mathbf{m}$ when the dipole is in stable equilibrium (zero couple), and its magnitude is the couple per unit dipole oriented with its axis perpendicular to the direction of $\mathbf{B}$. Thus $B = T/m_{\perp}$ defines $\mathbf{B}$ in magnitude but the complete definition is embodied in

$$\mathbf{T} = \mathbf{m} \times \mathbf{B} = I\,\mathrm{d}\mathbf{S} \times \mathbf{B}. \tag{2.3}$$

This equation, in the form $\mathbf{T} = \mathbf{m} \times \mathbf{B}$, can be extended to any type of magnetic dipole by using it to define **m** in magnitude and direction. The two definitions of **B** in (2.1) and (2.3) are completely equivalent (as demonstrated in problem 2.2)—we choose to develop the subject in terms of current elements.

The flux of **B** over any surface S is given the special symbol Φ:

$$\Phi = \int_S \mathbf{B} \,.\, \mathrm{d}\mathbf{S} \tag{2.4}$$

and its unit in the MKSA system used in this book is the volt-second or weber (Wb). The unit of **B** is therefore the $\mathrm{Wb/m^2}$, for which the name tesla, symbol T, is now internationally recommended.

2.1 Current-carrying conductors *in vacuo*

With definition (2.1) we can complete the statement of the basic law governing magnetic interactions by quoting the magnetic flux density due to a current element. This is

$$\mathbf{B} = \frac{\mu_0 I \,\mathrm{d}\mathbf{l} \times \mathbf{r}}{4\pi r^3} = \frac{\mu_0 \mathbf{J} \times \mathbf{r}}{4\pi r^3}\,\mathrm{d}\tau \tag{2.5}$$

where μ_0 takes the value $4\pi \times 10^{-7}$ H/m in MKSA units and 4π in CGS e.m.u.

The force between two filamentary current-carrying circuits, denoted by subscripts 1 and 2, would thus be given by

$$\mathbf{F} = \oint_2 \oint_1 \frac{\mu_0 I_1 I_2 \,\mathrm{d}\mathbf{l}_1 \times (\mathrm{d}\mathbf{l}_2 \times \mathbf{r}_{12})}{4\pi r_{12}^3} \tag{2.6}$$

and this is the magnetic law corresponding to Coulomb's law in chapter 1. Direct experimental evidence for (2.6) is relatively inexact, but accurate confirmation is afforded by the agreement between measurements of current, using current balances of various designs, carried out at the national standardizing laboratories (see *Electricity and Magnetism*, chapter 16). We shall also see in chapter 11 that acceptance of the principle of special relativity would mean that the accuracy with which the electrostatic law (1.2) is known could be carried over to the magnetic law (see section 11.7).

Equation (2.5) is not directly verifiable by experiment because the field of a current element cannot be produced separately from that of the rest of the circuit, and it should be noted that any term which integrates to zero round a complete circuit could be added to (2.5) without altering (2.6). Although (2.6) is apparently not symmetrical between circuits 1 and 2, problem 2.3 shows that it is possible for the expression to be put into a symmetrical form, thus ensuring that Newton's third law (equality of action and reaction) is not violated. The considerations of this paragraph should make us cautious in extending (2.5) and (2.6) to moving charges.

The principle of superposition is found to apply to forces given by (2.6) when more than two circuits are involved so that all steady electric and magnetic interactions obey the principle.

B *as a vector field.* The magnetic flux density forms a vector field whose divergence and curl we now derive.

First, divergence. From (2.5), the value of **B** at a point *in vacuo* due to a current-carrying circuit is

$$\mathbf{B} = \oint_{\text{cct}} \frac{\mu_0 I\, \mathrm{d}\mathbf{l} \times \mathbf{r}}{4\pi r^3} = \oint_{\text{cct}} -\frac{\mu_0 I\, \mathrm{d}\mathbf{l} \times \mathbf{grad}\,(1/r)}{4\pi}. \tag{2.7}$$

Using the general vector identity (A.25), we obtain from this

$$\mathbf{B} = \oint_{\text{cct}} \left[\frac{\mu_0 I}{4\pi}\,\mathbf{curl}\,(\mathrm{d}\mathbf{l}/r) - \frac{\mu_0 I}{4\pi r}\,\mathbf{curl}\,(\mathrm{d}\mathbf{l})\right].$$

The second term is zero because **dl** does not depend on the co-ordinates of the field point and the first term yields, by changing the order of differentiation and integration:

$$\mathbf{B} = \mathbf{curl}\left(\oint_{\text{cct}} \frac{\mu_0 I\, \mathrm{d}\mathbf{l}}{4\pi r}\right). \tag{2.8}$$

The second form of (2.5) would similarly yield, for a volume distribution of currents:

$$\mathbf{B} = \mathbf{curl}\left(\int_{\tau} \frac{\mu_0 \mathbf{J}\, \mathrm{d}\tau}{4\pi r}\right) \tag{2.9}$$

and, in either case, since div **curl** is always zero,

$$\operatorname{div} \mathbf{B} = 0. \tag{2.10}$$

Because of superposition this will apply to the magnetic flux density at a point *in vacuo* due to any system of steady currents.

Second, we derive **curl B** by first forming the line integral of **B** round a closed path and then using Stokes's theorem. In Fig. 2.1, the magnetic flux density at P due to the circuit C is given by (2.7). For a small displacement ds to P′ the value of **B . ds** will thus be

$$\mathbf{B}\,.\,\mathrm{d}\mathbf{s} = \oint_C \frac{\mu_0 I\,(\mathrm{d}\mathbf{l} \times \mathbf{r})\,.\,\mathrm{d}\mathbf{s}}{4\pi r^3}$$

$$= \frac{\mu_0 I}{4\pi}\oint_C \frac{(\mathrm{d}\mathbf{s} \times \mathrm{d}\mathbf{l})\,.\,\mathbf{r}}{r^3}. \qquad (2.11)$$

The term under the integral can be interpreted as follows. If C were displaced by $-\mathrm{d}\mathbf{s}$ to C' (Fig. 2.1), $\mathrm{d}\mathbf{l}$ would trace out an area

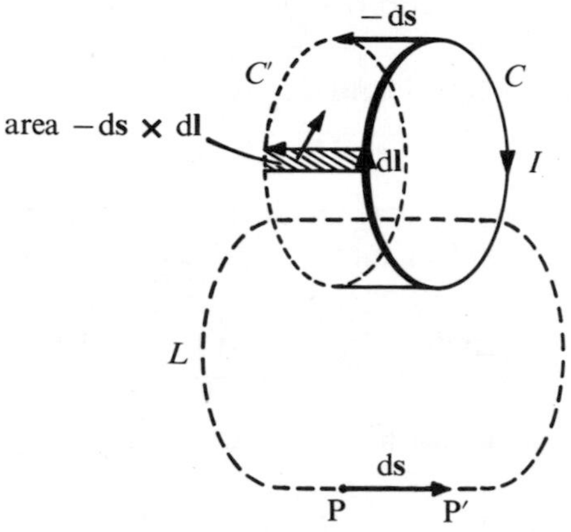

Fig. 2.1 Evaluation of the line integral of **B** due to a filamentary current-carrying circuit C

$-(\mathrm{d}\mathbf{s} \times \mathrm{d}\mathbf{l})$ and this would subtend a solid angle $\mathrm{d}^2\Omega = -(\mathrm{d}\mathbf{s} \times \mathrm{d}\mathbf{l})\,.\,\mathbf{r}/r^3$ at P by (A.20). The complete solid angle subtended at P by the area covered by C as it moves to C' is therefore the negative of the integral in (2.11). But the same geometrical relation occurs between P and C' as between P′ and C so that we may write from (2.11)

$$\mathbf{B}\,.\,\mathrm{d}\mathbf{s} = -\frac{\mu_0 I\,\mathrm{d}\Omega}{4\pi} \qquad (2.12)$$

where $\mathrm{d}\Omega$ is the change in solid angle produced by a movement of P to P′ with C stationary. If the line integral of **B** is evaluated round a closed path L encircling C, then Ω will change by 4π and hence

$$\oint_L \mathbf{B}\,.\,\mathrm{d}\mathbf{s} = \mu_0 I. \qquad (2.13)$$

For the sign to be positive, the path L must encircle I according to the right-hand screw rule (a simple way of remembering this is to realize that the line integral must be positive if L follows a magnetic line of force always in the positive direction). Equation (2.13) is often known as *Ampère's circuital theorem* and the path L as an *Amperian path.*

Using Stokes's theorem, (A.37), the left-hand side of (2.13) is converted into a surface integral of **curl B** over the surface S bounded by L. At the same time, I is written as the flux of **J** over S so that

$$\int_S (\mathbf{curl\ B} - \mu_0 \mathbf{J}) \cdot \mathrm{d}\mathbf{S} = 0$$

for *any* surface S. The integrand must therefore be zero and

$$\mathbf{curl\ B} = \mu_0 \mathbf{J}. \qquad (2.14)$$

The properties of the magnetic fields of steady currents *in vacuo* are thus summarized by equations (2.10) and (2.14), namely

$$\boxed{\mathrm{div}\ \mathbf{B} = 0; \qquad \mathbf{curl\ B} = \mu_0 \mathbf{J}.} \qquad (2.15)$$

Taking the divergence of both sides of (2.14) yields div $\mathbf{J} = 0$ as in (1.23).

2.2 Magnetic potentials

The only universal potential which can be used as a result of (2.15) arises from the solenoidal nature of **B** (i.e., its zero divergence), and it is a vector potential. Under certain circumstances, however, a scalar potential may be used and we look at this first.

Magnetic scalar potential. A quantity V_m may be defined such that

$$\mathbf{B} = -\mu_0\,\mathbf{grad}\ V_m \quad \text{and} \quad B_s = -\mu_0\,\partial V_m/\partial s \qquad (2.16)$$

so that by (2.10)

$$\nabla^2 V_m = 0. \qquad (2.17)$$

It would also follow that between two points A and B in the field

$$V_{mB} - V_{mA} = \int_A^B -\mathbf{B} \cdot \mathrm{d}\mathbf{s}/\mu_0. \qquad (2.18)$$

By equations (2.16) and (2.12) we should find that, for a small displacement of the field point near a current-carrying circuit

$$\mathrm{d}V_m = -\mathbf{B} \cdot \mathrm{d}\mathbf{s}/\mu_0 = I\,\mathrm{d}\Omega/4\pi \qquad (2.19)$$

and it follows that we could use as a scalar potential

$$V_m = \frac{I\Omega}{4\pi} \tag{2.20}$$

for the purpose of calculating **B** at a point *in vacuo* due to a complete current-carrying circuit, Ω being the solid angle subtended at the field point by the circuit. This method (discussed in chapter 8 of *Electricity and Magnetism*) leads to the concept of an equivalent magnetic shell, since a sheet of magnetized material whose periphery coincides with the circuit gives the same V_m as (2.20) provided it is everywhere magnetized perpendicular to its plane with a magnetic moment per unit area equal to I.

The scalar potential is, nevertheless, severely limited in its applications. First, it is clear by virtue of (2.13) that V_m cannot be single-valued even when a zero is chosen—it will have an infinity of values all differing by multiples of I. Second, it follows from (2.16) that **curl B** $= 0$ since **curl grad** is always zero. This contradicts the general law (2.14) unless $\mathbf{J} = 0$. Hence V_m cannot be used at points within materials carrying volume currents.

The main reason why a scalar potential is used at all is that it makes certain magnetic problems identical in mathematical form with electrostatic ones as we shall see in chapter 6. Thus, a small current loop of moment $\mathbf{m} = I\,\mathrm{d}\mathbf{S}$ subtends a solid angle $(\mathrm{d}S\cos\theta)/r^2$ at a distant point, θ being the angle between **m** and **r**. By (2.20), the scalar potential due to an ideal magnetic dipole is thus

$$V_m = \frac{I\,\mathrm{d}S\cos\theta}{4\pi r^2} \tag{2.21}$$

and therefore

$$V_m = \frac{m\cos\theta}{4\pi r^2} = \frac{\mathbf{m}\cdot\mathbf{r}}{4\pi r^3} = -\frac{\mathbf{m}\cdot\mathbf{grad}\,(1/r)}{4\pi} \tag{2.22}$$

as in (1.16). **B** can then be obtained by using (2.16).

Magnetic vector potential. The relation div $\mathbf{B} = 0$ is universally true for steady fields and **B** may therefore be expressed always as the **curl** of some vector **A**, known as the magnetic vector potential.

$$\mathbf{B} = \mathbf{curl}\,\mathbf{A}. \tag{2.23}$$

It will be remembered that scalar potentials, both electrostatic and magnetic, are undetermined by an additive constant which can be chosen as convenient—the choice corresponds to fixing a zero. The vector potential is similarly undetermined, for if $\mathbf{A}_1$ is one possible potential then so is $\mathbf{A}_2 = \mathbf{A}_1 + \mathbf{grad}\, f$ where f is any differentiable scalar field.

Now, if we compare (2.23) with (2.8), we see that

$$\mathbf{A} = \oint_C \frac{\mu_0 I \, \mathrm{d}\mathbf{l}}{4\pi r} \tag{2.24}$$

is an adequate expression for the vector potential due to a filamentary current-carrying circuit C. For surface or volume distributions of current:

$$\mathbf{A} = \int_S \frac{\mu_0 \mathbf{J}_s \, \mathrm{d}S}{4\pi r} \quad \text{and} \quad \mathbf{A} = \int_\tau \frac{\mu_0 \mathbf{J} \, \mathrm{d}\tau}{4\pi r} \tag{2.25}$$

where we must remember that the integrations are carried out over the *sources* (see Appendix A and problem 2.5). Each cartesian component of the second equation of (2.25) is of the form of V in (1.15), and like V will therefore satisfy Poisson's equation in the form $\nabla^2 A_x = -\mu_0 J_x$, etc. We may therefore say that our choice makes $\mathbf{A}$ satisfy

$$\nabla^2 \mathbf{A} = -\mu_0 \mathbf{J}. \tag{2.26}$$

In co-ordinate systems other than cartesian, (2.26) is still true but by (A.34) can only mean

$$\mathbf{grad}\, \mathrm{div}\, \mathbf{A} - \mathbf{curl}\, \mathbf{curl}\, \mathbf{A} = -\mu_0 \mathbf{J}.$$

From (2.23) and (2.14) we see that $\mathbf{curl}\, \mathbf{curl}\, \mathbf{A} = \mu_0 \mathbf{J}$ and hence $\mathbf{grad}\, \mathrm{div}\, \mathbf{A} = 0$. This means that div $\mathbf{A}$ forms a uniform scalar field with a constant value which does not affect $\mathbf{B}$. We therefore choose

$$\mathrm{div}\, \mathbf{A} - 0 \tag{2.27}$$

a choice resulting from the decision to use (2.24) or (2.25) without a **grad** f added. We shall see that there is always a certain freedom in the choice of potential functions yielding quite definite fields, a freedom used to make equations as simple and as useful as possible.

The great power of the vector potential lies in problems concerning radiation and further development of electromagnetic theory rather than in finding **B** due to current distributions. In general, finding **A** from (2.24), (2.25), or (2.26) is difficult and **B** is often better calculated from the scalar potential above where possible or from the current element formula (2.7).

Vector potential of a magnetic dipole. For future use, we shall calculate the vector potential of an ideal magnetic dipole using the notation of Fig. 2.2. From (2.24) the vector potential at P is

$$\mathbf{A} = \frac{\mu_0 I}{4\pi}\oint_C \frac{\mathrm{d}\mathbf{l}}{r} = -\frac{\mu_0 I}{4\pi}\int_S \left(\mathbf{grad}\,\frac{1}{r}\right) \times \mathrm{d}\mathbf{S}$$

using identity (A.38) with $V = 1/r$. The gradient is clearly taken here

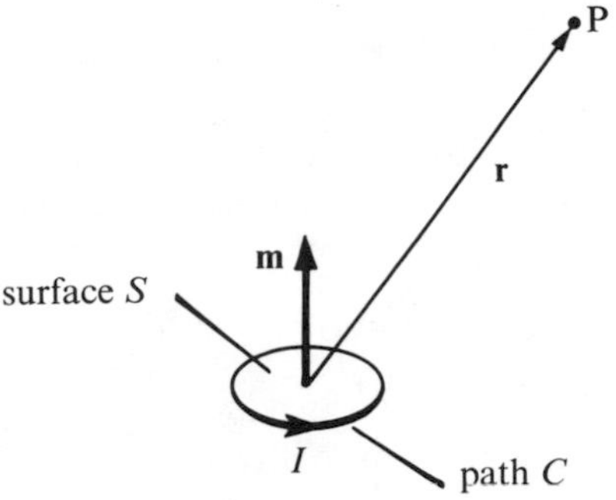

Fig. 2.2 Calculation of the vector potential due to an ideal magnetic dipole

with respect to the source co-ordinates, and so we must change the sign if we want **A** in terms of field co-ordinates. Moreover, if the circuit is small compared with the distances **r**, the gradient of $1/r$ will not change appreciably over the surface S and in the limit may be taken outside the integral. Hence

$$\mathbf{A} = \frac{\mu_0}{4\pi}\,\mathbf{grad}\,(1/r) \times \int_S I\,\mathrm{d}\mathbf{S}$$

and since $\mathbf{m} = \int I\,\mathrm{d}\mathbf{S}$ is the magnetic dipole moment of the loop, and $\mathbf{curl}\,\mathbf{m} = 0$:

$$\mathbf{A} = -\frac{\mu_0}{4\pi}\mathbf{m} \times \mathbf{grad}\,(1/r) = \frac{\mu_0 \mathbf{m} \times \mathbf{r}}{4\pi r^3} = \mathbf{curl}\,(\mu_0 \mathbf{m}/4\pi r). \qquad (2.28)$$

2.3 Magnetic media

Magnetized media are characterized by a magnetization **M** defined as the magnetic dipole moment per unit volume. For an element of volume $\mathrm{d}\tau$, the dipole moment is therefore given by

$$\mathbf{m} = \mathbf{M}\,\mathrm{d}\tau. \qquad (2.29)$$

Once again this is a smoothed-out model which corresponds with observations made on all kinds of materials. **M** may arise under the influence of external applied magnetic fields, but can exist independently of such fields in ferromagnetic and ferrimagnetic materials.

We now carry out an analysis similar to that in section 1.5 to find the effect of a piece of magnetized material and we again use Fig. 1.2 with **M** replacing **P**. The vector potential at the point P due to an element of material is, by (2.28) and (2.29)

$$\mathbf{A} = \frac{\mu_0}{4\pi}\mathbf{M} \times \mathbf{grad}_s\,(1/r)\,\mathrm{d}\tau \tag{2.30}$$

where the sign has changed once more since we wish to integrate over source points. Using (A.25) and integrating over the volume of material:

$$\mathbf{A} = \frac{\mu_0}{4\pi}\int_\tau \left[\frac{\mathbf{curl\,M}}{r} - \mathbf{curl}\,(\mathbf{M}/r)\right]\mathrm{d}\tau. \tag{2.31}$$

Transforming the second term to a surface integral using (A.36),

$$\mathbf{A} = \int_\tau \frac{\mu_0\,\mathbf{curl\,M}}{4\pi r}\,\mathrm{d}\tau + \oint_S \frac{\mu_0\mathbf{M}\times\mathrm{d}\mathbf{S}}{4\pi r}. \tag{2.32}$$

Comparison of (2.32) with (2.25) shows that the material behaves as if it were a combination of volume currents of density $\mathbf{J}_\mathrm{M} = \mathbf{curl\,M}$

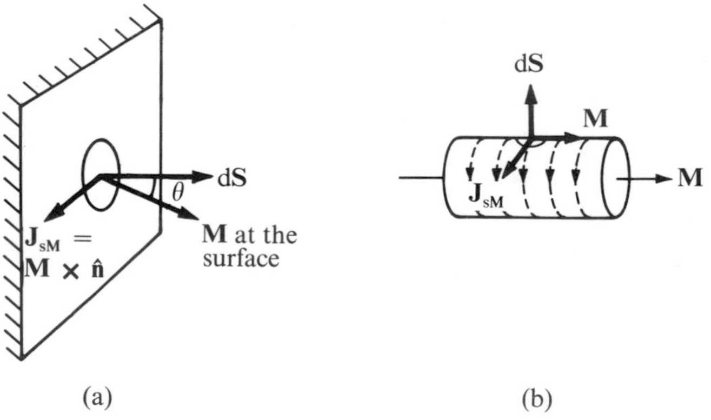

Fig. 2.3 Equivalent surface magnetization currents. In (a) the equivalent current is tangential to the surface and has a magnitude $M \sin\theta$; (b) shows the situation in a uniformly magnetized material in which $\mathbf{J}_\mathrm{M} = \mathbf{curl\,M} = 0$ and the whole material can be replaced by surface currents

and surface currents of density $\mathbf{J}_{sM} = \mathbf{M} \times \hat{\mathbf{n}}$, where $\hat{\mathbf{n}}$ is the unit vector normal to the surface, and of magnitude $M \sin \theta$ (see Fig. 2.3). The equivalent distributions

$$\mathbf{J}_M = \mathbf{curl\ M}; \qquad \mathbf{J}_{sM} = \mathbf{M} \times \hat{\mathbf{n}} \tag{2.33}$$

play the same part in magnetism as Poisson's distribution in electrostatics (see also problem 2.9 for equivalent pole distribution).

Magnetic field strength. We now see how the presence of magnetic materials affects the general relations (2.15). The magnetic flux density at any point, inside or outside material, is now defined as arising from both conduction currents $\mathbf{J}_c$ (giving an applied flux density $\mathbf{B}_0$) and magnetization currents $\mathbf{J}_M$ and $\mathbf{J}_{sM}$ (giving a magnetization flux density $\mathbf{B}_m$), so that

$$\mathbf{B} = \mathbf{B}_0 + \mathbf{B}_m. \tag{2.34}$$

The vector potential exists for all the currents—given by (2.25) for $\mathbf{J}_c$ and by (2.32) for $\mathbf{J}_M$ and $\mathbf{J}_{sM}$. $\mathbf{B}$ thus remains solenoidal with no sources, i.e., div $\mathbf{B} = 0$ still. We now have, however, that

$$\mathbf{curl\ B} = \mu_0(\mathbf{J}_c + \mathbf{J}_M) = \mu_0(\mathbf{J}_c + \mathbf{curl\ M})$$

or

$$\mathbf{curl}\left(\frac{\mathbf{B}}{\mu_0} - \mathbf{M}\right) = \mathbf{J}_c.$$

The magnetic field strength $\mathbf{H}$ is defined by

$$\mathbf{H} = \frac{\mathbf{B}}{\mu_0} - \mathbf{M} \tag{2.35}$$

and so

$$\mathbf{curl\ H} = \mathbf{J}_c. \tag{2.36}$$

The properties of magnetic fields due to steady currents in the presence of magnetic media are therefore summarized by

$$\boxed{\text{div}\ \mathbf{B} = 0; \qquad \mathbf{curl\ H} = \mathbf{J}_c.} \tag{2.37}$$

The units of $\mathbf{H}$ and $\mathbf{M}$ in the MKSA system are both the A/m.

The integral forms corresponding to (2.37) are easily obtained in the usual way by integrating over a volume or a surface and using

Gauss's divergence theorem and Stokes's theorem. The relations are

$$\oint_S \mathbf{B} \cdot \mathrm{d}\mathbf{S} = 0 \tag{2.38}$$

$$\oint_C \mathbf{H} \cdot \mathrm{d}\mathbf{s} = I_c \tag{2.39}$$

where S is any closed surface and C is any closed path encircling a conduction current I_c. These two are respectively the magnetic form of Gauss's electrostatic theorem (absence of monopoles) and the generalized Ampère's circuital theorem. The quantity $\oint \mathbf{H} \cdot \mathrm{d}\mathbf{s}$ is often known as the *magnetomotive force* (m.m.f.) by analogy with e.m.f.

Magnetic susceptibility and permeability. For most materials there is a relation between **M** and **H** in the medium expressed by

$$\mathbf{M} = \chi_m \mathbf{H} \tag{2.40}$$

where χ_m is a scalar constant, the *magnetic susceptibility*, in LIH materials but otherwise has the same types of variation as χ_e. From (2.35) and (2.40):

$$\mathbf{B} = \mu_0(1 + \chi_m)\mathbf{H} \tag{2.41}$$

and if we define the *relative permeability* of a material by

$$\mu_r = 1 + \chi_m \tag{2.42}$$

then

$$\mathbf{B} = \mu_r\mu_0\mathbf{H}. \tag{2.43}$$

Equations (2.40)–(2.43) should not be applied to ferromagnetic materials without care.

Boundary conditions. Equations (2.37) imply that at any boundary

$$B_n \text{ is continuous} \tag{2.44}$$

$$H_t \text{ is discontinuous by } J_{sc}\text{, the surface density of conduction current.} \tag{2.45}$$

Discontinuities in **M** can be treated as if they were sources of **H** (because div **H** = −div **M**) known as *poles* (see problems 2.9 and 2.11).

2.4 Energy and forces in magnetic systems

To calculate the energy associated with electric currents and their magnetic interactions, we have to assemble the currents in some way, either by moving them to their final positions or by making them grow to their final magnitudes rather as we did with electric charge in section 1.6. Either method involves time variations in magnetic flux linking the various circuits and produces electromagnetic induction, dealt with in the next chapter. At this stage, therefore, questions about magnetic energy cannot be answered fully and we shall deal only with the more restricted question of potential energy U, from which forces and couples may be obtained using

$$F_s = -\partial U/\partial s \quad \text{or} \quad \mathbf{F} = -\mathbf{grad}\, U; \qquad T_\theta = -\partial U/\partial \theta. \quad (2.46)$$

In calculating U, we are concerned only with the work done by an external mechanical force in changing the position or configuration of the system, and ignore any extra energy input needed to form the various dipoles and currents initially or to maintain them constant—these are matters for the next chapter.

Currents in vacuo and in linear media. The force exerted by a magnetic field of flux density **B** on a current-carrying circuit is, by (2.1)

$$\mathbf{F} = I\oint_C (\mathrm{d}\mathbf{l} \times \mathbf{B}) \quad (2.47)$$

and an external force will have to do work

$$\mathrm{d}W = -\mathbf{F}\,.\,\mathrm{d}\mathbf{s} = -I\oint_C (\mathrm{d}\mathbf{l} \times \mathbf{B})\,.\,\mathrm{d}\mathbf{s}$$

in displacing the circuit by ds. If the multiple product is changed:

$$\mathrm{d}W = -I\oint_C \mathbf{B}\,.\,(\mathrm{d}\mathbf{s} \times \mathrm{d}\mathbf{l}) = -I\int_{S'} \mathbf{B}\,.\,\mathrm{d}\mathbf{S}$$
$$= -I\Phi_{\mathrm{in}}$$

where S' is the curved surface traced out by the movement of the circuit and Φ_{in} is the magnetic flux crossing S' from outside to inside. Problem 2.14 shows that $+\Phi_{\mathrm{in}}$ is equal to the change in flux linking the circuit itself, $\mathrm{d}\Phi = (\Phi_{\mathrm{final}} - \Phi_{\mathrm{initial}})$, and so

$$\mathrm{d}U = \mathrm{d}W = -I\,\mathrm{d}\Phi \quad (2.48)$$

where Φ is the external magnetic flux linking the circuit. Thus a suitable U for such a circuit is

$$U = -I\Phi \tag{2.49}$$

and forces and torques on the circuit will be given by

$$F_s = I\frac{\partial \Phi}{\partial s}; \qquad T_\theta = I\frac{\partial \Phi}{\partial \theta} \tag{2.50}$$

from which it can be seen that a circuit always tends to move in such a way as to link a greater external flux.

The external field giving rise to Φ has a flux density $\mathbf{B}_0$ given by the **curl** of a vector potential $\mathbf{A}_0$ and so Φ can be written

$$\Phi = \int_S \mathbf{B}_0 \cdot d\mathbf{S} = \int_S (\mathbf{curl}\ \mathbf{A}_0) \cdot d\mathbf{S}$$

$$= \oint_C \mathbf{A}_0 \cdot d\mathbf{l} \tag{2.51}$$

where the surface S spans the circuit C. If now the external flux is due to a second circuit labelled 2 (our original circuit being labelled 1), then by (2.24)

$$\mathbf{A}_0 = \oint_2 \frac{\mu_0 I_2\, d\mathbf{l}_2}{4\pi r_{12}} \tag{2.52}$$

and hence the mutual potential energy of two current-carrying circuits is

$$U = -I_1 I_2 \oint_1 \oint_2 \frac{\mu_0\, d\mathbf{l}_2 \cdot d\mathbf{l}_1}{4\pi r_{12}}. \tag{2.53}$$

The geometrical quantity

$$M = \oint_1 \oint_2 \frac{\mu_0\, d\mathbf{l}_2 \cdot d\mathbf{l}_1}{4\pi r_{12}} \tag{2.54}$$

is clearly symmetrical under an interchange of the subscripts and is known as the *mutual inductance* between the circuits. Formula (2.54) is known as Neumann's formula. It follows that for two circuits

$$U = -MI_1 I_2 \tag{2.55}$$

and

$$F_s = I_1 I_2 \frac{\partial M}{\partial s}; \qquad T_\theta = I_1 I_2 \frac{\partial M}{\partial \theta}. \tag{2.56}$$

Comparison of (2.55) with (2.49) shows that M is the magnetic flux linking either circuit due to unit current in the other, i.e., that

$$\Phi_1 = MI_2; \qquad \Phi_2 = MI_1 \tag{2.57}$$

and the unit of M is the Wb/A, called the henry H.

In linear magnetic media, expressions for forces, torques, and mutual inductance all increase by a factor μ_r in the numerator.

Permanent dipoles and magnetic materials. A small current loop in an external magnetic flux density $\mathbf{B}_0$ has a potential energy given by (2.49):

$$U = -\int I\mathbf{B}_0 \,.\, \mathrm{d}\mathbf{S}.$$

If the loop is small enough, the variation of $\mathbf{B}_0$ over it is negligible and U may be written

$$U = -\mathbf{B}_0 \,.\, \int I \,\mathrm{d}\mathbf{S} = -\mathbf{m} \,.\, \mathbf{B}_0 \tag{2.58}$$

where $\mathbf{m}$ is the magnetic dipole moment. The force on such a dipole in a non-uniform field is thus given by $\mathbf{F} = \mathbf{grad}\,(\mathbf{m} \,.\, \mathbf{B}_0)$ and because $\mathbf{m}$ is not a function of the co-ordinates and curl $\mathbf{B}_0 = 0$ in the region, (A.27) gives

$$\mathbf{F} = (\mathbf{m} \,.\, \mathbf{grad})\, \mathbf{B}_0 \tag{2.59}$$

as for an electric dipole. Thus we obtain the same formula as if we had treated the dipole as two monopoles, and the x-component of it is

$$F_x = m_x \frac{\partial B_{0x}}{\partial x} + m_y \frac{\partial B_{0x}}{\partial y} + m_z \frac{\partial B_{0x}}{\partial z}. \tag{2.60}$$

For an element of magnetic material, (2.29) gives $\mathrm{d}U = -\mathbf{M} \,.\, \mathbf{B}_0 \,\mathrm{d}\tau$ and for a finite volume

$$U = -\int_{\text{space}} \mathbf{M} \,.\, \mathbf{B}_0 \,\mathrm{d}\tau \tag{2.61}$$

since outside the material $\mathbf{M} = 0$. For linear materials, $\mathbf{M}$ can be replaced by $\chi_m\mathbf{H}$ where $\mathbf{H}$ is the magnetic field strength *inside* the material and is *not* $\mathbf{B}_0/\mu_r\mu_0$. Any further extension of these formulae to find forces on materials must be made with care.

2.5 Moving charges

The formulae developed throughout this chapter have involved steady fields at all points in space. If we regard a steady current as a collection of moving charges with volume density ρ and mean velocity $\mathbf{v}$, then $\mathbf{J} = \rho\mathbf{v}$ from (1.21), and the force on any element in a field $\mathbf{B}$ would be, from (2.1):

$$\mathbf{F} = \rho\mathbf{v} \times \mathbf{B}\, d\tau = Q\mathbf{v} \times \mathbf{B} \tag{2.62}$$

where Q is the total charge in the volume element. Corresponding expressions can be obtained from other formulae in this chapter by substituting $\rho\mathbf{v}$ for $\mathbf{J}$ or $Q\mathbf{v}$ for $I\, d\mathbf{l}$. For instance, (2.5) gives the flux density due to a moving charge element as

$$\mathbf{B} = \frac{\mu_0 \rho\mathbf{v} \times \mathbf{r}}{4\pi r^3}\, d\tau = \frac{\mu_0 Q\mathbf{v} \times \mathbf{r}}{4\pi r^3}. \tag{2.63}$$

The assumption in (2.62) and (2.63) is, however, that the formulae will be used for integrating over continuous steady currents and any extension of them to isolated charges may not be justified. A moving isolated charge constitutes a non-stationary system and must be treated by the methods of chapter 4. Thus (2.63) turns out to be an approximation for low velocities, though (2.62) is known to be accurate when applied to a single charge Q.

The complete force on a charge or charge element *in vacuo* is given by the Lorentz force formula

$$\mathbf{F} = Q(\mathbf{E} + \mathbf{v} \times \mathbf{B}) = (\rho\mathbf{E} + \mathbf{J} \times \mathbf{B})\, d\tau \tag{2.64}$$

which must be regarded as an independent postulate or derived using the special principle of relativity (chapter 11).

Formulae (2.64) are sufficient to calculate trajectories of charged particles in any combinations of steady $\mathbf{E}$ and $\mathbf{B}$. For any current consisting of moving charges we see that the rate of working of any fields producing the motion must be $\mathbf{F} \cdot \mathbf{v}$ where $\mathbf{F}$ is given by (2.64). This is $\rho(\mathbf{E} + \mathbf{v} \times \mathbf{B}) \cdot \mathbf{v}$ per unit volume. The second term is zero and so

$$P = \int \rho\mathbf{v} \cdot \mathbf{E}\, d\tau = \int \mathbf{J} \cdot \mathbf{E}\, d\tau$$

as in (1.24). No work is done by the magnetic field, which always produces a force perpendicular to the velocity.

PROBLEMS

2.1 There is great similarity between the treatments in chapters 1 and 2. Prepare a list of the major differences between steady electric and magnetic fields.

2.2 Show that the definition of **B** through $\mathbf{F} = I\,d\mathbf{l} \times \mathbf{B}$ leads to a torque $\mathbf{T} = \mathbf{m} \times \mathbf{B}$ on an infinitesimally small current loop of moment $\mathbf{m} = I\,d\mathbf{S}$. This shows the equivalence of (2.1) and (2.3).

2.3 Under what circumstances are $\mathbf{A} \times (\mathbf{B} \times \mathbf{C})$ and $\mathbf{B} \times (\mathbf{A} \times \mathbf{C})$ equal? Show that the forces between two current elements (integrand of (2.6)) are not in general equal and opposite. Expand the multiple vector product and show that when integrated round the two complete circuits as in (2.6), the forces on circuits 1 and 2 are equal and opposite.

2.4 A uniform magnetic flux density $\mathbf{B}_0$ has only a z-component. Show that a suitable vector potential in cylindrical co-ordinates is $A_r = 0, A_z = 0$, $A_\theta = rB_0/2$. Express **A** also in terms of (a) cartesian co-ordinates, (b) the position vector **r** from the origin 0. What shape are the lines of **A**?

2.5 Surface current density $\mathbf{J}_s$ is not such a familiar quantity as volume current density **J**. $\mathbf{J}_s$ is defined as the current per unit length in a thin sheet (see *Electricity and Magnetism*, section 1.7) and is necessary when considering equivalent current distributions as in section 2.3 above. Show that the various forms for the vector potential in (2.24) and (2.25) are equivalent and in particular note the meaning of dS in (2.25).

2.6 An infinite plane current sheet has a uniform surface current density $\mathbf{J}_s$. Find the magnetic flux density outside the sheet. If the current is flowing in the surface of a semi-infinite conductor, check that the boundary conditions (2.44) and (2.45) are satisfied.

2.7 Show that the vector potential at a point a distance R from the centre of a finite straight wire of length $2L$ and carrying a current I is $(\mu_0 I/2\pi)\log_e[p + (1 + p^2)^{1/2}]$ where $p = L/R$. Hence show that **B** tends to $\mu_0 I/2\pi R$ as L tends to infinity, even though **A** itself tends to infinity.

2.8 Find the vector potential A_z due to two parallel infinite straight currents I flowing in the $+z$ and $-z$ directions. Hence show that the cross-sections through equipotential surfaces are the same as those of V in problem 1.4. Show, on the lines of problem 1.3, that the equations of lines of **B** are $\mathbf{B}\,.\,\mathbf{grad}\,A_z = 0$ and thus that the lines of **B** are the curves A_z = constant.

2.9 The derivation of the equivalent distribution in section 2.3 could be carried out on lines *exactly* similar to those in chapter 1 by using the scalar potential (2.22) instead of (2.30). Carry through this calculation and show that the magnetic material can also be replaced by a volume distribution of sources $\rho_m = -\text{div}\,\mathbf{M}$ together with a surface distribution $\sigma_m = M_\perp$. By analogy with electrostatics, define **H** as a field whose sources are ρ_m and show that the usual formulae follow. (Sources of **H** form magnetic *poles*.)

2.10 Find the magnetic field strength and flux density due to a sphere of radius a with a permanent uniform magnetization $\mathbf{M}$. Take the field point both inside and outside the sphere.

2.11 Sketch the $\mathbf{B}$ and $\mathbf{H}$ fields of the sphere in problem 2.10. If the magnetization is induced by an external flux density $\mathbf{B}_0$ instead of being permanent, show that the internal $\mathbf{B}$ field in an isotropic homogeneous ferromagnetic is always in the same direction as that of $\mathbf{B}_0$, while the internal $\mathbf{H}$ field is always in the opposite direction.

2.12 Use the answers to problem 2.10 for the following: (a) show that the same $\mathbf{B}$ and $\mathbf{H}$ fields as in problem 2.10 would be produced by an unmagnetized sphere with a surface density of charge σ rotating with an angular velocity $M/\sigma a$; (b) how should the windings on a spherical former be spaced to produce a uniform magnetic field within the former?

2.13 Show that round a tube of magnetic flux of cross-section A, the m.m.f. is equal to the product of flux and reluctance where the reluctance is defined as $\sum l/\mu_r \mu_0 A$ round the tube (magnetic circuit). Draw the analogy between the magnetic circuit and electric circuit, emphasizing where the analogy breaks down.

2.14 Prove that when a rigid circuit moves in a magnetic field the flux of $\mathbf{B}$ cut by the moving circuit is equal and opposite to the change in flux linking the circuit.

2.15 Show that equation (2.53) follows from problem 2.3.

2.16 Equation (2.59) or (2.60) could be obtained by treating the dipole as two poles, i.e., there is assumed to be extension along the direction of $\mathbf{m}$. In fact, a current-loop dipole only has extension in directions perpendicular to $\mathbf{m}$. How then does the force arise?

2.17 Treating a thin cylindrical beam of electrons as a continuous charge distribution, find the electric and magnetic fields at a distance r from the axis of the beam at points inside it and hence find the resultant focusing or defocusing force. (Density of electrons n, charge e, velocity v.)

2.18 Show that the kinetic energy K of a charged particle moving in a magnetic field of flux density $\mathbf{B}$ is a constant of the motion and that, if $\mathbf{B}$ is uniform, the kinetic energies parallel to $\mathbf{B}$ ($K_{\parallel}$) and perpendicular to $\mathbf{B}$ ($K_{\perp}$) are separately constant. Show that the orbit in a uniform $\mathbf{B}$ field is, in general, a helix and that the orbital magnetic moment of the particle has a magnitude $K_{\perp}/B$ and a direction opposite to that of $\mathbf{B}$.

2.19 A convergent magnetic field has axial symmetry about the z-axis, so that $B_\phi = 0$, and the variation $\partial B_z/\partial z$ is constant. Show that to a first order a charged particle still moves in a helix and experiences a force which acts towards the weaker field. Show that the *mirror effect* occurs and that the flux linking the orbit and the magnetic moment of the charge in its orbit are constants of the motion.

2.20 Show that the motion of a charged particle in a uniform electric field **E** and a uniform magnetic flux density **B** at right angles ($\mathbf{E} \cdot \mathbf{B} = 0$) is a combination of circular motion about the direction of **B** as axis and a *plasma drift velocity* $(\mathbf{E} \times \mathbf{B})/B^2$ independent of the type of particle.

2.21 A particle has a magnetic moment **m** and an angular momentum **L** related by $\mathbf{m} = \gamma \mathbf{L}$. Show that it will precess in a uniform **B** field with the Larmor precession frequency $\omega_L = -\gamma \mathbf{B}$. Show that the Larmor frequency for an orbiting electron is half the cyclotron frequency $\omega_c = eB/m$.

2.22 Show that for a collection of permanent magnets (i.e., no conduction currents anywhere) the integral of $\mathbf{B} \cdot \mathbf{H}$ over all space is zero and that, therefore, $\frac{1}{2}\mathbf{B} \cdot \mathbf{H}$ is not a correct expression in this case for the energy density.

2.23 Argue that the potential energy of a set of permanent magnets in each others field is given not by (2.61) but by $U = -\int \frac{1}{2}\mathbf{M} \cdot \mathbf{B}\, d\tau$. Using problem 2.22, show that this is equivalent to an energy density $B^2/2\mu_0$.

2.24 Check that the scalar magnetic potential (2.22) and the vector potential (2.28) due to a magnetic dipole of moment **m** give the same **B** at the point (r, θ).

3

Slowly-varying currents

The first two chapters were concerned entirely with stationary phenomena and we now turn to situations in which variations with time occur. Any equations obtained must be generalizations of those already established, in the sense that the new must reduce to the old when all time variations are equated to zero. In this chapter, we shall see the effect of allowing currents and their associated magnetic fields to vary slowly with time. The term 'slowly' is qualitative, but is taken to mean that conditions are effectively steady or *quasi-steady*, i.e., that at any instant time variations are slow enough for conducting and insulating media to possess equilibrium values for all varying quantities. The law which is particularly concerned with quasi-steadiness is (1.22): $\operatorname{div} \mathbf{J} = -\partial\rho/\partial t$. In this chapter, we assume that $\operatorname{div} \mathbf{J}$ is so much greater than $-\partial\rho/\partial t$ that the steady current law is valid: $\operatorname{div} \mathbf{J} = 0$. All currents are thus to be solenoidal with no sources. We shall see in chapter 4 what this condition means physically.

We end by considering motional e.m.f.s and induced currents in slowly moving conductors.

3.1 Electromagnetic induction in stationary media

An e.m.f. is generated in any closed path whenever there is a change of magnetic flux across it, and if the path passes through conducting material an induced current flows. The changes in flux may occur because the circuit is stationary and $\mathbf{B}$ varies with time (*changing-field* or *transformer e.m.f.s*), or because the circuit is moving through a steady $\mathbf{B}$ (*motional e.m.f.s*) or both. We defer the consideration of motional e.m.f.s until section 3.5, noting only for the moment that the magnitude of both types of e.m.f. are well established experimentally, the highest accuracy occurring in the Lorenz disc determination of resistance and in phenomena involving alternating currents in self- and mutual inductances. While it is possible to deduce the existence of motional e.m.f.s from the steady current laws, that of changing-field e.m.f.s cannot be deduced without invoking relativistic principles or something equivalent (see *Electricity and Magnetism*, chapter 9). We therefore state as a fundamental law that the e.m.f. induced in a rigid closed conducting circuit which is stationary in a magnetic field is given by

$$\mathscr{E} = -\frac{\partial \Phi}{\partial t} \tag{3.1}$$

where Φ is the instantaneous magnetic flux linking the circuit C. If the surface spanning C is S, then (3.1) may be written

$$\oint_C \mathbf{E} \cdot d\mathbf{s} = \int_S -\frac{\partial \mathbf{B}}{\partial t} \cdot d\mathbf{S} \tag{3.2}$$

using (1.35). These integral forms of the law of electromagnetic induction can be put into differential form by a transformation of the left-hand side with Stokes's theorem (A.37):

$$\int_S \left(\mathbf{curl\ E} + \frac{\partial \mathbf{B}}{\partial t} \right) \cdot d\mathbf{S} = 0 \tag{3.3}$$

for any surface S. The integrand must therefore be zero and

$$\mathbf{curl\ E} = -\frac{\partial \mathbf{B}}{\partial t} \tag{3.4}$$

which reduces to the first equation of (1.46) in the absence of time variations. By taking the divergence of both sides and using the fact that div **curl** is always zero, we have $\partial(\text{div}\ \mathbf{B})/\partial t = 0$ showing that div **B** at any point is constant in time. Since we know that div $\mathbf{B} = 0$ when there are no time variations, we equate the constant to zero:

$$\text{div}\ \mathbf{B} = 0. \tag{3.5}$$

Although the original e.m.f. occurred round a conducting path, the differential form (3.4) refers to **E** and **B** *in vacuo* as well, and in any case the presence of an e.m.f. round a closed path does not need a conductor any more than the electric field of (1.1) needs the test charge. Thus, these formulae apply to any points *in vacuo* or in conductors and we may summarize the properties of electric and magnetic fields in any media for slowly-varying currents by

$$\boxed{\begin{aligned} \operatorname{div} \mathbf{B} &= 0; \qquad & \mathbf{curl\ H} &= \mathbf{J} \\ \operatorname{div} \mathbf{D} &= \rho; \qquad & \mathbf{curl\ E} &= -\frac{\partial \mathbf{B}}{\partial t}. \end{aligned}} \tag{3.6}$$

3.2 Vector and scalar potentials

We can still define a vector potential **A** satisfying

$$\mathbf{B} = \mathbf{curl\ A} \tag{3.7}$$

but (3.4) now yields $\mathbf{E} = -\partial \mathbf{A}/\partial t$ + a quantity whose **curl** is zero, i.e., a quantity of the form **grad** f, where f is a scalar field. Since, for static fields, we want $\mathbf{E} = -\mathbf{grad}\ V$ where V satisfies Poisson's equation, we must have

$$\mathbf{E} = -\frac{\partial \mathbf{A}}{\partial t} - \mathbf{grad}\ V. \tag{3.8}$$

If the divergence of both sides is taken and we use $\operatorname{div} \mathbf{E} = \rho/\varepsilon_r\varepsilon_0$ and Poisson's equation for V in LIH media, $\nabla^2 V = -\rho/\varepsilon_r\varepsilon_0$, we find that $\partial(\operatorname{div} \mathbf{A})/\partial t$ is zero and by the same argument as that leading to (3.5):

$$\operatorname{div} \mathbf{A} = 0. \tag{3.9}$$

It is then easily shown, using $\mathbf{curl\ H} = \mathbf{J}$, that both **A** and V obey Poisson's equations as they did in chapters 1 and 2.

The above analysis shows that in the approximation now being used, the magnetic flux density **B** and magnetic field **H** have the same sources and vortices as in chapter 2, but that **E** is a superposition of the electrostatic field given by $\mathbf{E}_Q = -\mathbf{grad}\ V$, whose sources are charges, and the induced electric field $\mathbf{E}_M = -\partial \mathbf{A}/\partial t$, whose vortices are time-varying magnetic fields and in which **A** is given by (2.24) or (2.25).

3.3 Magnetic energy

We return now to the problem of the energy associated with the magnetic interaction between currents, and choose an approach equivalent to that used for charges in chapter 1: we find the input of energy needed when the currents in the system grow from zero to their final value. At a point where the current density is **J** there will, in general, be an electric field $\mathbf{E}_M$ from e.m.f.s due to changing magnetic fields, an irrotational field $\mathbf{E}_Q$ arising from charges and an electric field $\mathbf{E}_M'$ due to external sources of e.m.f. Both $\mathbf{E}_M$ and $\mathbf{E}_M'$ are non-electrostatic fields, but $\mathbf{E}_M'$ is solely responsible for the input of energy from outside the system.

The conduction current at any point is now given by

$$\mathbf{J} = \gamma(\mathbf{E}_M' + \mathbf{E}_M + \mathbf{E}_Q). \tag{3.10}$$

Taking the scalar product of both sides with **J** and rearranging:

$$\mathbf{J} \cdot \mathbf{E}_M' = J^2/\gamma - \mathbf{J} \cdot (\mathbf{E}_M + \mathbf{E}_Q). \tag{3.11}$$

The term on the left gives the rate at which energy is supplied to the system from external sources (equation (1.24)) and the first term on the right gives the rate of dissipation of energy as heat (equation (1.37)), both per unit volume. The final term thus gives the rate of energy storage in the system and since $\mathbf{E}_M + \mathbf{E}_Q$ is the field **E** given by (3.8) and appearing in (3.6), we may write for the magnetic energy U_M

$$\frac{\mathrm{d}U_M}{\mathrm{d}t} = \int -\mathbf{J} \cdot (\mathbf{E}_M + \mathbf{E}_Q)\,\mathrm{d}\tau = \int -\mathbf{J} \cdot \mathbf{E}\,\mathrm{d}\tau. \tag{3.12}$$

The volume τ may extend over the whole of space if the system of currents is finite since the contribution to the integral is zero where $\mathbf{J} = 0$. For steady currents, problem 1.14 showed that the contribution of $\mathbf{E}_Q$ to the integral is then zero and so under quasi-steady conditions we may simply put

$$\frac{\mathrm{d}U_M}{\mathrm{d}t} = \int -\mathbf{J} \cdot \mathbf{E}_M\,\mathrm{d}\tau. \tag{3.13}$$

U_M in terms of **B** *and* **H**. Substituting $\mathbf{J} = \mathbf{curl\,H}$ into (3.12) and using (A.26)—$\mathrm{div}\,(\mathbf{E} \times \mathbf{H}) = \mathbf{H} \cdot \mathbf{curl\,E} - \mathbf{E} \cdot \mathbf{curl\,H}$,

$$\frac{\mathrm{d}U_M}{\mathrm{d}t} = \int_\tau \mathbf{H} \cdot \frac{\partial \mathbf{B}}{\partial t}\,\mathrm{d}\tau + \oint_S (\mathbf{E} \times \mathbf{H}) \cdot \mathrm{d}\mathbf{S} \tag{3.14}$$

where S is the surface bounding τ. The last term tends to zero as S recedes to infinity since **E** decreases at least as $1/r^2$, **H** at least as $1/r^2$ while $\mathrm{d}\mathbf{S}$ increases as r^2 (note that this will not be true with radiation fields). Thus, for an increment of current the rate of storage of magnetic energy can be written as the integral over all space of $\mathbf{H} \cdot \partial\mathbf{B}/\partial t$ or

$$\delta U_{\mathrm{M}} = \int_{\mathrm{space}} (\mathbf{H} \cdot \delta\mathbf{B})\, \mathrm{d}\tau. \tag{3.15}$$

For linear systems in which $\mathbf{B} = \mu_r\mu_0\mathbf{H}$, the integration from zero currents to final values can be carried out and (3.15) yields

$$U_{\mathrm{M}} = \int_{\mathrm{space}} \tfrac{1}{2}\mathbf{B} \cdot \mathbf{H}\, \mathrm{d}\tau \quad \text{linear systems} \tag{3.16}$$

which is analogous to (1.55).

U_{M} in terms of sources. The $\mathbf{E}_{\mathrm{M}}$ in (3.13) is the $-\partial\mathbf{A}/\partial t$ term of (3.8) and thus we can write the increment of U_{M} as

$$\delta U_{\mathrm{M}} = \int \mathbf{J} \cdot \delta\mathbf{A}\, \mathrm{d}\tau \tag{3.17}$$

instead of (3.15) and again for linear systems this can be integrated to

$$U_{\mathrm{M}} = \int \tfrac{1}{2}\mathbf{J} \cdot \mathbf{A}\, \mathrm{d}\tau \quad \text{linear systems.} \tag{3.18}$$

We now confine ourselves to linear systems while converting this to a form suitable for use when the currents flow in filamentary circuits. For the kth circuit, $I_k = \int \mathbf{J} \cdot \mathrm{d}\mathbf{S}$ integrated over the cross-section S_k of the filament. The volume integral of (3.18) separates into a line integral round the circuit and a surface integral over S_k, so that for this circuit

$$U_{\mathrm{M}k} = \oint_C \int_{S_k} \tfrac{1}{2}\mathbf{J} \cdot \mathbf{A}\, \mathrm{d}S\, \mathrm{d}l = \oint_C \int_{S_k} \tfrac{1}{2}JA\cos\theta\, \mathrm{d}S\, \mathrm{d}l$$

$$= \tfrac{1}{2}I \oint_C \mathbf{A} \cdot \mathrm{d}\mathbf{l}. \tag{3.19}$$

The integral, by (2.51), is the magnetic flux linking the kth circuit—now, however, from all sources in the system including the kth circuit itself. Hence

$$U_{\mathrm{M}} = \sum_k \tfrac{1}{2}I_k\Phi_k \quad \text{linear systems.} \tag{3.20}$$

For non-linear systems, we should only have been able to say that

$$\delta U_{\mathrm{M}} = \sum_k I_k\, \delta\Phi_k. \tag{3.21}$$

The flux in (3.20) can be expressed as the sum of a self-flux Φ_{kk} and mutual fluxes Φ_{jk} for the kth circuit, where

$$\Phi_{kk} = L_k I_k; \qquad \Phi_{jk} = M_{jk} I_j. \tag{3.22}$$

L_k is the *self-inductance* of the kth circuit and M_{jk} is the mutual inductance between the jth and kth (compare (2.57)). In linear systems, $M_{jk} = M_{kj}$ and (3.20) can then be written

$$U_M = \sum_k \tfrac{1}{2} L_k I_k^2 + \sum_k \sum_j M_{jk} I_j I_k \quad \text{linear systems.} \tag{3.23}$$

This expression can be obtained more directly and the previous ones derived from it (see *Electricity and Magnetism*, section 9.8).

Mutual inductance may be calculated from the geometrical expression (2.54) or from (3.22). The same series of steps from (2.51) onwards applied to the self-flux of a circuit would yield

$$L_{kk} = \oint_k \oint_k \frac{\mu_0 \, \mathbf{dl}_k \, . \, \mathbf{dl}_k}{4\pi r_{kk}} \tag{3.24}$$

but this becomes infinite for truly filamentary currents and L must be calculated using (3.22) or by equating the magnetic energy $\frac{1}{2}LI^2$ to that calculated from the volume integral of $\frac{1}{2}\mathbf{B} \, . \, \mathbf{H}$ (see problem 3.8).

3.4 Induced currents in stationary conductors

In a stationary conductor of conductivity γ, the e.m.f. set up by a changing $\mathbf{B}$ field produces a current density $\mathbf{J}$ related to $\mathbf{E}$ by $\mathbf{J} = \gamma\mathbf{E}$. We now obtain a differential equation satisfied by these induced currents when the medium is linear isotropic and homogeneous. From $\mathbf{curl\ E} = -\partial\mathbf{B}/\partial t$, we have

$$\mathbf{curl\ curl\ E} = -\partial/\partial t\,(\mathbf{curl\ B}) = -\partial(\mathbf{curl}\ \mu_r\mu_0\mathbf{H})/\partial t = -\mu_r\mu_0\mathbf{J}.$$

Thus, using (A.34), replacing $\mathbf{E}$ by $\mathbf{J}/\gamma$ and from the quasi-steady condition div $\mathbf{J} = 0$, we have

$$\nabla^2\mathbf{J} = \mu_r\mu_0\gamma\,\frac{\partial\mathbf{J}}{\partial t} \tag{3.25}$$

and the same equation is clearly obeyed by $\mathbf{B}$ and $\mathbf{E}$. This is a diffusion type equation governing the spread and decay of currents and fields throughout the conductor.

By considering a one-dimensional case with an alternating field of angular frequency ω, it is easily shown from (3.25) that the amplitude of the current density will fall off with distance x from a plane conducting surface according to the law

$$\mathbf{J} = \mathbf{J}_0\, e^{-x/\alpha}. \tag{3.26}$$

Here $\mathbf{J}_0$ is the current density at the surface and α is the *penetration depth* given by

$$\alpha = (2/\mu_r\mu_0\gamma\omega)^{1/2} \tag{3.27}$$

(see problem 3.1). Clearly the fields will obey the same law, and at high frequencies in good conductors will be confined to a thin layer near the surface. This is the *skin effect*, considered further in section 7.4.

The skin effect is accentuated by high conductivity. In the limit of perfect conduction ($\gamma = \infty$), there can be no finite current density within the material unless $\mathbf{E} = 0$ everywhere inside it. In that case, $\partial\mathbf{B}/\partial t$ must be zero by (3.6) so that the magnetic flux density could never change: it would be kept constant by surface currents. Superconductors approximate to this condition but go further and always have $\mathbf{B} = 0$, a condition which cannot be deduced from Maxwell's equations. This complete expulsion of all magnetic fields on achieving the superconducting state is known as the *Meissner effect*.

3.5 Moving conductors and magnetohydrodynamics

Accurate treatment of moving systems requires the use of special relativity which is considered in some detail in chapter 11. Here, we look at a first order treatment accurate for velocities much less than that of light.

When a conductor moves through a magnetic flux density $\mathbf{B}$, any charge within it experiences a force $Q(\mathbf{v} \times \mathbf{B})$ by (2.62), $\mathbf{v}$ being the velocity of the conductor in the immediate vicinity of the charge. Thus, *in the frame of reference of the conductor*, an electric field $\mathbf{E}'$ given by

$$\mathbf{E}' = \mathbf{v} \times \mathbf{B} \tag{3.28}$$

exists at every point. Note, particularly, that $\mathbf{v}$ and $\mathbf{B}$ are measured in the laboratory frame. Round a closed path in the conductor, there is therefore an e.m.f.

$$\mathscr{E}_m' = \oint (\mathbf{v} \times \mathbf{B}) \cdot d\mathbf{s} \tag{3.29}$$

known as a *motional e.m.f.* This can be used as a current-element type formula or can be expressed as rate of flux cut by the circuit in question (see *Electricity and Magnetism*, section 9.2), and these forms are useful when only a part of a circuit moves, as in the Lorenz disc. We note that it is not necessary for all parts of the conductor to have the same **v** for these formulae to apply so that a filamentary circuit need not be rigid.

Now, consider cases where a conductor moves through a time-varying **B** so that we expect both motional and transformer e.m.f.s to occur. In general, the electric field at any point is the sum of (a) any electrostatic field present given by $\mathbf{E}_Q = -\mathbf{grad}\, V$, which is assumed to be the same in the frame of the conductor as in the laboratory frame, (b) a field $\mathbf{E}_M = -\partial\mathbf{A}/\partial t$ due to the time-varying **B** also assumed the same in both frames (true at low velocities), (c) the field given by (3.28) which only appears in the conductor's frame. Thus

$$\mathbf{E}' = -\frac{\partial \mathbf{A}}{\partial t} - \mathbf{grad}\, V + (\mathbf{v} \times \mathbf{B}) = \mathbf{E} + (\mathbf{v} \times \mathbf{B}) \qquad (3.30)$$

where **E** and **E′** are the electric fields in the frames of the laboratory and conductor respectively. The e.m.f. round a path C in the conductor is

$$\begin{aligned}\mathscr{E}' &= \oint_C \mathbf{E}' \cdot d\mathbf{s} = \oint_C \mathbf{E} \cdot d\mathbf{s} + \oint_C (\mathbf{v} \times \mathbf{B}) \cdot d\mathbf{s} \\ &= \int_S (\mathbf{curl}\, \mathbf{E}) \cdot d\mathbf{S} + \oint_C \mathbf{B} \cdot (d\mathbf{s} \times \mathbf{v}) \\ &= \int_S -\frac{\partial \mathbf{B}}{\partial t} \cdot d\mathbf{S} + \oint_C \mathbf{B} \cdot (d\mathbf{s} \times \mathbf{v}) \qquad (3.31)\end{aligned}$$

where C bounds the area S and both move with the conductor. If Φ is the flux of **B** over S at any instant, the first term on the right can be written as $-\partial\Phi/\partial t$ (reversing the order of differentiation and integration) provided the rate of change in the area S is small compared with the rate at which C sweeps out area. The second term gives the rate at which flux is *cut* by C because $(d\mathbf{s} \times \mathbf{v})$ is the rate at which $d\mathbf{s}$ sweeps out area. By problem (2.14), however, the rate at which flux is cut by a moving circuit is equal to the rate of change of Φ across S due to spatial variations in **B**. Thus the right-hand side of

(3.31) is the total rate of change of Φ taking into account both time and space variations in **B**. We may therefore write

$$\mathscr{E}' = -\frac{d\Phi}{dt} \tag{3.32}$$

(see also problem 3.11).

The current density at any point in the conductor is

$$\mathbf{J} = \gamma\left(-\frac{\partial \mathbf{A}}{\partial t} - \mathbf{grad}\, V + (\mathbf{v} \times \mathbf{B})\right) \tag{3.33}$$

or

$$\mathbf{J} = \gamma(\mathbf{E} + (\mathbf{v} \times \mathbf{B})) \tag{3.34}$$

a generalized ohm's law.

There are many difficult problems associated with moving conductors in magnetic fields and the reader is referred to Birss (1961) and Cullwick (1959). The former, in particular, discusses the phenomenon frequently referred to as *unipolar induction* and the question whether it is meaningful to talk of the rotation of lines of force when a cylindrical magnet rotates about its axis of symmetry.

Magnetohydrodynamics. When the conductor moving in the magnetic field is a fluid (liquid, gas, or plasma) the induced currents given by (3.33) are subject to forces which cause pressure changes in the fluid. We must then use both hydrodynamic equations and electromagnetic equations to investigate the motion, giving us the subject of *magnetohydrodynamics* (MHD). This subject strictly treats fluids as continua and where the particulate nature of the medium becomes important other approaches must be used. This is particularly true of plasmas or highly ionized gases of density low enough for mean free paths to be of the same order of magnitude as the extent of the plasma: the motion of individual ions in electric and magnetic fields then becomes more of interest.

In many cases, however, the continuum model is valid and MHD has become a branch of physics of some importance because of its applications in the production of electric power, in the production of high temperatures for controlled thermonuclear energy, and in explaining stellar and cosmic processes. We have space to consider only one or two topics in this large and increasing field of study. Our treatment to some extent parallels that of Cowling (1957).

Suppose the conducting fluid has a velocity **v** with respect to a frame of reference in which **E** and **B** exist. Then, as above,

$$\mathbf{curl\ E} = -\partial \mathbf{B}/\partial t; \qquad \mathbf{J} = \gamma(\mathbf{E} + \mathbf{v} \times \mathbf{B}). \tag{3.35}$$

Eliminating **E** between these two yields

$$\frac{\partial \mathbf{B}}{\partial t} = \mathbf{curl}\ (\mathbf{v} \times \mathbf{B}) - \frac{\mathbf{curl\ J}}{\gamma}$$

and since **curl H** $=$ **J**, and $\mathbf{H} = \mathbf{B}/\mu_r\mu_0$, we obtain

$$\frac{\partial \mathbf{B}}{\partial t} = \mathbf{curl}\ (\mathbf{v} \times \mathbf{B}) + \nabla^2 \mathbf{B}/\mu_r\mu_0\gamma. \tag{3.36}$$

Special cases of this equation when $\mathbf{v} = 0$ have been considered in section 3.4. If the conductor is moving, much depends upon whether one of the two terms on the right is overwhelmingly predominant. If the last term is much greater, then we revert to (3.25) with **B** instead of **J** and obtain the diffusion type of equation. If the last term is negligible, then

$$\mathbf{curl}\ (\mathbf{v} \times \mathbf{B}) = \partial \mathbf{B}/\partial t = -\mathbf{curl\ E}. \tag{3.37}$$

When both sides of this are integrated over any area moving with the conductor and the surface integrals are converted to line integrals using Stokes's theorem, we obtain from (3.30) and (3.32)

$$\mathbf{curl\ E'} = 0 \quad \text{and} \quad \mathscr{E}' = -\mathrm{d}\Phi/\mathrm{d}t = 0 \tag{3.38}$$

i.e., the magnetic flux across any moving closed path in the fluid does not change with time—a condition often summarized by saying that the lines of **B** are 'frozen in' the fluid and are carried along with it, although in practice this is never quite true.

The condition for the first term on the right of (3.36) to predominate greatly over the second is that $\mathbf{curl}\ (\mathbf{v} \times \mathbf{B}) \gg \nabla^2 \mathbf{B}/\mu_r\mu_0\gamma$. Some idea of the situations in which this will be so can be obtained using a simple dimensional argument. If L is a characteristic dimension of the body of fluid, then $\mathbf{curl}\ (\mathbf{v} \times \mathbf{B}) \sim vB/L$, while $\nabla^2 \mathbf{B}/\mu_r\mu_0\gamma \sim B/L^2\mu_r\mu_0\gamma$ so that

$$vL\mu_r\mu_0\gamma \gg 1 \tag{3.39}$$

is the condition for the characteristically MHD effect associated with (3.37) to occur. In the laboratory, the condition is not easy to satisfy (e.g., for mercury moving at 100 cm/s, $vL\mu_r\mu_0\gamma \sim 1$, and the lines of **B** can slip through the fluid without difficulty) but there are several important cases where (3.39) applies:

(1) In laboratory plasmas, because v is very high
(2) In superconductors, because γ is very high
(3) In cosmic phenomena, because L is very large.

In addition, there must exist a sufficiently large magnetic field in the first place otherwise the phenomena become simple hydrodynamic ones.

MHD waves. The existence of a magnetic flux density $\mathbf{B}_0$ in a fluid to which (3.39) applies confers a rigidity on the fluid in that any tendency to motion perpendicular to $\mathbf{B}_0$ is countered by strong electromagnetic restoring forces (see Fig. 3.1a). The possibility that this could lead to a new kind of wave motion was recognized by Alfvén (1942). The following simple treatment neglects second order effects.

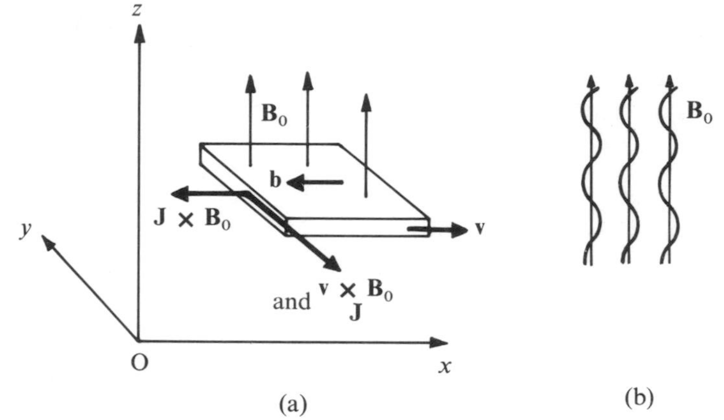

Fig. 3.1 (a) Infinite slab of conducting fluid moving along the x direction with a velocity $\mathbf{v}$ and through a magnetic flux density $\mathbf{B}_0$ along z. The induced currents $\mathbf{J}$ and the body forces $\mathbf{J} \times \mathbf{B}_0$ are shown; (b) resultant wave profile of magnetic field lines and fluid motion in transverse MHD waves

Consider the small motion of a slab of fluid as in Fig. 3.1a, where $\mathbf{B}_0$ is a steady uniform field along z and where $\mathbf{v}$ and $\mathbf{b}$ (the additional small field produced by the motionally induced currents) have only x components. The slab is homogeneous and effectively infinite in area so that no variations occur in the xy-plane. The general equation of motion of such a fluid would be, per unit mass,

$$\rho_m \, \mathrm{d}\mathbf{v}/\mathrm{d}t = (\mathbf{J} \times \mathbf{B}) - \mathbf{grad}\, p \tag{3.40}$$

where ρ_m is the fluid density and p the pressure. The $(\mathbf{J} \times \mathbf{B})$ term has only an x component JB_0 since $\mathbf{J} \times \mathbf{b} = 0$, while $\mathbf{grad}\, p$ has no x component. The total derivative $\mathrm{d}/\mathrm{d}t$ is equal to $(\partial/\partial t + \mathbf{v} \, . \, \mathbf{grad})$

as in problem 3.11 and in this case (**v . grad**)**v** is zero. Hence (3.40) becomes simply

$$\rho_{\mathrm{m}}\, \partial v/\partial t = JB_0.$$

The general relation **J** = **curl H** here yields $|\mu_0 \mathbf{J}| = |\mathbf{curl\ b}| = \partial b/\partial z$ and so

$$\rho_{\mathrm{m}}\, \partial v/\partial t = (B_0/\mu_0)\, \partial b/\partial z. \tag{3.41}$$

The MHD condition (3.37) degenerates in our case to **curl** ($\mathbf{v} \times \mathbf{B}_0$) = $-\partial \mathbf{B}/\partial t = -\partial \mathbf{b}/\partial t$, and because ($\mathbf{v} \times \mathbf{B}_0$) has only a y component:

$$B_0\, \partial v/\partial z = \partial b/\partial t. \tag{3.42}$$

Elimination of either b or v from (3.41) and (3.42) leads to the wave equations

$$\frac{\partial^2 b}{\partial z^2} - \frac{1}{{v_{\mathrm{A}}}^2}\frac{\partial^2 b}{\partial t^2} = 0; \qquad \frac{\partial^2 v}{\partial z^2} - \frac{1}{{v_{\mathrm{A}}}^2}\frac{\partial^2 v}{\partial t^2} = 0 \tag{3.43}$$

where $v_{\mathrm{A}} = ({B_0}^2/\mu_0\rho_m)^{1/2}$. These are transverse waves propagating in the direction of $\mathbf{B}_0$ as shown in Fig. 3.1b and are known as slow MHD or *Alfvén waves*.

Motion of the fluid parallel to $\mathbf{B}_0$ is unrestricted and ordinary longitudinal acoustic waves may be propagated along $\mathbf{B}_0$ with the velocity of sound, v_{s}, in the medium. In a compressible fluid, longitudinal waves can be propagated perpendicular to $\mathbf{B}_0$ with a velocity $({v_{\mathrm{A}}}^2 + {v_{\mathrm{s}}}^2)^{1/2}$. In practice, MHD waves are very complex and fluids will clearly behave anisotropically. For details and applications the reader is referred to Cowling (1957), Alfvén (1963), and Ferraro and Plumpton (1961).

Plasmas will support MHD waves at low frequencies where charge separation and displacement current (chapter 4) may be neglected. The higher frequency electromagnetic waves propagated in plasmas are considered in section 8.8.

PROBLEMS

3.1 Show that $J = J_0 \exp\left[-(1 + j)x/\alpha\right] \exp(j\omega t)$ is a solution of the one-dimensional form of (3.25) where α is given by (3.27). Calculate the penetration depth for copper at (a) a.c. frequencies of 50 Hz, 1 MHz, (b) microwave frequencies of wavelength 3 cm, (c) optical frequencies, (d) X-ray frequencies. Comment on the result for (d).

3.2 Show that the scalar and vector potentials of section 3.2 both satisfy a Poisson's equation if div $\mathbf{A} = 0$.

3.3 How is the expression (3.16) compatible with problem (2.22)?

3.4 Questions about magnetic energy are more complicated, in general, than the corresponding electric cases because of the energy needed to keep constant those currents producing the external field $\mathbf{B}_0$. This extra energy is often twice the decrease in potential energy so that an apparent change of sign occurs. Discuss this in relation to (a) the energy of a magnetic dipole in a field, (b) the mutual energy of two circuits between which there is a mutual inductance M.

3.5 Show that the energy loss per unit volume due to hysteresis in a ferromagnetic material is given by the area of the **B**–**H** loop for one complete cycle of the magnetizing field. How is this related to the area of the **M**–**H** loop?

3.6 The most common examples in which forces on magnetic materials are required are those connected with the measurement of susceptibilities of non-ferromagnetic materials. Use the method of problem 1.26 to show that the change in magnetic energy when a linear material is introduced into a pre-existing field *in vacuo*, $\mathbf{B}_0$, is given by the volume integral of $+\frac{1}{2}\mathbf{M} \cdot \mathbf{B}_0$ (note the difference in sign from the dielectric case). Hence show that if the specimen is so weakly magnetic that the internal and external fields can be equated, the force per unit volume on the specimen is $\frac{1}{2}\mu_0\chi_m \,\mathbf{grad}\,(\mathbf{H}^2)$. If the space occupied by the specimen was originally occupied by air of susceptibility χ_m', what modification is made to the force?

3.7 Show that the same results as in problem 3.6 follow from (2.59) under the same assumption, i.e., that the specimen is weakly magnetic.

3.8 Calculate the magnetic flux density within a long wire carrying a current distributed uniformly over its cross-section. Hence find the magnetic energy associated with the magnetic flux inside the wire. Equate the result to $\frac{1}{2}LI^2$ and show that the self-inductance $L = \mu_0/8\pi$ per unit length. (Compare this with the method in *Electricity and Magnetism*, section 9.6.)

3.9 A torsional pendulum consisting of a horizontal circular metal disc of thickness x and conductivity γ oscillates about a vertical axis through its centre. The suspension has a torsional constant c. What effect on the equation of motion has a vertical uniform magnetic field of flux density $\mathbf{B}$ over the central portion of radius a of the disc?

3.10 Using the technique involved in deriving (3.39), estimate from the diffusion equation (3.25) a characteristic time for the spread of currents and fields through a conductor.

3.11 Show that when a quantity varies both in space and time, its total rate of change with time, $\mathrm{d}/\mathrm{d}t$, is equal to $(\partial/\partial t + \mathbf{v} \cdot \mathbf{grad})$ where $\mathbf{v}$ is the velocity of the point at which the rates are evaluated. Interpret the result physically. Show that the assumption of (3.32) as a fundamental law would lead to both motional and transformer e.m.f.s.

4

Maxwell's equations and electromagnetic radiation

In this chapter, the electromagnetic field equations are generalized further by allowing rapid time variations. The quasi-steady condition of the last chapter is no longer valid and we see how this leads to a displacement current term (section 4.1), thus completing Maxwell's equations for stationary media. We then look at generalizations concerning electromagnetic energy (section 4.2).

The rest of the chapter is concerned with solutions of Maxwell's equations *in vacuo*, other than those encountered in previous chapters. These solutions, arising from the presence of the displacement current term, show that time variations in **E** and **B** are propagated with a finite velocity and carry energy away from the source. We thus call the energy *electromagnetic radiation* and when the variations are continuously propagated we talk of *electromagnetic waves*.

For the moment, we concern ourselves only with the propagation of radiation *in vacuo* without boundaries and with the generation of fields from oscillating and accelerating charges. Interaction of radiation with matter is dealt with in Part 3 and only enters this chapter generally in connection with electromagnetic momentum.

4.1 Varying electric fields and displacement current: Maxwell's equations

The clue to the existence of displacement current lies rather surprisingly in the equation of continuity (1.22). For steady currents this degenerates into div **J** = 0, which is consistent with the equation

curl H = **J** of (3.6) as can be seen by taking the divergence of both sides. It is clear, however, that there will be cases in which time variations are too rapid for even the quasi-steady condition to be valid and we must use the full equation (1.22):

$$\text{div}\,\mathbf{J} = -\frac{\partial \rho}{\partial t} \tag{4.1}$$

if the law of conservation of charge is to be obeyed. This is not consistent with **curl H** = **J**, which must be modified to

$$\mathbf{curl\ H} = \mathbf{J} + \mathbf{K} \tag{4.2}$$

where **K** is such that div **K** = $\partial\rho/\partial t$. Provided the sources of **D** are not affected by the time variations, ρ = div **D** and div **K** = div $(\partial \mathbf{D}/\partial t)$. Thus

$$\mathbf{curl\ H} = \mathbf{J} + \frac{\partial \mathbf{D}}{\partial t} \tag{4.3}$$

is a satisfactory generalization in that it both implies (4.1) and reduces to (2.36) when time variations are zero. The term $\partial \mathbf{D}/\partial t$ is known as the *displacement current density* at the point and its flux (see below) as the *displacement current*.

The above argument only shows that the addition of the displacement current term is the minimum necessary modification to be made to the field equations to achieve self-consistency when time variations occur: the existence of electromagnetic waves can only be predicted if this term is added and provides additional justification for it. On the basis that we adopt the minimum number of assumptions in a theory consistent with the explanation of all observations, we take (4.3) as our required generalization together with div **D** = ρ as the source equation consistent with it. No further additions are found necessary.

Integral form. The integral form of (4.3) is obtained by integrating both sides over an area S bounded by a path C and transforming the left-hand side by Stokes's theorem to a line integral:

$$\oint_C \mathbf{H}\,.\,d\mathbf{s} = \int_S \mathbf{J}\,.\,d\mathbf{S} + \int_S \frac{\partial \mathbf{D}}{\partial t}\,.\,d\mathbf{S} \tag{4.4}$$

or

$$\oint_C \mathbf{H}\,.\,d\mathbf{s} = I_c + I_d \tag{4.5}$$

where I_c is the conduction current across S and I_d the displacement current $\partial\Psi/\partial t$ (writing Ψ for the flux of **D** across S). Thus a change of electric flux across any closed surface is accompanied by an m.m.f. round the boundary (closed lines of **H** and **B** *in vacuo*).

Maxwell's equations. We now have the complete set of equations governing electric and magnetic fields within stationary media, known as Maxwell's equations. We collect them here in their differential form:

	Homogeneous equations	Inhomogeneous (source) equations
scalar equations	$\text{div}\,\mathbf{B} = 0$	$\text{div}\,\mathbf{D} = \rho$
vector equations	$\textbf{curl}\,\mathbf{E} + \dfrac{\partial \mathbf{B}}{\partial t} = 0$	$\textbf{curl}\,\mathbf{H} - \dfrac{\partial \mathbf{D}}{\partial t} = \mathbf{J}.$

(4.6)

Before these can be used, relations between the various field quantities, known as constitutive relations, must be stipulated according to the media occurring in the problem. The most common form is that expressed by $\mathbf{H} = \mathbf{B}/\mu_r\mu_0$ and $\mathbf{D} = \varepsilon_r\varepsilon_0\mathbf{E}$ for linear materials, but it should be remembered that μ_r and ε_r cannot be treated as constants unless the materials are also isotropic and homogeneous and that they vary with frequency in general. For ferromagnetic materials **H** is not a function of **B** at all, since the previous history is involved and general solutions to Maxwell's equations cannot be obtained. The same applies to ferroelectric materials in relation to **D** and **E**. In many cases, it may be advantageous to include the properties of the medium explicitly by writing $\mathbf{D} = \varepsilon_0\mathbf{E} + \mathbf{P}$ and $\mathbf{H} = \mathbf{B}/\mu_0 - \mathbf{M}$ so that the source equations become

$$\text{div}\,\mathbf{E} = \frac{\rho}{\varepsilon_0} - \frac{\text{div}\,\mathbf{P}}{\varepsilon_0} \tag{4.7}$$

and

$$\textbf{curl}\,\mathbf{B} = \mu_0\left(\mathbf{J} + \varepsilon_0\frac{\partial \mathbf{E}}{\partial t} + \frac{\partial \mathbf{P}}{\partial t} + \textbf{curl}\,\mathbf{M}\right). \tag{4.8}$$

Thus we have as sources of **E** both the given or conduction charges, ρ, and the polarization charges, $-\text{div}\,\mathbf{P}$. And we have as vortices of **B** (see appendix A) not only the given or conduction current **J** and the vacuum displacement current $\varepsilon_0\,\partial\mathbf{E}/\partial t$, but also the *polarization* *current* $\partial \mathbf{P}/\partial t$ and the magnetization current **curl M**. The polarization current is the only one of these we have not met before: it clearly arises from the motion of displaced charges in dielectrics, and that it gives rise to a magnetic field has been demonstrated by experiments of Röntgen (1888).

The sources ρ and $\mathbf{J}$ may be given quantities and $\mathbf{J}$ may in general be replaced by $\rho\mathbf{v}$ in accordance with (1.21), but in a conductor we must have the further constitutive relation $\mathbf{J} = \gamma\mathbf{E}$ where γ is subject to the same limitations as μ_r and ε_r. Finally, where the fields interact with currents and charges we may need the Lorentz force formula (2.64).

Relative magnitudes of conduction and displacement currents. Since the only new term introduced in this chapter is the displacement current density, it is useful to ask under what circumstances the term will be appreciable or negligible compared with the conduction current density. If it is negligible, then we only need the quasi-steady treatment of chapter 3.

To compare $\mathbf{J}$ and $\partial\mathbf{D}/\partial t$ we choose conditions under which both are present: $\mathbf{J}$ as a conduction current given by $\gamma\mathbf{E}$, and $\partial\mathbf{D}/\partial t$ as a result of sinusoidal variations at an angular frequency ω. Thus $\mathbf{J} = \gamma\mathbf{E} = \gamma\mathbf{E}_0 \sin \omega t$ and $\partial\mathbf{D}/\partial t = \omega\varepsilon_r\varepsilon_0\mathbf{E}_0 \cos \omega t$. Hence

$$\frac{\text{magnitude of displacement current}}{\text{magnitude of conduction current}} = \frac{\omega\varepsilon_r\varepsilon_0}{\gamma} = \omega\tau \qquad (4.9)$$

where τ is the relaxation time of the conductor as derived in problem 1.11. Even poor conductors have τ in the range 10^{-6}–10^{-12} sec and metals have $\tau \sim 10^{-18}$ sec. Displacement currents are thus likely to be negligible in conductors at lower frequencies, providing a justification for the quasi-steady approximation in chapter 3.

Boundary conditions. The scalar equations of (4.6) are the same as those for steady fields and thus lead to the same boundary conditions on the normal components of **B** and **D**. The vector equations differ by the addition only of the $\partial\mathbf{B}/\partial t$ and $\partial\mathbf{D}/\partial t$ terms, but provided these remain finite at a boundary their contributions disappear in the standard derivation (see appendix A). Thus we have, in general,

$$\left.\begin{aligned} &\delta B_n = 0; \qquad \delta E_t = 0; \\ &\delta D_n = \sigma_c, \text{ the surface density of conduction charge} \\ &\delta H_t = J_{sc}, \text{ the surface conduction current density} \end{aligned}\right\} \qquad (4.10)$$

We consider the possible potentials in section 4.4.

4.2 Electromagnetic energy and Poynting's theorem

In previous chapters, we have shown that under quasi-steady conditions we could write $\mathbf{E} \cdot \partial \mathbf{D}/\partial t$ and $\mathbf{H} \cdot \partial \mathbf{B}/\partial t$ for the rates of increase of electric and magnetic energy per unit volume associated with accumulation of charge and growth of currents. We now extend the argument.

In section 3.3, we showed that the rate of input of energy from external sources $\mathbf{E}'$ due to the growth of currents was $\mathbf{J} \cdot \mathbf{E}'$ per unit volume, and that this could be written as $J^2/\gamma - \mathbf{J} \cdot \mathbf{E}$ (equation (3.11)) where $\mathbf{E}$ is the electric field excluding that of the external source. This expression will still be valid under the same argument, where $\mathbf{J}$ and $\mathbf{E}$ are now the quantities occurring in Maxwell's equations and where consequently we can no longer ignore displacement current. Replacing $\mathbf{J}$ by $\mathbf{curl\,H} - \partial \mathbf{D}/\partial t$ and using the same transformation as in the derivation of (3.14), we now transform $-\mathbf{J} \cdot \mathbf{E}$:

$$-\mathbf{J} \cdot \mathbf{E} = \mathbf{H} \cdot \frac{\partial \mathbf{B}}{\partial t} + \mathbf{E} \cdot \frac{\partial \mathbf{D}}{\partial t} + \operatorname{div} (\mathbf{E} \times \mathbf{H}). \tag{4.11}$$

Integrating over a finite volume enclosing the whole system and using Gauss's divergence theorem on the last term gives

$$-\int_{\tau} \mathbf{J} \cdot \mathbf{E}\, \mathrm{d}\tau = \int_{\tau} \left(\mathbf{H} \cdot \frac{\partial \mathbf{B}}{\partial t} + \mathbf{E} \cdot \frac{\partial \mathbf{D}}{\partial t} \right) \mathrm{d}\tau + \oint_{S} (\mathbf{E} \times \mathbf{H}) \cdot \mathrm{d}\mathbf{S} \tag{4.12}$$

where S is the surface bounding τ.

The left-hand side we recognize as the rate at which energy is supplied to the system by external sources less the rate of loss due to Joule heating (see (3.11)): it thus gives the total rate at which electromagnetic energy is created in the system. The right-hand side separates this into two terms, a volume integral which can be interpreted as the rate of increase of electromagnetic energy within the volume, and a surface integral over S which can then only be equal to the rate of outward flow of energy, if energy is to be conserved. This interpretation of (4.12) is known as *Poynting's theorem* and

$$\mathbf{N} = \mathbf{E} \times \mathbf{H} \tag{4.13}$$

as the *Poynting vector*, after their originator. If we use U_{EM} to stand for the electromagnetic field energy,

$$\frac{\mathrm{d}U_{\mathrm{EM}}}{\mathrm{d}t} = \int_\tau \left(\mathbf{H} \cdot \frac{\partial \mathbf{B}}{\partial t} + \mathbf{E} \cdot \frac{\partial \mathbf{D}}{\partial t}\right) \mathrm{d}\tau$$

and

$$U_{\mathrm{EM}} = \int_\tau (\tfrac{1}{2}\mathbf{B} \cdot \mathbf{H} + \tfrac{1}{2}\mathbf{D} \cdot \mathbf{E})\, \mathrm{d}\tau \quad \text{linear media.} \tag{4.14}$$

While (4.12) is correct, the interpretation must be treated with some care. The Poynting vector gives the energy flow per unit area per unit time over any *closed surface*:

$$P_S = \oint_S \mathbf{N} \cdot \mathrm{d}\mathbf{S}. \tag{4.15}$$

It is an *extension* of Poynting's theorem to say that **N** at any *point* on the closed surface gives the magnitude and direction of energy flow at that point, and because this extension leads to unacceptable results with steady fields Poynting's theorem is sometimes criticized incorrectly. Certainly, if **B** and **D** are steady, if the integral of **N** over S is zero and if $\mathbf{J} = 0$ within τ, the extension will be invalid because all the terms of (4.12) are zero and no energy exchanges occur. Moreover, the localization of either electric or magnetic energy in steady conditions is without physical content. When time variations occur, however, the extension of Poynting's theorem so that **N** may be considered a point function is a fruitful idea and has physical meaning as well. We shall see that the finite time taken for the propagation of electromagnetic interactions over large distances forces us to accept a localization of energy in the fields if we are to preserve the conservation of energy principle.

Other forms of Poynting's theorem have been derived and, in particular, Tonks (1938) has shown that when the volume τ contains charges free to move *in vacuo* (as in many electronic devices), the work done by external fields can be split into an increase in kinetic energy of the particles within the volume together with a loss of kinetic energy through particles escaping over the bounding surface.

In the special case of (4.12) when no conduction currents flow within τ, it is possible to obtain a value for the velocity of energy flow, v_e, in terms of the Poynting vector and the energy *density*

$$u_{\mathrm{EM}} = \tfrac{1}{2}\mathbf{B} \cdot \mathbf{H} + \tfrac{1}{2}\mathbf{D} \cdot \mathbf{E}. \tag{4.16}$$

In time $\mathrm{d}t$ the energy crossing an element $\mathrm{d}S$ perpendicular to $\mathbf{N}$ is $N\,\mathrm{d}S\,\mathrm{d}t$. If $\mathrm{d}S$ is part of the closed surface bounding τ, equation (4.12) with $\mathbf{J} = 0$ tells us that the outflow of energy is entirely lost from U_{EM} and can also be expressed as $u_{\mathrm{EM}}(v_{\mathrm{e}}\,\mathrm{d}t\,\mathrm{d}S)$. Thus, equating these two expressions, we obtain

$$v_{\mathrm{e}} = N/u_{\mathrm{EM}}. \tag{4.17}$$

4.3 Propagation of electromagnetic radiation *in vacuo*

We first examine solutions of Maxwell's equations in regions containing no sources, so that for the moment we ignore the way in which any fields arise: this will be the concern of succeeding sections. We also consider only a region of space which is a vacuum because any medium can be regarded in some sense as a collection of sources. Maxwell's equations with $\mathbf{J} = 0$, $\rho = 0$, $\mathbf{D} = \varepsilon_0\mathbf{E}$, and $\mathbf{H} = \mathbf{B}/\mu_0$ become

$$\operatorname{div}\mathbf{B} = 0; \qquad \mathbf{curl}\,\mathbf{B} = \frac{1}{c^2}\frac{\partial\mathbf{E}}{\partial t} \tag{4.18a, b}$$

$$\operatorname{div}\mathbf{E} = 0; \qquad \mathbf{curl}\,\mathbf{E} = -\frac{\partial\mathbf{B}}{\partial t} \tag{4.19a, b}$$

in which

$$c = 1/(\varepsilon_0\mu_0)^{1/2} \tag{4.20}$$

a universal constant which can be determined from electrical measurements (see *Electricity and Magnetism*, section 16.7). Taking the **curl** of both sides of either vector equation gives, for instance,

$$\mathbf{curl}\,\mathbf{curl}\,\mathbf{E} = -\partial(\mathbf{curl}\,\mathbf{B})/\partial t = -\frac{1}{c^2}\frac{\partial^2\mathbf{E}}{\partial t^2}. \tag{4.21}$$

If cartesian co-ordinates are going to be used, it is useful to write **curl curl E** as **grad** div $\mathbf{E} - \nabla^2\mathbf{E}$ and because of (4.19a) we have

$$\nabla^2\mathbf{E} - \frac{1}{c^2}\frac{\partial^2\mathbf{E}}{\partial t^2} = 0 \quad \text{or} \quad \Box^2\mathbf{E} = 0 \tag{4.22}$$

and, similarly,

$$\nabla^2\mathbf{B} - \frac{1}{c^2}\frac{\partial^2\mathbf{B}}{\partial t^2} = 0 \quad \text{or} \quad \Box^2\mathbf{B} = 0 \tag{4.23}$$

where we have used the D'Alembertian operator $\Box^2$ (which can be read 'dal squared'):

$$\Box^2 \equiv \nabla^2 - \frac{1}{c^2}\frac{\partial^2}{\partial t^2} \tag{4.24}$$

In cartesian co-ordinates, (4.22) and (4.23) each separate into three equations, one for each component of **E** and **B**, of the form

$$\nabla^2 E_x - \frac{1}{c^2}\frac{\partial^2 E_x}{\partial t^2} = 0 \tag{4.25}$$

the solutions of which are equations of wave motion. In other co-ordinate systems the wave equation retains the form of (4.21).

The prediction of the existence of these electromagnetic waves and their identification with light waves were great triumphs of nineteenth century physics, due entirely to the inclusion of the displacement current term in Maxwell's equations and to the value of the velocity c given by (4.20): almost exactly 3×10^8 m/s, the velocity of light. We are here concerned to examine the properties of the waves as predicted by electromagnetic theory.

Solutions of (4.21) can be obtained in many forms corresponding for instance either to stationary or progressive waves, or having wave fronts of particular types such as plane, cylindrical, or spherical surfaces. Where no boundary conditions are imposed, as in this chapter, progressive solutions are more appropriate and we shall look at plane waves in most detail with a glance at spherical waves of high symmetry. The co-ordinate system is chosen in every case according to shape of the wavefronts or of the boundaries.

4.4 Plane electromagnetic waves *in vacuo*

It is easily shown that a general solution of the one-dimensional wave equation $\partial^2 f/\partial x^2 - \partial^2 f/v_p{}^2\, \partial t^2 = 0$ is $f_1(x - v_p t) + f_2(x + v_p t)$, where f_1 represents a wave travelling in the positive x-direction and f_2 one travelling in the opposite direction both with phase velocities v_p. In three dimensions, cartesian co-ordinates are most suitable for plane wave solutions and we therefore seek solutions to (4.25) similar to f_1. A function of the form $E_x(lx + my + nz - ct)$ would be adequate, for it represents a disturbance travelling with a phase velocity c in a direction normal to the planes $lx + my + nz =$ constant and has a value which is the same at any time t over these same planes. (The reader should check carefully that he understands the representation: for an elementary account, see Braddick (1965), chapter 3.) The quantities l, m, n are the direction cosines of the normal to the planes and are inter-related by $l^2 + m^2 + n^2 = 1$.

We prefer to use a vector notation in which the planes are specified by the relation $\hat{\mathbf{s}} \cdot \mathbf{r} =$ constant, **s** being the direction of the normal to the planes and **r** the position of any point on the plane (Fig. 4.1). The unit vector $\hat{\mathbf{s}}$ has components $\hat{s}_x$, $\hat{s}_y$, $\hat{s}_z$ if needed and these

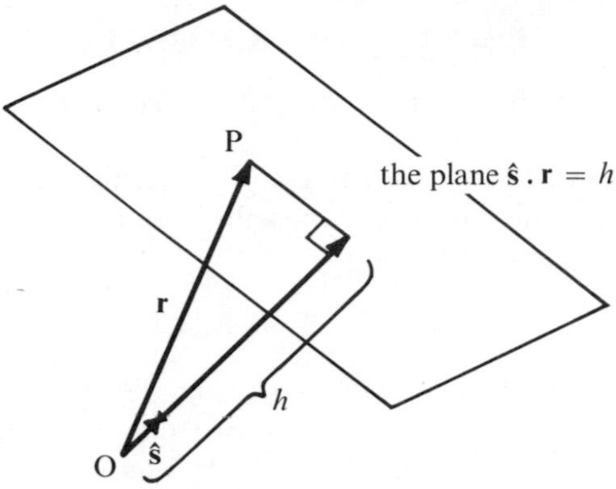

Fig. 4.1 Specification of a plane whose perpendicular distance from 0 is h. P is any point on the plane and its position **r** always satisfies $\hat{\mathbf{s}} \cdot \mathbf{r} = h$

replace the l, m, n, above. Thus the general solutions of (4.22) and (4.23) representing plane waves of phase velocity c are

$$\mathbf{E} = \mathbf{E}(\hat{\mathbf{s}} \cdot \mathbf{r} - ct); \qquad \mathbf{B} = \mathbf{B}(\hat{\mathbf{s}} \cdot \mathbf{r} - ct). \tag{4.26}$$

Because these must also satisfy Maxwell's equations, some properties of plane waves can be deduced. If, for convenience, we put

$$\hat{\mathbf{s}} \cdot \mathbf{r} - ct = p \tag{4.27}$$

then it is easy to show that the following replacements can be made for operations on **E** or **B**:

$$\left.\begin{array}{ll} \textbf{curl} \text{ or } \nabla \times \rightarrow \hat{\mathbf{s}} \times \partial/\partial p; & \text{div or } \nabla . \rightarrow \hat{\mathbf{s}} \cdot \partial/\partial p; \\ \partial/\partial t \rightarrow -c\, \partial/\partial p. & \end{array}\right\} \tag{4.28}$$

For instance,

$$(\textbf{curl}\ \mathbf{E})_x = \frac{\partial E_z}{\partial y} - \frac{\partial E_y}{\partial z} = \hat{s}_y \frac{\partial E_z}{\partial p} - \hat{s}_z \frac{\partial E_y}{\partial p} = (\hat{\mathbf{s}} \times \partial \mathbf{E}/\partial p)_x.$$

Hence (4.18b) and (4.19b) give

$$\hat{\mathbf{s}} \times \frac{\partial \mathbf{E}}{\partial p} = c\frac{\partial \mathbf{B}}{\partial p} \tag{4.29}$$

$$\hat{\mathbf{s}} \times \frac{\partial \mathbf{B}}{\partial p} = -\frac{1}{c}\frac{\partial \mathbf{E}}{\partial p}. \tag{4.30}$$

Both (4.29) and (4.30) can be integrated with respect to p to yield:

$$\hat{\mathbf{s}} \times \mathbf{E} = c\mathbf{B} \quad \text{or} \quad \mathbf{B} = (\hat{\mathbf{s}} \times \mathbf{E})/c \tag{4.31}$$

$$\hat{\mathbf{s}} \times \mathbf{B} = -\mathbf{E}/c \quad \text{or} \quad \mathbf{E} = -c(\hat{\mathbf{s}} \times \mathbf{B}) \tag{4.32}$$

omitting fields which are independent of p, i.e., are constant in space and time and thus are not wave-type solutions. It follows from these or from (4.18a) and (4.19a) that

$$\hat{\mathbf{s}} \,.\, \mathbf{B} = 0; \qquad \hat{\mathbf{s}} \,.\, \mathbf{E} = 0 \tag{4.33}$$

and so *both* **E** *and* **B** *are transverse* (giving so-called TEM—transverse electric and magnetic—waves. See chapter 10). Equations (4.31) and (4.32) make it clear that **E**, **B**, *and* $\hat{\mathbf{s}}$ *are mutually perpendicular and such that they form a right-handed system in the order* **E**, **B**, $\hat{\mathbf{s}}$. In fact, $\mathbf{E} \times \mathbf{B} = \hat{\mathbf{s}}E^2/c$. The magnitudes of **E** and **B** are related by

$$E = cB \tag{4.34}$$

and because $\mathbf{H} = \mathbf{B}/\mu_0$

$$E/H = (\mu_0/\varepsilon_0)^{1/2} \approx 120\pi \text{ or } 376{\cdot}6 \text{ ohms} \tag{4.35}$$

a quantity known as the *impedance of free space*.

Monochromatic plane waves. We now consider the form and properties of waves whose magnitude varies in the direction of propagation with a single frequency ν and repeats itself in a single wave-length λ related by $v_p = \nu\lambda$. Using the complex representation with $v_p = c$,

$$\mathbf{E} = \mathbf{E}_0 \, e^{i\frac{2\pi}{\lambda}(\hat{\mathbf{s}}\,.\,\mathbf{r} - ct)} \tag{4.36}$$

so that instantaneous values must be obtained by taking real or imaginary parts. The amplitude $\mathbf{E}_0$ is constant in magnitude and direction over the planes $\hat{\mathbf{s}} \,.\, \mathbf{r}$ = constant. Whether the complete exponent is positive or negative is irrelevant, some authors preferring one, some the other. The form (4.36) is in general use when dealing with waves but it leads to the unusual form $e^{-i\omega t}$ in a.c. theory so we shall replace i by $-j$ where the form $e^{j\omega t}$ is needed.

A more compact form of (4.36) is obtained by using the wave number $k = 2\pi/\lambda$ and defining a *wave vector* in the direction of propagation:

$$\mathbf{k} = k\hat{\mathbf{s}} \tag{4.37}$$

so that, because $2\pi c/\lambda = \omega$, the angular frequency, (4.36) becomes

$$\mathbf{E} = \mathbf{E}_0 \, e^{i(\mathbf{k}\,.\,\mathbf{r}-\omega t)} \tag{4.38}$$

with a similar expression for **B**:

$$\mathbf{B} = \mathbf{B}_0 \, e^{i(\mathbf{k}\,.\,\mathbf{r}-\omega t+\alpha)} \tag{4.39}$$

where α is the phase difference between the two. From (4.31), however, we should obtain

$$\mathbf{k} \times \mathbf{E}_0 \, e^{i(\mathbf{k}\,.\,\mathbf{r}-\omega t)} = \mathbf{B}_0 \, e^{i(\mathbf{k}\,.\,\mathbf{r}-\omega t+\alpha)}$$

This must be satisfied for all **r** and t so that α must be zero and **E** *and* **B** *are in phase.*

Using the form of (4.38) means that the operator ∇ can be replaced by $i\mathbf{k}$, as is easily checked, and $\partial/\partial t$ by $-i\omega$. Thus

$$\textbf{curl} \rightarrow i\mathbf{k} \times; \qquad \text{div} \rightarrow i\mathbf{k}\,.; \qquad \textbf{grad} \rightarrow i\mathbf{k}; \qquad \partial/\partial t \rightarrow -i\omega \tag{4.40}$$

Nearly monochromatic waves. A perfectly monochromatic wave is an abstraction in so far as it must extend to infinity both backwards and forwards in time. A sinusoidal wave train which terminates at both ends contains a small range of frequencies about the mean, a range constituting what is known as the *natural broadening* of a spectral line—it is inescapable however much other causes of broadening may be minimized. A finite wave train can be represented by the superposition of monochromatic waves each of which is a solution of Maxwell's equations as above. Because the equations are linear, the superposed waves are also a solution and we thus have a means of dealing with more practicable types of plane wave. The finite wave train forms a wave *group* having a group velocity defined by

$$v_g = \frac{d\omega}{dk} \tag{4.41}$$

instead of the *phase* velocity

$$v_p = \frac{\omega}{k}. \tag{4.42}$$

For electromagnetic waves *in vacuo*, the ratio of ω to k is c at all frequencies so that $v_p = v_g = c$—there is no dispersion.

Polarization. Before light was recognized as electromagnetic in character, it was known that light waves were transverse and that the 'light vibrations' were in some cases confined to a plane perpendicular to the wave front and containing the direction of propagation. This plane became known as the *plane of polarization* and the light as *plane-polarized.*

An electromagnetic wave in which the vector amplitudes $\mathbf{E}_0$ and $\mathbf{B}_0$ remain in the same plane throughout the whole wave would be an adequate representation of a plane-polarized light wave (see Fig. 4.2). Traditional optics would then identify the plane of polarization

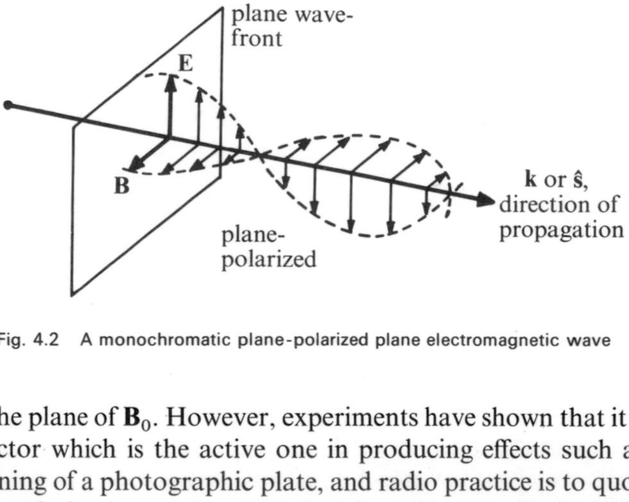

Fig. 4.2 A monochromatic plane-polarized plane electromagnetic wave

with the plane of $\mathbf{B}_0$. However, experiments have shown that it is the $\mathbf{E}_0$ vector which is the active one in producing effects such as the darkening of a photographic plate, and radio practice is to quote $\mathbf{E}_0$ as the polarization vector. Anisotropic media (chapter 7) make the situation even more complicated so that we shall merely refer where necessary to the 'plane of **E**' or 'plane of **B**' and avoid the more general term where ambiguity might arise.

Other forms of polarization are possible as can be seen by writing the electric field amplitude $\mathbf{E}_0$ as the sum of two perpendicular components both lying in the wave-front:

$$\mathbf{E}_0 = \mathbf{E}_1 \, e^{i\alpha} + \mathbf{E}_2 \, e^{i\beta} = \mathbf{E}_1 + \mathbf{E}_2 \, e^{i\delta} \tag{4.43}$$

using $\mathbf{E}_1$ as providing the standard phase and putting $\beta - \alpha = \delta$. Then

$$\mathbf{E} = \mathbf{E}_0 \, e^{i(\mathbf{k}\,.\,\mathbf{r}-\omega t)} = \mathbf{E}_1 \, e^{i(\mathbf{k}\,.\,\mathbf{r}-\omega t)} + \mathbf{E}_2 \, e^{i(\mathbf{k}\,.\,\mathbf{r}-\omega t+\delta)}. \tag{4.44}$$

In general (see problem 4.4), the tip of $\mathbf{E}_0$ will trace out an ellipse (either at a single point as time goes on or along the wave at any instant) and we have *elliptically polarized* waves. Degenerate cases occur when $\delta = 0$, giving plane-polarized waves, and when $\delta = \frac{1}{2}\pi$ and $|\mathbf{E}_1| = |\mathbf{E}_2|$ giving *circularly polarized* waves. In *unpolarized* waves, the vector $\mathbf{E}_0$ is subject to random changes of amplitude and phase due to the combination of many incoherent wave trains from different parts of the source. An unpolarized wave could never be truly monochromatic for this would mean that the two components of (4.44), which are independent solutions of Maxwell's equations, would have the same ω at all times and the phase difference could never vary.

In all cases, the magnetic vector has components $\mathbf{B}_1$ and $\mathbf{B}_2$ related to $\mathbf{E}_1$ and $\mathbf{E}_2$ by (4.31) and (4.32) and need not be considered separately.

Propagation of energy. The Poynting vector is a quadratic function of the fields and it is not correct to use for $\mathbf{N}$ the real part of $(\mathbf{E} \times \mathbf{H})$ when the fields are given in the complex form (4.38). Instead we must use

$$\mathbf{E} = \mathbf{E}_0 \cos(\mathbf{k}\,.\,\mathbf{r} - \omega t); \qquad \mathbf{H} = \mathbf{H}_0 \cos(\mathbf{k}\,.\,\mathbf{r} - \omega t) \tag{4.45}$$

and, since $H_0 = \varepsilon_0 c E_0$, by (4.35)

$$\mathbf{N} = \mathbf{E} \times \mathbf{H} = \hat{\mathbf{s}} \varepsilon_0 c E_0{}^2 \cos^2(\mathbf{k}\,.\,\mathbf{r} - \omega t). \tag{4.46}$$

The average value over a number of periods would thus be

$$\overline{N} = \tfrac{1}{2}\varepsilon_0 c E_0{}^2 \quad \text{or} \quad \varepsilon_0 c E_{\text{rms}}^2. \tag{4.47}$$

If it is desired to use the complex representation, then $\overline{\mathbf{N}}$ is given by

$$\overline{\mathbf{N}} = \tfrac{1}{2} \operatorname{Re}(\mathbf{E} \times \mathbf{H}^*) \tag{4.48}$$

where $\mathbf{H}^*$ is the complex conjugate of $\mathbf{H}$ and Re means 'take the real part of'.

4.5 Spherical waves *in vacuo*

The wave equation **curl curl E** $= -\partial^2\mathbf{E}/c^2\,\partial t^2$ becomes very complicated in spherical polar co-ordinates and we shall restrict ourselves to solutions with complete spherical symmetry about the origin such as would be appropriate where a point source at the origin generates waves in an unbounded LIH medium. If, then, all variations with respect to θ and ϕ are put equal to zero, the expressions (A.15) and (A.16) for div and **curl** show that div $\mathbf{E} = 0$ implies $\partial E_r/\partial r = 0$, and that because **curl B** has a zero radial component, (4.18b) gives that $\partial E_r/\partial t = 0$. Thus E_r does not vary in space or time and is of no interest in a wave solution. A similar conclusion can be arrived at for **B** so that the waves are completely transverse.

From (A.16),

$$\mathbf{curl\,E} = -\frac{1}{r}\frac{\partial(rE_\phi)}{\partial r}\hat{\boldsymbol{\theta}} + \frac{1}{r}\frac{\partial(rE_\theta)}{\partial r}\hat{\boldsymbol{\phi}}$$

and therefore

$$\mathbf{curl\,curl\,E} = -\frac{1}{r}\frac{\partial^2(rE_\theta)}{\partial r^2}\hat{\boldsymbol{\theta}} - \frac{1}{r}\frac{\partial^2(rE_\phi)}{\partial r^2}\hat{\boldsymbol{\phi}}.$$

Equating the components of this to the appropriate ones of $-\partial^2\mathbf{E}/c^2\,\partial t^2$, it is found that both E_θ and E_ϕ satisfy scalar wave equations

$$\frac{\partial^2(rE_{\theta,\phi})}{\partial r^2} - \frac{1}{c^2}\frac{\partial^2(rE_{\theta,\phi})}{\partial t^2} = 0 \tag{4.49}$$

so that the general solution will be of the form

$$rE_{\theta,\phi} = \mathrm{f}_1(r - ct) + \mathrm{f}_2(r + ct). \tag{4.50}$$

Since we are usually concerned only with waves propagated outwards from the origin, we keep only the f_1 term, so that

$$E_{\theta,\phi} = \frac{1}{r}\,\mathrm{f}(r - ct) \tag{4.51}$$

a wave propagated outwards with a velocity c and with an amplitude decreasing as $1/r$.

4.6 Generalized potentials *in vacuo*

Solutions of Maxwell's equations with sources are often facilitated by the use of potentials similar to those encountered in previous chapters, and these will now be derived for use in the next sections.

Because div $\mathbf{B} = 0$ is universally valid, it is always possible to define a vector potential **A** such that

$$\mathbf{B} = \mathbf{curl\,A}. \tag{4.52}$$

The other homogeneous Maxwell equation $\mathbf{curl\ E} + \partial\mathbf{B}/\partial t = 0$ then gives

$$\mathbf{E} = -\frac{\partial \mathbf{A}}{\partial t} - \mathbf{grad}\ V \qquad (4.53)$$

where V is any differentiable scalar field. Equations (4.52) and (4.53) leave much latitude in the choice of **A** and V, but certain restrictions come into play when the inhomogeneous or source equations are introduced. Moreover, we shall always demand that when steady or quasi-steady conditions prevail, the expressions for **A** and V shall reduce to those in chapters 1 to 3.

The source equations involve the **H** and **D** fields so that constitutive relations must be assumed. *In vacuo* and with **J** and ρ *given*,

$$\mathbf{curl\ B} = \mu_0 \mathbf{J} + \frac{1}{c^2}\frac{\partial \mathbf{E}}{\partial t} \qquad (4.54)$$

and therefore

$$\mathbf{curl\ curl\ A} = \mu_0 \mathbf{J} - \frac{1}{c^2}\frac{\partial^2 \mathbf{A}}{\partial t^2} - \frac{1}{c^2}\mathbf{grad}\left(\frac{\partial V}{\partial t}\right) \qquad (4.55)$$

or

$$\nabla^2 \mathbf{A} - \frac{1}{c^2}\frac{\partial^2 \mathbf{A}}{\partial t^2} = -\mu_0 \mathbf{J} + \mathbf{grad}\left[\operatorname{div} \mathbf{A} + \frac{1}{c^2}\frac{\partial V}{\partial t}\right]. \qquad (4.56)$$

Moreover, from $\operatorname{div} \mathbf{D} = \rho$,

$$\nabla^2 V = -\frac{\rho}{\varepsilon_0} - \frac{\partial}{\partial t}(\operatorname{div} \mathbf{A}). \qquad (4.57)$$

In the absence of time variations, (4.56) and (4.57) should reduce to (2.26) and (1.17) and this could be achieved by putting $\operatorname{div} \mathbf{A} = 0$, a choice known as the *Coulomb gauge*. Alternatively, the bracketed term of (4.56) could be equated to zero so that

$$\operatorname{div} \mathbf{A} = -\frac{1}{c^2}\frac{\partial V}{\partial t}. \qquad (4.58)$$

This is known as the *Lorentz gauge* and it has the advantage that it separates **A** and V into two independent equations:

$$\Box^2 \mathbf{A} = -\mu_0 \mathbf{J} \qquad (4.59)$$

$$\Box^2 V = -\rho/\varepsilon_0. \qquad (4.60)$$

Gauge invariance. Only the **curl** of **A** is fixed by (4.52) so that any vector field expressible as **grad** f can be added to **A** without altering **B**. Thus if $\mathbf{A}_0$ is an acceptable vector potential, so is

$$\mathbf{A} = \mathbf{A}_0 + \mathbf{grad}\, f. \tag{4.61}$$

Moreover, if V_0 is the scalar potential corresponding to $\mathbf{A}_0$, then

$$V = V_0 - \frac{\partial f}{\partial t} \tag{4.62}$$

leaves **E** unchanged (using (4.53)) and so is also acceptable. The transformations (4.61) and (4.62) are known as *gauge transformations* and show that the potentials are very much a matter of choice for maximum convenience: it is **E** and **B** which are the physically important quantities. Maxwell's equations are invariant under the choice of gauge.

The choice of f is linked with that of div **A**, for with the Coulomb gauge, div $\mathbf{A} =$ div $\mathbf{A}_0 = 0$ and hence $\nabla^2 f = 0$; while with the Lorentz gauge, we find similarly that $\Box^2 f = 0$. The Coulomb gauge has a certain advantage in that V is exactly the electrostatic potential so that **E** is separable into an electrostatic field and a wave field given by $-\partial\mathbf{A}/\partial t$. The Lorentz gauge is more often to be preferred, however, because it yields relativistically invariant expressions (see chapter 11). *We shall henceforth assume that the Lorentz gauge is being used.*

Retarded potentials. The problem of calculating **E** and **B** from given sources is now reduced to that of obtaining **A** and V from (4.59) and (4.60) and then using (4.52) and (4.53). We confine ourselves to the solution of (4.60) in detail. Because the equation is linear, we look at the solution for a charge element $\rho\, d\tau$ situated at the origin and obtain the solution for a general charge distribution by superposition.

A charge element situated at the origin means that at every point except the origin, V satisfies $\Box^2 V = 0$ and that the solution will have complete spherical symmetry. Using spherical polars in which variations with θ and ϕ are put equal to zero, V must satisfy

$$\frac{1}{r^2}\frac{\partial}{\partial r}\left(r^2\frac{\partial V}{\partial r}\right) - \frac{1}{c^2}\frac{\partial^2 V}{\partial t^2} = 0$$

using (A.17), or

$$\frac{\partial^2(rV)}{\partial r^2} - \frac{1}{c^2}\frac{\partial^2(rV)}{\partial t^2} = 0. \tag{4.63}$$

This is identical in form to (4.49) and leads to a solution like (4.50)

$$V = \frac{1}{r}\,\mathrm{f}_1\!\left(t - \frac{r}{c}\right) + \frac{1}{r}\,\mathrm{f}_2\!\left(t + \frac{r}{c}\right) \tag{4.64}$$

where we have expressed the arguments slightly differently by dividing them through by $\pm c$. The potential f_1/r is known as a *retarded potential* and f_2/r as an *advanced potential*. Because we wish to impose the physical boundary condition that the potentials and hence the fields at infinity shall not be affected by changes in the source until *after* they occur, we keep only the retarded potential

$$V = \frac{1}{r}\,\mathrm{f}_1\!\left(t - \frac{r}{c}\right). \tag{4.65}$$

To find the form of the function f_1, we use the fact that very near the origin $V = \rho\,\mathrm{d}\tau/4\pi\varepsilon_0 r$ and because ρ is to be a function of time:

$$V \to \frac{\rho(t)\,\mathrm{d}\tau}{4\pi\varepsilon_0 r} \quad \text{as } r \to 0. \tag{4.66}$$

But, at the same time, $\mathrm{f}_1(t - r/c) \to \mathrm{f}_1(t)$ as $r \to 0$, so we identify $\mathrm{f}_1(t)$ as $\rho(t)\,\mathrm{d}\tau/4\pi\varepsilon_0$. In that case, (4.65) must be

$$V = \frac{\rho(t - r/c)\,\mathrm{d}\tau}{4\pi\varepsilon_0 r} \tag{4.67}$$

and by superposition of many such sources we have that generally

$$V(x, y, z, t) = \int \frac{\rho(x', y', z', t - r/c)}{4\pi\varepsilon_0 r}\,\mathrm{d}\tau' \tag{4.68}$$

and, in a similar way, each component of **A** will satisfy the same type of equation so that

$$\mathbf{A}(x, y, z, t) = \int \frac{\mu_0 \mathbf{J}(x', y', z', t - r/c)}{4\pi r}\,\mathrm{d}\tau'. \tag{4.69}$$

These retarded potentials mean that the potentials at the field point (x, y, z, t) are determined by the sources at (x', y', z') as they were at a time $(t - r/c)$, i.e., as if the effect of any changes travels to the field point with a velocity c. This ties up with the results of section 4.3 where it was seen that the wave fields of **E** and **B** were propagated with velocity c *in vacuo*. Equations (4.68) and (4.69) are often concisely written

$$V = \int \frac{[\rho]}{4\pi\varepsilon_0 r}\,d\tau'; \qquad \mathbf{A} = \int \frac{\mu_0[\mathbf{J}]}{4\pi r}\,d\tau' \tag{4.70}$$

where the square brackets indicate that ρ and $\mathbf{J}$ are to be given values corresponding to a time r/c before that at which V and $\mathbf{A}$ are to be evaluated. Apart from this, the expressions (4.70) are identical with (1.15) and (2.25). It should not be forgotten that $\mathbf{A}$ and V are related through the Lorentz condition (4.58).

4.7 Radiation from an oscillating dipole

An important example of a radiating system is afforded by the Hertzian dipole (Fig. 4.3). This consists of an electric dipole with

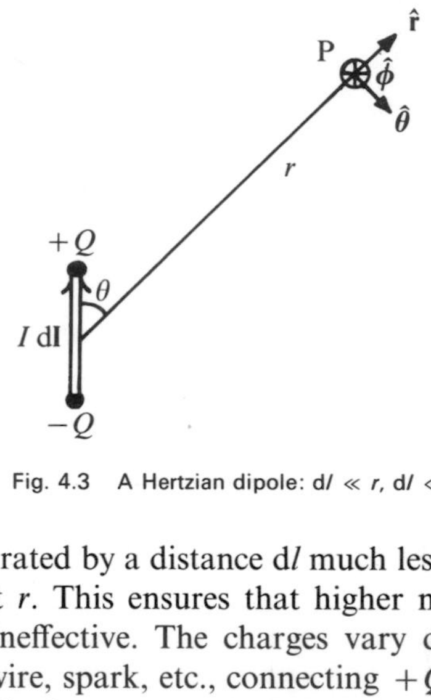

Fig. 4.3 A Hertzian dipole: $dl \ll r$, $dl \ll \lambda$

charges $\pm Q$ separated by a distance dl much less than the distance of the field point r. This ensures that higher multipole moments (chapter 5) are ineffective. The charges vary due to a current I flowing along a wire, spark, etc., connecting $+Q$ and $-Q$, so that $I = dQ/dt$. The dipole moment $\mathbf{p}$ is $Q\,\mathbf{dl}$ and hence

$$\dot{\mathbf{p}} = \dot{Q}\,\mathbf{dl} = I\,\mathbf{dl} \tag{4.71}$$

the dot denoting differentiation with respect to time.

The element is situated at the origin and to find the fields at P we use polar co-ordinates (r, θ) only, because of the axial symmetry. If λ is the wave-length corresponding to any periodic time variations, we also stipulate that $dl \ll \lambda$ so that all source points have the same retarded time and no phase differences occur at P between waves from different parts of the source.

By (4.69), we have

$$\mathbf{A} = \frac{\mu_0[I]\,\mathbf{dl}}{4\pi r} = \frac{\mu_0[\dot{\mathbf{p}}]}{4\pi r}. \tag{4.72}$$

Since the direction of **p** is constant, **A** lies along the axis of symmetry and has components

$$A_r = \frac{\mu_0[\dot{p}]\cos\theta}{4\pi r}; \qquad A_\theta = -\frac{\mu_0[\dot{p}]\sin\theta}{4\pi r}. \tag{4.73}$$

Thus, using (A.15), and remembering that $\partial\dot{p}(t - r/c)/\partial r = -[\ddot{p}]/c$, we obtain

$$\operatorname{div}\mathbf{A} = -\frac{\mu_0\cos\theta}{4\pi}\left(\frac{[\dot{p}]}{r^2} + \frac{[\ddot{p}]}{rc}\right).$$

This is equal to $-\partial V/c^2\,\partial t$ by the Lorentz condition and so

$$V = \frac{\cos\theta}{4\pi\varepsilon_0}\left(\frac{[p]}{r^2} + \frac{[\dot{p}]}{rc}\right). \tag{4.74}$$

The fields are now obtained from (4.74) and (4.73) using (4.52) and (4.53). The working is not difficult using (A.14) and (A.16) and the results are:

$$\mathbf{B} = \left(\frac{\mu_0[\dot{p}]\sin\theta}{4\pi r^2}\right)\hat{\boldsymbol{\phi}} + \left(\frac{\mu_0[\ddot{p}]\sin\theta}{4\pi rc}\right)\hat{\boldsymbol{\phi}} \tag{4.75}$$

$$\mathbf{E} = \left(\frac{2[p]\cos\theta}{4\pi\varepsilon_0 r^3}\hat{\mathbf{r}} + \frac{[p]\sin\theta}{4\pi\varepsilon_0 r^3}\hat{\boldsymbol{\theta}}\right) + \left(\frac{2[\dot{p}]\cos\theta}{4\pi\varepsilon_0 r^2 c}\hat{\mathbf{r}} + \frac{[\dot{p}]\sin\theta}{4\pi\varepsilon_0 r^2 c}\hat{\boldsymbol{\theta}}\right) + \frac{[\ddot{p}]\sin\theta}{4\pi\varepsilon_0 rc^2}\hat{\boldsymbol{\theta}}. \tag{4.76}$$

The first bracketed term in **E** is the only *static* field: it is the field of an electric dipole as would be given by (1.16) and because it falls off as $1/r^3$ it is the dominant field only at small distances. The first term in **B** and the second in **E** depend on $\dot{p}$ or the current I and are fields which would arise from steady currents: they fall off as $1/r^2$ and are called *induction* fields. The important new terms are the last in (4.75) and (4.76): they fall off only as $1/r$ and predominate at large distances.

They are *radiation* fields because the energy given by integrating **N** over a sphere round the dipole does not decrease as the radius gets larger: in this they are unlike the static and induction fields. The radiation fields are then

$$\mathbf{E}_{\text{rad}} = \frac{[\ddot{p}]\sin\theta}{4\pi\varepsilon_0 c^2 r}\hat{\boldsymbol{\theta}}; \qquad \mathbf{B}_{\text{rad}} = \frac{[\ddot{p}]\sin\theta}{4\pi\varepsilon_0 c^3 r}\hat{\boldsymbol{\phi}}. \tag{4.77}$$

The Poynting vector is

$$\mathbf{N} = \mathbf{E}\times\mathbf{H} = \frac{[\ddot{p}]^2\sin^2\theta}{16\pi^2\varepsilon_0 c^3 r^2}\hat{\mathbf{r}} \tag{4.78}$$

and when integrated over a sphere this gives the total energy radiated from the dipole per unit time as

$$P = \left(\frac{\mu_0}{4\pi}\right)\frac{2[\ddot{p}]^2}{3c} = \frac{2[\ddot{p}]^2}{3(4\pi\varepsilon_0)c^3}. \tag{4.79}$$

If the time variations in the source are sinusoidal, then the retardation in $\ddot{p}$ is immaterial and when $p = p_0\cos\omega t$, the mean value of $(\ddot{p})^2$ is $\omega^4 p_0{}^2/2$. Hence the mean radiated power is

$$\bar{P} = \frac{\omega^4 p_0{}^2}{12\pi\varepsilon_0 c^3} \tag{4.80}$$

i.e., it is proportional to the 4th power of the frequency. Under these circumstances, the radiation terms predominate when $r \gg \lambda$ in what is known as the *wave zone*. Notice particularly that the radiation fields (4.77) are transverse and related to each other exactly as they are in a plane wave (Fig. 4.4).

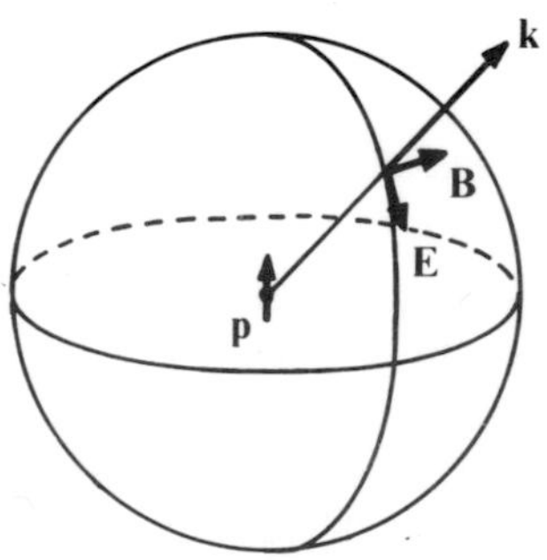

Fig. 4.4 Radiation fields from a Hertzian dipole

In terms of the current I, $\ddot{p} = \dot{I}\, \mathrm{d}l$ and if $I = I_0 \cos \omega t$, (4.79) gives

$$\bar{P} = \frac{2\pi}{3\varepsilon_0 c}\left(\frac{\mathrm{d}l}{\lambda}\right)^2 I_{\mathrm{rms}}^2. \tag{4.81}$$

The magnetic dipole is considered in problem 4.12.

4.8 Radiation from an accelerated charge

For a charge Q occupying a small volume and moving with a velocity v, we cannot just use (4.70) with $\int [\rho]\, \mathrm{d}\tau = Q$ and $\int [\mathbf{J}]\, \mathrm{d}\tau = Q\mathbf{v}$ because different parts of the charge have different retarded times even if $v \ll c$. When integrating over the source, we are interested in the charge which was at the various source points a time r/c ago. To calculate this, imagine a sphere collapsing towards the field point P so that its surface moves with a velocity c and finally reaches P at time t. In all cases, the surface is passing through the source exactly at time $t - r/c$. Consider the element of volume $\mathrm{d}\tau'$ (Fig. 4.5a) traversed by the surface element $\mathrm{d}S$ in time $\mathrm{d}t$. Were the charge

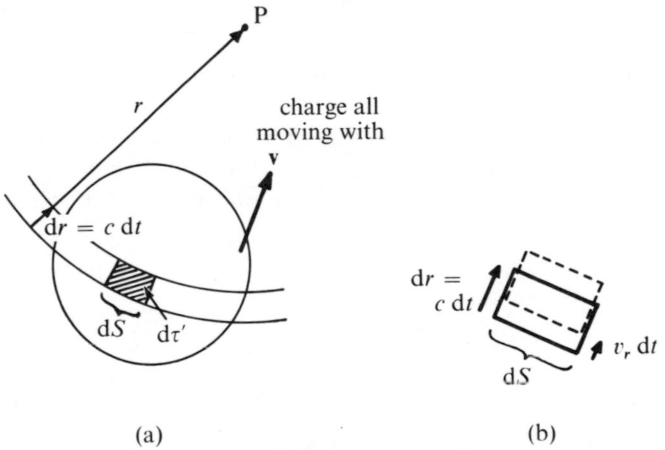

Fig. 4.5 (a) Method of calculating charge having the same retarded time; (b) the collapsing sphere does not cover as much charge as it would when $\mathbf{v} = 0$, provided v_r is towards P

stationary we should simply say that the charge $\mathrm{d}Q$ with retarded time $t - r/c$ is $[\rho]\, \mathrm{d}\tau'$ so that we could replace $[\rho]\, \mathrm{d}\tau'$ in (4.70) by $\mathrm{d}Q$. But the charge is moving with velocity $[\mathbf{v}]$ whose component towards P is $[v_r]$. Thus, by the time $\mathrm{d}S$ has travelled $\mathrm{d}r$, the charge itself has moved on by $[v_r]\,dt$ (Fig. 4.5b) so that the amount of charge actually covered by dS is reduced to $[\rho]\,(dr - [v_r]\,dt)\,dS$ or, since $d\tau' = dr\,dS$, to $[\rho](1 - [v_r]/c)\,d\tau'$. This is the element of charge dQ with the appropriate retarded time so that

$$dQ = [\rho](1 - [v_r]/c)\,d\tau' = [\rho](1 - [\mathbf{v}\,.\,\mathbf{r}/rc])\,d\tau'. \quad (4.82)$$

Thus, replacing $[\rho]\,d\tau'$ by $dQ/(1 - [v_r]/c)$ in (4.70),

$$V = \int \frac{dQ}{4\pi\varepsilon_0(r - \mathbf{v}\,.\,\mathbf{r}/c)} \quad (4.83)$$

in which all quantities are retarded. If the charge is small enough, the variation in r over the volume is also small and in the limit the denominator of (4.83) may be taken out of the integration. This gives

$$V = \frac{Q}{4\pi\varepsilon_0(r - \mathbf{v}\,.\,\mathbf{r}/c)} = \frac{Q}{4\pi\varepsilon_0 s} \quad (4.84)$$

and, in a similar way,

$$\mathbf{A} = \frac{\mu_0 Q\mathbf{v}}{4\pi(r - \mathbf{v}\,.\,\mathbf{r}/c)} = \frac{\mu_0 Q\mathbf{v}}{4\pi s}. \quad (4.85)$$

In both (4.84) and (4.85), all $\mathbf{v}$ and $\mathbf{r}$ are retarded quantities and $s = r - \mathbf{v}\,.\,\mathbf{r}/c$.

These expressions are known as the *Liénard-Wiechert potentials* for a small moving charge and it is from these that $\mathbf{E}$ and $\mathbf{B}$ are obtained using $\mathbf{E} = -\partial\mathbf{A}/\partial t - \mathbf{grad}\,V$ and $\mathbf{B} = \mathbf{curl}\,\mathbf{A}$. The complete solution is lengthy to obtain (see appendix C) and we here quote the result:

$$\mathbf{E} = \frac{Q}{4\pi\varepsilon_0 s^3}\left(1 - \frac{v^2}{c^2}\right)\left(\mathbf{r} - \frac{r\mathbf{v}}{c}\right) + \frac{Q}{4\pi\varepsilon_0 c^2 s^3}\left[\mathbf{r} \times \left\{\left(\mathbf{r} - \frac{\mathbf{v}r}{c}\right) \times \dot{\mathbf{v}}\right\}\right] \quad (4.86)$$

$$\mathbf{B} = \frac{\mathbf{r} \times \mathbf{E}}{rc} \quad (4.87)$$

in which all quantities are retarded. These fields can be analysed into three types much as those of the oscillating dipole in the last section. Thus, $\mathbf{v} = \dot{\mathbf{v}} = 0$ gives the static field of a *stationary charge* which consists only of an electric field falling off with distance as $1/r^2$ and no magnetic field. A charge moving with *uniform velocity* has $\dot{\mathbf{v}} = 0$ and now gives rise to both electric and magnetic fields falling off as

$1/r^2$: for small velocities $\mathbf{B}$ is given by $\mu_0 Q(\mathbf{v} \times \mathbf{r})/4\pi r^3$ as would be obtained from (2.5) by replacing $I\,d\mathbf{l}$ by $Q\mathbf{v}$ (see section 2.5). For further discussion of the fields of a uniformly moving charge, see problems 4.15 and 4.16.

When the charge *accelerates*, extra terms in $\dot{\mathbf{v}}$ appear:

$$\mathbf{E}_{\text{acc}} = \frac{Q}{4\pi\varepsilon_0 c^2 s^3}\left(\mathbf{r} \times \left\{\left(\mathbf{r} - \frac{r\mathbf{v}}{c}\right) \times \dot{\mathbf{v}}\right\}\right) \tag{4.88}$$

$$\mathbf{B}_{\text{acc}} = \frac{\mathbf{r} \times \mathbf{E}_{\text{acc}}}{rc} \tag{4.89}$$

where all quantities are retarded. These fields are both transverse to the retarded position vector and fall off with distance as $1/r$. At large distances, therefore, the acceleration fields will predominate over the others. Evaluation of the Poynting vector over a closed surface shows that the energy from these fields is lost to the charge and that the fields are therefore to be identified as radiation fields like (4.77).

Examples of accelerating charges which radiate are to be found in synchrotron radiation and in bremsstrahlung. In a circular orbit, the acceleration is perpendicular to the velocity, and radiation from charges forms a serious source of energy loss in the larger accelerators. *Bremsstrahlung* or *braking radiation* occurs when electrons are slowed down in a target and gives rise to the continuous spectrum observed in X-ray tubes.

We consider briefly the case in which the charge is moving so slowly that the distinction between present and retarded positions

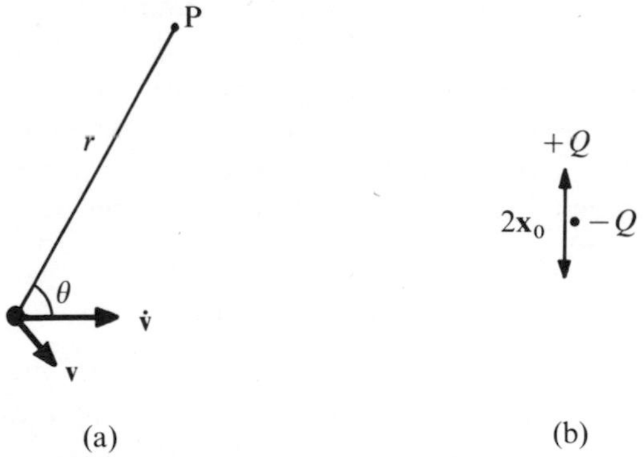

Fig. 4.6 (a) A moving charge with its velocity and acceleration; (b) an oscillating dipole in which Q vibrates with amplitude x_0

vanishes and $s = r$. Then, using the notation of Fig. 4.6a, (4.88) and (4.89) give

$$\mathbf{E}_{\text{acc}} = \frac{Q[\dot{v}] \sin\theta}{4\pi\varepsilon_0 c^2 r}\hat{\boldsymbol{\theta}}; \qquad \mathbf{B}_{\text{acc}} = \frac{Q[\dot{v}] \sin\theta}{4\pi\varepsilon_0 c^3 r}\hat{\boldsymbol{\phi}} \tag{4.90}$$

so that **E** and **B** satisfy the same conditions as in a plane wave. Computing the energy lost over a sphere by using the Poynting vector, we obtain

$$\text{Radiated power } P = \frac{Q^2[\dot{v}]^2}{6\pi\varepsilon_0 c^3}. \tag{4.91}$$

For a generalization of this, see problem 11.11.

An oscillating dipole of the type shown in Fig. 4.6b has a dipole moment $\mathbf{p} = Q\mathbf{x}$ where $\mathbf{x}$ is the instantaneous displacement $\mathbf{x}_0 \sin\omega t$. It follows that $\ddot{p} = Q\dot{v}$ and the formulae of (4.90) and (4.91) are thus identical with those of (4.77) and (4.79). The condition $v \ll c$ in this type of dipole corresponds to the condition $\mathrm{d}l \ll \lambda$ in the last section.

4.9 Radiation pressure and electromagnetic momentum

When an electromagnetic wave meets a conducting surface, the transverse **E** vector sets up conduction currents **J** in the direction of **E**. The magnetic vector **B** then exerts a force $\mathbf{J} \times \mathbf{B}$ per unit volume on these currents in the direction of the original wave. This force constitutes a *radiation pressure* whose existence can be demonstrated experimentally (see *Electricity and Magnetism*, section 15.6, for an elementary treatment). The pressure can communicate momentum to the conductor and so, unless we attribute momentum also to the impinging wave, the principle of conservation of momentum will not be obeyed. We thus look for an expression giving the momentum to be associated with an electromagnetic wave in such a way that the total linear momentum in the universe is always conserved. This will also imply a recoil in any system emitting radiation.

From the general expression (2.64), the force per unit volume on a region containing both charges and currents is:

$$\mathbf{f} = \rho\mathbf{E} + \mathbf{J} \times \mathbf{B}. \tag{4.92}$$

Using Maxwell's equations to eliminate ρ and **J** and introducing a zero term **H** div **B** to obtain a symmetrical expression, we find

$$\mathbf{f} = \mathbf{E}\,\mathrm{div}\,\mathbf{D} + \mathbf{H}\,\mathrm{div}\,\mathbf{B} - \mathbf{B} \times (\mathbf{curl\,H}) - \frac{\partial \mathbf{D}}{\partial t} \times \mathbf{B}.$$

The last term can be written as $-\partial(\mathbf{D} \times \mathbf{B})/\partial t + \mathbf{D} \times \partial\mathbf{B}/\partial t$ or as $-\partial(\mathbf{D} \times \mathbf{B})/\partial t - \mathbf{D} \times (\mathbf{curl\ E})$, and integrating over a volume:

$$\mathbf{F} = \int_\tau [\mathbf{E} \operatorname{div} \mathbf{D} - \mathbf{D} \times (\mathbf{curl\ E}) + \mathbf{H} \operatorname{div} \mathbf{B} - \mathbf{B} \times (\mathbf{curl\ H})]\, d\tau$$

$$- \frac{d}{dt}\int (\mathbf{D} \times \mathbf{B})\, d\tau. \quad (4.93)$$

It is shown below that the first volume integral here can be expressed as a surface integral over S bounding τ. If the volume is large enough, the field quantities over S may under some circumstances be zero and (4.93) would then be

$$\mathbf{F} = -\frac{d\mathbf{G}}{dt} \quad (4.94)$$

where

$$\mathbf{G} = \int_\tau (\mathbf{D} \times \mathbf{B})\, d\tau. \quad (4.95)$$

Since $\mathbf{F}$ can be written as $d\mathbf{p}_{\text{mech}}/dt$ where $\mathbf{p}_{\text{mech}}$ is the mechanical linear momentum of the system, we have that

$$\frac{d}{dt}(\mathbf{p}_{\text{mech}} + \mathbf{G}) = 0 \quad (4.96)$$

and the total momentum of the system is not conserved unless we interpret $\mathbf{G}$ as an electromagnetic momentum of density

$$\mathbf{g} = \mathbf{D} \times \mathbf{B}. \quad (4.97)$$

In vacuo, using $\mathbf{D} = \varepsilon_0\mathbf{E}$, $\mathbf{B} = \mu_0\mathbf{H}$ and (problem 4.9) $N = u_{\text{EM}}c$

$$\mathbf{g} = \frac{\mathbf{N}}{c^2} = \frac{u_{\text{EM}}}{c}\hat{\mathbf{s}} \quad \textit{in vacuo}. \quad (4.98)$$

Radiation pressure. We now turn to a case in which the first term of (4.93) is not zero: that of a steady monochromatic wave impinging on the surface of an LIH medium. Here it is the final term of (4.93) which has a zero mean value. The equation for the force is then

$$\mathbf{F} = \int_\tau [(\mathbf{E} \operatorname{div} \mathbf{D} - \mathbf{D} \times \mathbf{curl\ E}) + (\mathbf{H} \operatorname{div} \mathbf{B} - \mathbf{B} \times \mathbf{curl\ H})]\, d\tau$$

$$(4.99)$$

and problem 4.18 shows how this can be transformed into the surface integral

$$\mathbf{F} = \oint [\mathbf{E}(\mathbf{D} \cdot \mathrm{d}\mathbf{S}) + \mathbf{H}(\mathbf{B} \cdot \mathrm{d}\mathbf{S}) - u_{\mathrm{EM}} \, \mathrm{d}S] \tag{4.100}$$

where u_{EM} is the energy density $\frac{1}{2}\mathbf{B} \cdot \mathbf{H} + \frac{1}{2}\mathbf{D} \cdot \mathbf{E}$. This can be expressed as $\int T \, \mathrm{d}S$ where T is the Maxwell stress tensor, but for a

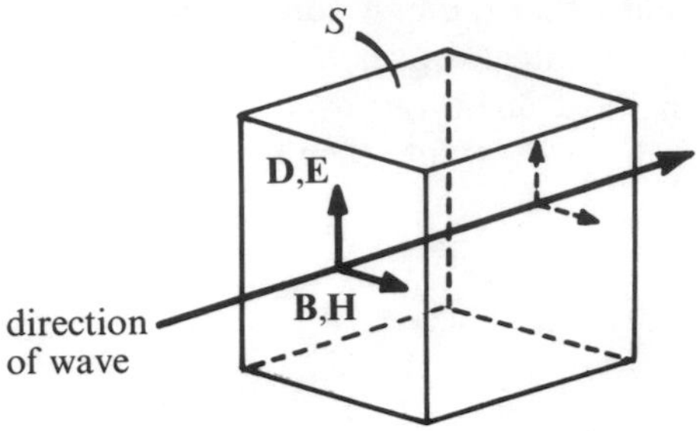

Fig. 4.7 An electromagnetic wave striking a block of material normally

block of LIH material as in Fig. 4.7 it will be found that the contributions to the integral over the sides are either zero or they cancel, and that the only contribution over the front and rear surfaces is from the u_{EM} term. The force per unit area or the radiation pressure is thus the difference between the energy density entering and emerging from the material. If the radiation is completely absorbed, we simply have that the radiation pressure is the incident u_{EM} (see also problems 4.19 and 4.20).

PROBLEMS

4.1 Estimate the electric field strength at 3 m from a 150 W lamp and 150 miles from a 15 kW transmitting aerial assuming that they radiate energy as point sources and that 20 per cent of the energy input is emitted as electromagnetic radiation.

4.2 A cylindrical conductor of finite resistance R carries a steady current I along its length. Calculate the value of the Poynting vector at the surface of the conductor and show that the electromagnetic field energy flowing into the material is RI^2 per unit time. (Remember that E_{tan} is continuous across the boundary.) On this picture, where does the energy come from?

4.3 Use the form (4.38) for monochromatic waves to show that $\mathbf{E}$ and $\mathbf{B}$ are transverse and spatially perpendicular.

4.4 To find the amplitude of a wave at any instant, the real or imaginary part of the complex representation must be taken. Show from (4.44) that the tip of $\mathbf{E}_0$ traces out an ellipse at any point in the wave as time elapses. Take the z-axis as the direction of propagation and put $\mathbf{E}_1$ and $\mathbf{E}_2$ along the x- and y-axes so that $x = E_1 \cos(kz - \omega t)$, $y = E_2 \cos(kz - \omega t + \delta)$. Find the angle between the principal axes of the ellipse and the x-axis.

4.5 Show that circularly polarized light propagated along the z-axis can be represented by $\mathbf{E}_\pm = E_0(\hat{\mathbf{x}} \pm i\hat{\mathbf{y}}) \exp\{i(kz - \omega t)\}$ where $\hat{\mathbf{x}}$ and $\hat{\mathbf{y}}$ are unit vectors along the x- and y-axes. Optical usage defines right-handed polarization such that it corresponds to clockwise rotation when the wave approaches the observer. Which sign in $\mathbf{E}_\pm$ corresponds to right-handed polarization? In the physics of elementary particles, a positive *helicity* or *chirality* is possessed when the positive senses of the axial vector representing rotation axis and the polar vector representing translation are the same. Does right circularly polarized light have positive or negative helicity?

4.6 Show that any state of elliptical polarization can be represented by appropriate combinations of two circularly polarized waves of opposite helicity.

4.7 A plane electromagnetic wave of wave-length 3 cm is travelling in the x-direction *in vacuo*. The amplitude of $\mathbf{E}$ is 2 V/m and the wave is right circularly polarized. Find expressions for the cartesian components of $\mathbf{E}$ and $\mathbf{B}$ at any instant.

4.8 What is the mean energy flux carried by the waves of problem 4.7?

4.9 Show from (4.17) that the velocity of propagation of energy in a plane electromagnetic wave *in vacuo* is c.

4.10 Show that a potential $\boldsymbol{\Pi}_e$ (the electric Hertz vector) defined by $V = -\text{div}\, \boldsymbol{\Pi}_e$, $\mathbf{A} = (1/c^2)\, \partial \boldsymbol{\Pi}_e/\partial t$ automatically satisfies the Lorentz condition (4.58). Obtain $\mathbf{E}$ and $\mathbf{B}$ in terms of $\boldsymbol{\Pi}_e$ and note that it contains all the information necessary to find fields. What conditions are imposed on $\boldsymbol{\Pi}_e$ by Maxwell's equations when there are no sources ($\rho = 0$, $\mathbf{J} = 0$)?

4.11 Show that $\boldsymbol{\Pi}_e = [\mathbf{p}]/4\pi\varepsilon_0 r$ is the electric Hertz vector everywhere for the Hertzian dipole and that the fields (4.75) and (4.76) follow.

4.12 Show that a potential $\boldsymbol{\Pi}_m$ (the magnetic Hertz vector) defined by $V = 0$, $\mathbf{A} = \textbf{curl}\, \boldsymbol{\Pi}_m$ is another potential automatically satisfying the Lorentz condition (4.58) and also yielding $\mathbf{E}$ and $\mathbf{B}$. Using equation (2.28) to obtain $\boldsymbol{\Pi}_m$ for a magnetic dipole, show that the radiation fields from a varying magnetic dipole of moment $\mathbf{m}$ are given by

$$\mathbf{E} = -\frac{\mu_0[\ddot{m}] \sin\theta}{4\pi c r}\hat{\boldsymbol{\phi}}; \qquad \mathbf{B} = \frac{\mu_0[\ddot{m}] \sin\theta}{4\pi c^2 r}\hat{\boldsymbol{\theta}}$$

with the usual notation. Compare these fields and the total radiated power with those of the Hertzian dipole.

4.13 Show that if **E** and **B** are solutions of Maxwell's equations *in vacuo*, then so are $\mathbf{E}' = -c\mathbf{B}$ and $\mathbf{B}' = \mathbf{E}/c$.

4.14 Show that there exist two vectors $\mathbf{Q}_e$ and $\mathbf{Q}_m$ (known as stream functions) which automatically satisfy the equation of continuity div $\mathbf{J} + \partial\rho/\partial t = 0$ if suitably defined in terms of the sources ρ and **J**. (Use the analogy of the Hertz vectors.) Use Maxwell's equations with sources represented solely by $\mathbf{Q}_e$ to show that the electric Hertz vector introduced in problem 4.10 satisfies $\square^2 \boldsymbol{\Pi}_e = -\mathbf{Q}_e/\varepsilon_0$. Assume no media present so that $\mathbf{D} = \varepsilon_0\mathbf{E}$, $\mathbf{H} = \mathbf{B}/\mu_0$.

4.15 Using (4.86) and (4.87), write down expressions for the fields due to a charge moving with a uniform velocity **v**. In this case, it is possible to express **E** and **B** in terms of 'present' values rather than retarded values. Using the notation of Fig. 4.8, show that the retarded quantities $(\mathbf{r} - \mathbf{v}r/c)$ and s in

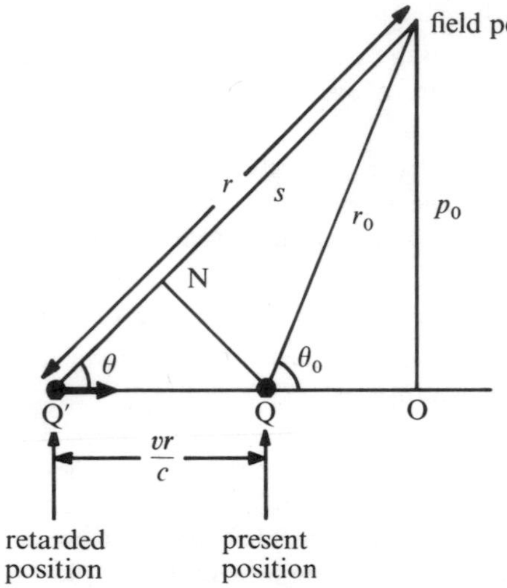

Fig. 4.8 Geometry for calculating the fields of a charge moving with a uniform velocity

(4.86) may be replaced by $\mathbf{r}_0$ and $r_0[1 - (v^2 \sin^2 \theta_0)/c^2]^{1/2}$ respectively. Find **E** and **B** in terms of $\mathbf{r}_0$, θ_0, and **v**. Show that as $v \to c$, the fields in the transverse plane ($\theta_0 = 90°$) become very large and those in the direction of **v** very small.

4.16 Find **E** and **B** from problem 4.15 for a slowly moving charge with constant velocity and confirm that they tally with the appropriate formulae in chapters 1 and 2.

4.17 Two equal point charges Q are moving with constant velocities v parallel to each other at a constant distance r_0 apart. What is the total force between them?

4.18 Show that the x component of $\mathbf{E}\,\mathrm{div}\,\mathbf{D} - (\mathbf{D} \times \mathbf{curl\,E})$ may be expressed as $\mathrm{div}\,(\mathbf{D}E_x) - \frac{1}{2}\varepsilon_r\varepsilon_0\,\mathrm{div}\,(\hat{\mathbf{x}}E^2)$ for LIH media, $\hat{\mathbf{x}}$ being a unit vector along the x-axis. Hence show that the volume integral of (4.99) is equivalent to the surface integral (4.100). For the block of material in Fig. 4.7, check that the resultant contribution to (4.100) from the whole surface is limited to that from u_{EM} over the front and rear.

4.19 A plane electromagnetic wave *in vacuo* impinges obliquely on an absorbent surface at an angle of incidence θ. What is the radiation pressure in terms of u_{EM} and θ? Show that when the radiation is incident at all angles with equal intensity the radiation pressure is $u_{\mathrm{EM}}/3$ normal to the surface.

4.20 The wave of problem 4.19 has a fraction f of the energy reflected at the surface and the rest completely absorbed. What is the radiation pressure?

4.21 Show that the relation between energy E and momentum p for an electromagnetic wave *in vacuo* is the same as that for photons.

Part 2

Potential Problems

In this part are grouped two types of electromagnetic problem frequently encountered in physical situations: both are best tackled by using potentials to obtain the fields. The first type (chapter 5) concerns the fields of complicated arrangements of charges or currents where these sources of the fields are *given*. The second type (chapter 6) deals with the solution of problems where media with specified boundaries modify the fields of given charge or current distributions.

5

Specified distributions of charge and current

Expressions for the fields due to charges and currents are only simple when the distributions are simple and the origin and co-ordinate system suitably chosen. As soon as any degree of complexity enters, for instance when considering molecules, atoms, or nuclei, formulae can become extremely unwieldly. Fortunately, a systematic method of dealing with general distributions of charge and current is possible when the field point is some distance from all sources. This is a common situation in physics, particularly in atomic and nuclear problems, and it is for this reason that a special chapter is devoted to such cases.

5.1 Discrete distributions of stationary charge

Let Q_i be the ith of a collection of point charges at a position $\mathbf{r}_i$ with respect to the origin. The collection is such that no charge is at a greater distance from the origin than a finite value R, i.e., all charges can be contained within a sphere radius R centre O. We evaluate the potential V at a point P (Fig. 5.1), whose position vector is $\mathbf{r}$, by summing all contributions from the Q_i: the electric field strength can then be obtained by using $\mathbf{E} = -\mathbf{grad}\, V$. We only stipulate that $|\mathbf{r}| > R$.

The potential due to Q_i alone is

$$V_i = \frac{Q_i}{4\pi\varepsilon_0 |\mathbf{r} - \mathbf{r}_i|}. \tag{5.1}$$

This expression needs expanding in such a way as to bring out the dependence on r and r_i separately. There are several equivalent ways of doing this, one of which uses the Taylor expansion about the origin of $1/|\mathbf{r} - \mathbf{r}_i|$ (see problem 5.1). We use a method leading more directly to the expressions needed for later discussion.

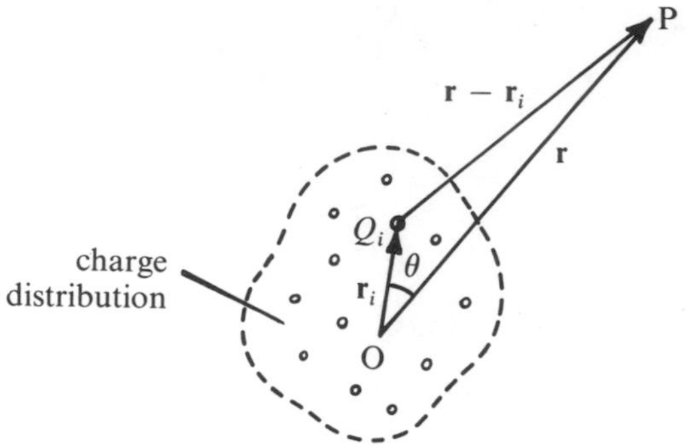

Fig. 5.1 Finding the potential due to a stationary charge distribution

In the triangle OPQ_i, we have

$$|\mathbf{r} - \mathbf{r}_i|^2 = r^2 - 2\mathbf{r}\cdot\mathbf{r}_i + r_i^2 = r^2 - 2rr_i\cos\theta + r_i^2 \qquad (5.2)$$

and thus

$$V_i = \frac{Q_i}{4\pi\varepsilon_0 r}\left(1 - 2\frac{\mathbf{r}\cdot\mathbf{r}_i}{r^2} + \frac{r_i^2}{r^2}\right)^{-1/2}$$

$$= \frac{Q}{4\pi\varepsilon_0 r}\left(1 - 2\frac{r_i\cos\theta}{r} + \frac{r_i^2}{r^2}\right)^{-1/2}$$

Expanding either form of this by the binomial theorem (convergent series since all $r_i < r$), collecting terms and arranging them in ascending powers of $1/r$, we get

$$V_i = \frac{Q_i}{4\pi\varepsilon_0 r}\left[1 + \frac{r_i\cos\theta}{r} + \frac{r_i^2(3\cos^2\theta - 1)}{2r^2} + \frac{r_i^3(5\cos^3\theta - 3\cos\theta)}{2r^3} + \cdots\right] \qquad (5.3)$$

$$= \frac{Q_i}{4\pi\varepsilon_0 r}\left[1 + \frac{\mathbf{r}_i\cdot\mathbf{r}}{r^2} + \frac{3(\mathbf{r}_i\cdot\mathbf{r})^2 - r_i^2 r^2}{2r^4} + \cdots\right] \qquad (5.4)$$

where the general term in the bracket in (5.3) is $(r_i/r)^n P_n(\cos\theta)$, $P_n(\cos\theta)$ being the Legendre polynomials. Summing (5.4) over all the charges, we obtain the resultant potential at P:

$$V_{\mathrm{P}} = \frac{\sum Q_i}{4\pi\varepsilon_0 r} + \frac{\sum Q_i \mathbf{r}_i \cdot \mathbf{r}}{4\pi\varepsilon_0 r^3} + \frac{\sum \frac{1}{2}[3Q_i(\mathbf{r}_i \cdot \mathbf{r})^2 - Q_i r_i^2 r^2]}{4\pi\varepsilon_0 r^5} + \cdots \tag{5.5}$$

which we write as

$$V_{\mathrm{P}} = V_0 + V_1 + V_2 + \cdots. \tag{5.6}$$

These terms, representing as they do the increasing powers of (r_i/r) in (5.3), will decrease in magnitude since all $r_i < r$. For many applications, $r_i \ll r$ and the first term or two will predominate. Equation (5.5) is known as the *multipole expansion* of the potential, and each term can be shown to be the potential of certain ideal distributions of charge *situated at the origin*, as we now see.

Charge and dipole terms. The V_0 term in (5.6) is simply the potential of a total charge $\sum Q_i$ situated at O and for very large r any collection of charges will behave very nearly like a single charge $\sum Q_i$ because V_1, V_2, etc., are very small compared with V_0. If, however, $\sum Q_i = 0$ then V_1 predominates (note that in the analogous gravitational case $\sum m_i$ can never be zero).

Now V_1 can be written

$$V_1 = \frac{\mathbf{r} \cdot \sum Q_i \mathbf{r}_i}{4\pi\varepsilon_0 r^3} \tag{5.7}$$

where under the summation we now have quantities dependent only on the charge distribution itself and not on P. The quantity

$$\mathbf{p} = \sum Q_i \mathbf{r}_i \tag{5.8}$$

is known as the *electric moment* or *dipole moment* of the system about the origin O. It has three cartesian components $p_x = \sum Q_i x_i$, $p_y = \sum Q_i y_i$, $p_z = \sum Q_i z_i$ which transform under a change of co-ordinates like x_i, y_i, z_i so that $\mathbf{p}$ is a vector. Equation (5.7) can now be written

$$V_1 = \frac{\mathbf{p} \cdot \mathbf{r}}{4\pi\varepsilon_0 r^3} = -\frac{\mathbf{p} \cdot (\mathbf{grad}\,(1/r))}{4\pi\varepsilon_0} \tag{5.9}$$

and these are identical with the potential at P which would be given by an ideal dipole at O (compare equation (1.16)).

The dipole moment of a system, unlike its total charge $\sum Q_i$, depends usually on the origin chosen. Two important properties possessed by $\mathbf{p}$ in (5.8) are, however, (1) if $\sum Q_i = 0$, then $\mathbf{p}$ is independent of the origin chosen (e.g., an ideal dipole); and (2) if $\sum Q_i \neq 0$, then it is always possible to choose an origin so that $\mathbf{p}$ and hence V_1 is zero.

To prove these, let O′ be a second origin at a position $\mathbf{s}$ with respect to O and let primed quantities be those measured with respect to O′. Then $\mathbf{r}_i' = \mathbf{r}_i - \mathbf{s}$ and

$$\mathbf{p}' = \sum Q_i\mathbf{r}_i' = \sum Q_i\mathbf{r}_i - \mathbf{s}\sum Q_i = \mathbf{p} - \mathbf{s}\sum Q_i.$$

Thus $\mathbf{p}' = \mathbf{p}$ if $\sum Q_i = 0$. Otherwise, $\mathbf{s}$ can always be chosen as $\mathbf{p}/\sum Q_i$ to make $\mathbf{p}'$ zero. It should be noted that if $\mathbf{s}$ is so chosen, its co-ordinates with respect to O are $s_x = \sum Q_i x_i/\sum Q_i$, etc., so that it is clearly the centroid of charge (analogous in a massive body to the centre of mass).

Quadrupole term. The next term in (5.5) is

$$V_2 = \frac{1}{4\pi\varepsilon_0 r^5}\sum \tfrac{1}{2}[3Q_i(\mathbf{r}\cdot\mathbf{r}_i)^2 - Q_i r^2 r_i^2]. \tag{5.10}$$

Expanding the terms after the summation in cartesian co-ordinates:

$$V_2 = \frac{1}{4\pi\varepsilon_0 r^5}\sum \tfrac{1}{2}Q_i[3(xx_i + yy_i + zz_i)^2 - r_i^2(x^2 + y^2 + z^2)] \tag{5.11}$$

$$\begin{aligned} &= \frac{1}{4\pi\varepsilon_0 r^5}\tfrac{1}{2}\{x^2\sum Q_i(3x_i^2 - r_i^2) + y^2\sum Q_i(3y_i^2 - r_i^2) \\ &\quad + z^2\sum Q_i(3z_i^2 - r_i^2) + xy\sum 6Q_ix_iy_i \\ &\quad + yz\sum 6Q_iy_iz_i + zx\sum 6Q_iz_ix_i\}. \end{aligned} \tag{5.12}$$

Each of the summations is now independent of the field point P and a property of the charge system. The last three terms of (5.12) can be split into two equal halves to form nine quantities in all, of the form

$$\mathbf{q}_{\alpha\beta} = \sum Q_i(3\alpha\beta - \delta_{\alpha\beta}r_i^2) \tag{5.13}$$

where α, β may take any of the values x_i, y_i, or z_i and $\delta_{\alpha\beta}$ is the Kronecker symbol ($\delta_{\alpha\beta} = 0$ if $\alpha \neq \beta$, $= 1$ if $\alpha = \beta$). The nine terms of (5.13) can be set out in an array

$$\mathbf{q} \equiv \begin{pmatrix} q_{xx} & q_{xy} & q_{xz} \\ q_{yx} & q_{yy} & q_{yz} \\ q_{zx} & q_{zy} & q_{zz} \end{pmatrix}$$

$$\equiv \begin{pmatrix} \sum Q_i(3x_i^2 - r_i^2) & \sum 3Q_i x_i y_i & \sum 3Q_i x_i z_i \\ \sum 3Q_i y_i x_i & \sum Q_i(3y_i^2 - r_i^2) & \sum 3Q_i y_i z_i \\ \sum 3Q_i z_i x_i & \sum 3Q_i z_i y_i & \sum Q_i(3z_i^2 - r_i^2) \end{pmatrix} \tag{5.14}$$

When the co-ordinate axes are changed, these quantities transform in a manner characteristic of a second-rank tensor (see appendix B). The quantity $\mathbf{q}$ is the *quadrupole moment* of the system: it has nine components (compared with the three of the dipole moment) each of which depends on second moments of the charges about the origin (compared with the dipole moment in which only first moments are involved). Because the tensor (5.14) is symmetric, only six of the components are independent, as is otherwise clear from (5.12), and since in addition $q_{xx} + q_{yy} + q_{zz} = 0$, only five independent components remain. It can be shown (problem 5.3) that the components of $\mathbf{q}$ are independent of the choice of origin if both $\sum Q_i$ and $\mathbf{p}$ are zero.

The components of the quadrupole moment are analogous to the moments and products of inertia in a massive body and, like the inertia tensor and other symmetric second-rank tensors, $\mathbf{q}$ can be diagonalized by a suitable choice of axes. Axes so chosen that only the diagonal terms of (5.14) are not zero are known as *principal* axes and when referred to them, $\mathbf{q}$ has only two independent components left.

A particularly important class of distribution is one in which there is an axis of symmetry. Such an axis can form a principal axis with any point on it as origin because $\sum Q_i x_i y_i$, $\sum Q_i y_i z_i$, and $\sum Q_i z_i x_i$ are all zero owing to the symmetry. If the z-axis is chosen to be the axis of symmetry, then $\sum Q_i x_i^2 = \sum Q_i y_i^2$ so that $q_{xx} = q_{yy}$ and each will equal $-\frac{1}{2}q_{zz}$. Thus only *one* independent component of the quadrupole moment remains and this is conventionally q_{zz}. Thus, for arrangements with a z-axis of symmetry, (5.12) reduces to

$$V_2 = \frac{1}{4}\frac{q_{zz}(3z^2 - r^2)}{4\pi\varepsilon_0 r^5} \tag{5.15}$$

where

$$q_{zz} = Q_i(3z_i^2 - r_i^2). \tag{5.16}$$

Comparison of this result with the potential due to an ideal linear quadrupole (problem 1.9, $q_{zz} = 4Qa^2$), shows that the whole axially symmetric system can be replaced by such a linear quadrupole along the z-axis. General systems cannot be replaced by less than five ideal quadrupoles at the origin corresponding to the five independent components of $\mathbf{q}$ in (5.14).

Higher electric multipoles. It would clearly be possible to consider at equal length the octopole term V_3 in (5.6) and higher terms, but it is sufficient to note that the dependence on r, the distance of the field point P from the origin, is $1/r^L$ for the 2^L-pole term V_L when the appropriate moments are taken as given. The electric fields will fall off as $1/r^{L+1}$.

5.2 Continuous distributions of stationary charge

A continuous distribution can be treated in exactly the same way as the discrete one in the last section. The typical charge Q_i is replaced by the volume element $\rho\, \mathrm{d}x'\, \mathrm{d}y'\, \mathrm{d}z' = \rho\, \mathrm{d}\tau'$ situated at (x', y', z'), the primes indicating source co-ordinates. We then have that the potential at a field point P (x, y, z) is

$$V_{\mathrm{P}} = V_0 + V_1 + V_2 + \cdots \tag{5.17}$$

in which

$$V_0 = Q/4\pi\varepsilon_0 r \tag{5.18}$$

$$V_1 = \mathbf{p} \cdot \mathbf{r}/4\pi\varepsilon_0 r^3 = (p_x x + p_y y + p_z z)/4\pi\varepsilon_0 r^3 \tag{5.19}$$

$$V_2 = (q_{xx}x^2 + q_{yy}y^2 + q_{zz}z^2 + 2q_{xy}xy + 2q_{yz}yz + 2q_{zx}zx)/8\pi\varepsilon_0 r^5 \tag{5.20}$$

where

$$Q = \int_{\tau'} \rho\, \mathrm{d}\tau' \tag{5.21}$$

$$p_x = \int_{\tau'} \rho x'\, \mathrm{d}\tau'; \qquad p_y = \int_{\tau'} \rho y'\, \mathrm{d}\tau'; \qquad p_z = \int_{\tau'} \rho z'\, \mathrm{d}\tau' \tag{5.22}$$

$$q_{xx} = \int_{\tau'} \rho(3x'^2 - r'^2)\, \mathrm{d}\tau'; \qquad q_{xy} = \int_{\tau'} \rho 3x'y'\, \mathrm{d}\tau', \quad \text{etc.} \tag{5.23}$$

The same considerations about dependence of **p** and **q** on choice of origin occur as in the last section. In particular, if a distribution has complete spherical symmetry all moments about the origin are zero and only V_0 remains. With axial symmetry about the z-axis, once again only one independent component of the quadrupole moment remains:

$$q_{zz} = \int_{\tau'} (3z'^2 - r'^2)\rho \, d\tau' \tag{5.24}$$

the potential being given by (5.15) as before.

If a continuous distribution of charge departs slightly from spherical symmetry but retains an axial symmetry so that it becomes a prolate (elongated) or oblate spheroid, q_{zz} is a measure of the departure from sphericity and is positive if prolate, negative if oblate.

In applying multipole theory to quantum systems such as nuclei, some care must be taken both in correlating usage with the above and in the interpretation of results. Nuclear quadrupole moments are quoted as q_{zz}/e, where e is the electronic charge, so that they have the dimensions of (length)^2 and they are calculated not about the angular momentum $I^* = \sqrt{\{I(I+1)\}}$ axis, but about the direction corresponding to the maximum projection of I^*. Moreover, while a non-zero q_{zz} indicates departure from sphericity, a zero value does not necessarily mean that a nucleus has spherical symmetry, for all multipole moments can be zero on grounds other than geometrical symmetry. For quantum systems in stationary states, it can be shown that 2^L-pole electric moments with L odd are all zero, while those with L even (including q_{zz}) are zero unless the angular momentum I is at least $L/2$ (see Blatt and Weisskopf, 1953). Thus $q_{zz} = 0$ if I is 0 or $\frac{1}{2}$.

5.3 Charge distributions in electric fields

Suppose a general charge distribution is situated in an external electric field so that the ith charge Q_i at (x_i, y_i, z_i) is at a point where the potential is $V(x_i, y_i, z_i)$. The potential energy of Q_i in the field is thus $Q_i V$ and for the whole system is

$$U = Q_i V(x_i, y_i, z_i). \tag{5.25}$$

Expanding V in terms of the potential V_0 at the origin by using Taylor's theorem:

$$V(x_i, y_i, z_i) = V_0 + \left(x_i \frac{\partial V_0}{\partial x} + y_i \frac{\partial V_0}{\partial y} + z_i \frac{\partial V_0}{\partial z}\right)$$
$$+ \left(\frac{1}{2} x_i^2 \frac{\partial^2 V_0}{\partial x^2} + x_i y_i \frac{\partial^2 V_0}{\partial x \, \partial y} + \cdots\right) + \cdots \quad (5.26)$$

and (5.25) becomes

$$U = V_0 \sum Q_i + \left(\frac{\partial V_0}{\partial x} \sum Q_i x_i + \frac{\partial V_0}{\partial y} \sum Q_i y_i + \frac{\partial V_0}{\partial z} \sum Q_i z_i\right)$$
$$+ \left(\frac{1}{2} \frac{\partial^2 V_0}{\partial x^2} \sum Q_i x_i^2 + \cdots\right) + \cdots \quad (5.27)$$

$$= U_0 + U_1 + U_2 + \cdots \quad (5.28)$$

say. Once again we see that the charge distribution behaves as a collection of ideal multipoles at the origin: U_0 is the potential energy of a charge $\sum Q_i$ in V_0, the potential at O, and U_1 can be written as $\mathbf{p} \cdot \mathbf{grad}\, V_0$ or $-\mathbf{p} \cdot \mathbf{E}_0$, the potential energy of an ideal dipole in the electric field $\mathbf{E}_0$ at O, as in (1.62). To correlate U_2 with the quadrupole moment as defined in (5.14) we write it as

$$U_2 = \frac{1}{6}\left(\frac{\partial^2 V_0}{\partial x^2} \sum 3Q_i x_i^2 + \frac{\partial^2 V_0}{\partial x \, \partial y} \sum 3Q_i x_i y_i\right.$$
$$\left. + \frac{\partial^2 V_0}{\partial y \, \partial x} \sum 3Q_i y_i x_i + \cdots\right) \quad (5.29)$$

from (5.27). Since V_0 is due to an external field, $\nabla^2 V_0 = 0$ and so subtracting $\nabla^2 V_0 \sum Q_i r_i^2/6$ from the right-hand side of (5.29) will not alter its value. This, however, enables U_2 to be written as

$$U_2 = \frac{1}{6}\left(q_{xx} \frac{\partial^2 V_0}{\partial x^2} + q_{xy} \frac{\partial^2 V_0}{\partial x \, \partial y} + q_{xz} \frac{\partial^2 V_0}{\partial x \, \partial z} + \cdots\right) \quad (5.30)$$

so that the quadrupole moment interacts with the second derivative of the potential at the origin to give a contribution to the potential energy. It is easy to see that, in general, the 2^L-pole moment interacts with the Lth gradient of V_0 to give a contribution to U.

An important example of this occurs in molecular spectra: we have seen above that nuclei have zero electric dipole moments so that

$U_1 = 0$. However, the non-uniformity in the electric field at a nucleus is sufficient for its quadrupole moment, if any, to contribute to the interaction energy, causing hyperfine splitting in the energy levels and thus in the molecular spectra.

5.4 Distributions of steady current

The treatment here parallels that of section 5.2 rather than section 5.1 because distributions of current are essentially continuous. The magnetic flux density at the field point P (Fig. 5.2) is this time found

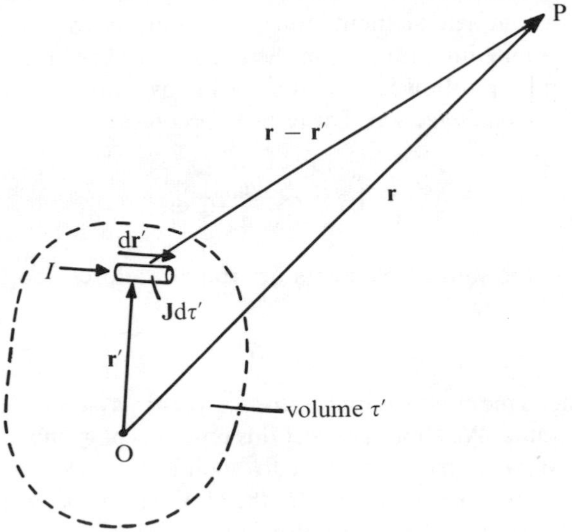

Fig. 5.2 Finding the potential due to a distribution of currents

using the vector potential **A**. If **J** dτ' is an element of current at the source point **r′**, then

$$\mathbf{A}_{\mathrm{P}} = \int_{\tau'} \frac{\mu_0 \mathbf{J}}{4\pi|\mathbf{r} - \mathbf{r}'|} \mathrm{d}\tau' \tag{5.31}$$

the integral being taken over the whole of the volume τ' containing currents. This volume, as in the charge distributions already considered, is such that $r' < r$ so that $1/|\mathbf{r} - \mathbf{r}'|$ can be expanded as in section 5.1. This gives

$$\mathbf{A}_\mathrm{P} = \frac{\mu_0}{4\pi r}\int_{\tau'} \mathbf{J}\,\mathrm{d}\tau' + \frac{\mu_0}{4\pi r^3}\int_{\tau'} \mathbf{J}(\mathbf{r}\,.\,\mathbf{r}')\,\mathrm{d}\tau' + \frac{\mu_0}{4\pi r^5}\int_{\tau'} \left[3\mathbf{J}(\mathbf{r}\,.\,\mathbf{r}')^2 - \mathbf{J}r^2r'^2\right]\mathrm{d}\tau' + \cdots \tag{5.32}$$

$$= \mathbf{A}_0 + \mathbf{A}_1 + \mathbf{A}_2 + \cdots. \tag{5.33}$$

We shall only look in detail at the first two terms of this expansion because no new points emerge in later terms. Because we are dealing with steady currents, each element $\mathbf{J}\,\mathrm{d}\tau'$ is best replaced by its equivalent filamentary element $I\,\mathrm{d}\mathbf{r}'$ (see Fig. 5.2) which must then be part of a complete filament loop in the whole of which the current is I. The volume integration can then be replaced by a line integral round each loop followed by a summation over all the loops.

Magnetic monopole term. The term $\mathbf{A}_0$ becomes the sum over loops of

$$\frac{\mu_0}{4\pi}\oint I\,\mathrm{d}\mathbf{r}' = \frac{\mu_0 I}{4\pi}\oint \mathrm{d}\mathbf{r}'$$

and the vector sum of elements $\mathrm{d}\mathbf{r}'$ round a closed loop is zero. Hence

$$\mathbf{A}_0 = 0. \tag{5.34}$$

The magnetic monopole term is thus zero for any system of complete steady currents. We should expect this on physical grounds because there are no magnetic entities corresponding to electric charges which could give rise to such a term: the Maxwell equation div $\mathbf{B} = 0$ denies the existence of sources of $\mathbf{B}$ of this type.

Magnetic dipole term. The second term in (5.33) is

$$\mathbf{A}_1 = \frac{\mu_0}{4\pi r^3}\int_{\tau'} \mathbf{J}(\mathbf{r}\,.\,\mathbf{r}')\,\mathrm{d}\tau' = \sum_{\text{loops}} \frac{\mu_0 I}{4\pi r^3}\oint(\mathbf{r}\,.\,\mathbf{r}')\,\mathrm{d}\mathbf{r}'. \tag{5.35}$$

The integrand can be transformed as follows. First, using (A.2):

$$\mathbf{r}\times(\mathbf{r}'\times\mathrm{d}\mathbf{r}') = \mathbf{r}'(\mathbf{r}\,.\,\mathrm{d}\mathbf{r}') - (\mathbf{r}\,.\,\mathbf{r}')\,\mathrm{d}\mathbf{r}' \tag{5.36}$$

and, in addition,

$$\mathrm{d}\left[\mathbf{r}'(\mathbf{r}\,.\,\mathbf{r}')\right] = \mathbf{r}'(\mathbf{r}\,.\,\mathrm{d}\mathbf{r}') + (\mathbf{r}\,.\,\mathbf{r}')\,\mathrm{d}\mathbf{r}'. \tag{5.37}$$

Subtracting (5.36) from (5.37) gives

$$(\mathbf{r}\,.\,\mathbf{r}')\,\mathrm{d}\mathbf{r}' = \tfrac{1}{2}\,\mathrm{d}\left[\mathbf{r}'(\mathbf{r}\,.\,\mathbf{r}')\right] - \tfrac{1}{2}\mathbf{r}\times(\mathbf{r}'\times\mathrm{d}\mathbf{r}').$$

Substituting in (5.35):

$$\mathbf{A}_1 = \sum_{\text{loops}} \frac{\mu_0 I}{4\pi r^3} \left\{ \oint \tfrac{1}{2}\, \mathrm{d}[\mathbf{r}'(\mathbf{r} \cdot \mathbf{r}')] - \oint \tfrac{1}{2}\mathbf{r} \times (\mathbf{r}' \times \mathrm{d}\mathbf{r}') \right\}. \tag{5.38}$$

The first integral is that of a perfect differential round a closed path and its value is thus zero. Replacing $I\,\mathrm{d}\mathbf{r}'$ in the second term by its equivalent $\mathbf{J}\,\mathrm{d}\tau'$, we thus obtain

$$\mathbf{A}_1 = -\frac{\mu_0}{4\pi r^3}\mathbf{r} \times \int_{\tau'} \tfrac{1}{2}(\mathbf{r}' \times \mathbf{J})\,\mathrm{d}\tau'. \tag{5.39}$$

The quantity

$$\mathbf{m} = \tfrac{1}{2} \int_{\tau'} (\mathbf{r}' \times \mathbf{J})\,\mathrm{d}\tau' \tag{5.40}$$

is a property of the current distribution and is independent of P. It defines the *magnetic dipole moment* about O of the currents and corresponds to $\mathbf{p}$ in (5.8) and (5.22). It is more complex than $\mathbf{p}$ in that $\mathbf{m}$ is the moment of a vector quantity about O while $\mathbf{p}$ is the moment of a scalar.

We can now write

$$\mathbf{A}_1 = \frac{\mu_0 \mathbf{m} \times \mathbf{r}}{4\pi r^3} \tag{5.41}$$

and comparison with (2.28) shows that $\mathbf{A}_1$ is the vector potential of an ideal magnetic dipole of moment given by (5.40) situated at the origin. Because $\mathbf{A}_0$ is zero, this is what current systems will appear to be at great distances.

Equation (5.40) seems somewhat different from the definition of the moment of a current loop given in (2.2), but it is in fact a generalization of that expression. For if we take only one loop consisting once more of elements $I\,\mathrm{d}\mathbf{r}'$, (5.40) gives for this

$$\mathbf{m} = I \oint \tfrac{1}{2}\mathbf{r}' \times \mathrm{d}\mathbf{r}' \tag{5.42}$$

and the integral is just the vector area of the loop (see problem 5.7).

Higher multipole terms. It is easily shown (problem 5.8) that the magnetic dipole moment about any origin is the same so that it is not possible, as with $\mathbf{p}$, to choose an origin so that $\mathbf{A}_1 = 0$. The higher multipole terms, which fall off as $1/r^3$, $1/r^4$, etc., are therefore normally small terms compared with $\mathbf{A}_1$. In quantum systems, it can be shown generally that 2^L-pole magnetic moments are zero for even L if the system is stationary (steady currents); for odd L the moments are zero if the angular momentum I is less than $L/2$ (see Blatt and Weisskopf, 1953).

Gyromagnetic ratio. If the system consists of moving charges each of mass m_i, velocity $\mathbf{v}_i$, charge Q_i at position $\mathbf{r}_i$, (5.40) gives

$$\mathbf{m} = \sum \tfrac{1}{2}(\mathbf{r}_i \times \mathbf{v}_i)Q_i. \tag{5.43}$$

The angular momentum about O is

$$\mathbf{L} = \sum m_i(\mathbf{r}_i \times \mathbf{v}_i). \tag{5.44}$$

If all the particles are identical, with charge e and mass m, these factors can be removed from the sums and the ratio of **m** to **L**, known as the gyromagnetic ratio γ, is

$$\gamma = e/2m. \tag{5.45}$$

Where more than one type of particle is moving or where there are other types of contribution to **m** or **L**, it is customary to retain the definition of γ as **m**/**L** and to write it as

$$\gamma = ge/2m \tag{5.46}$$

where the g-factor is characteristic of the complexity of the system giving rise to **m** and **L**.

5.5 Radiation from multipoles

Previous sections of this chapter have dealt entirely with fields of stationary systems of charge or current, but the most general system would naturally involve sources which varied in time. With such a system we should expect, as in sections 4.7 and 4.8, both static and radiation fields to be produced, the latter predominating in the wave zone at distances from the sources large compared with any wave-length involved. Having dealt with the static fields, we now look briefly at the radiation fields from a collection of moving charges occupying a region whose dimensions are small compared both with the distance of the field point and with any wave-length. Thus

$$|\mathbf{r}'| \quad \text{or} \quad |\mathbf{r}_i| \ll \lambda \ll |\mathbf{r}|. \tag{5.47}$$

Under these conditions we should expect any potential to be capable of expansion as in the static cases, the system behaving like a collection of time-varying electric and magnetic multipoles at the origin. Both types would occur because the charges giving rise to electric moments are moving and thus at the same time producing magnetic moments.

To see that this is so we need only examine the form of the retarded vector potential **A**, for we remember that from **A** we can obtain V through the Lorentz condition and thus the fields **E** and **B**. **J** is a function of the source co-ordinate **r′** and the retarded time of the source point with respect to the field point. Thus (4.70) gives:

$$\mathbf{A} = \int_{\tau'} \frac{\mu_0 \mathbf{J}(\mathbf{r}', t - |\mathbf{r} - \mathbf{r}'|/c)}{4\pi |\mathbf{r} - \mathbf{r}'|} \, d\tau'. \tag{5.48}$$

Since $r' \ll r$:

$$|\mathbf{r} - \mathbf{r}'| \approx r - \mathbf{r} \cdot \mathbf{r}'/r \tag{5.49}$$

using only the first two terms of equation (5.2) and taking the square root. Hence

$$\mathbf{A} \approx \int_{\tau'} \frac{\mu_0 \mathbf{J}(\mathbf{r}', t' + \mathbf{r} \cdot \mathbf{r}'/rc)}{4\pi(r - \mathbf{r} \cdot \mathbf{r}'/r)} \, d\tau', \tag{5.50}$$

where $t' = t - r/c$, the retarded time of the origin. Both the denominator and the numerator can be expanded, but if we keep only the two leading terms contributing to radiation, we can neglect the $\mathbf{r} \cdot \mathbf{r}'/r$ in the denominator since it gives no new non-static terms other than those of small orders of magnitude. The numerator of (5.50) can thus be written

$$\mathbf{J}(\mathbf{r}', t' + \mathbf{r} \cdot \mathbf{r}'/rc) \approx \mathbf{J}(\mathbf{r}', t') + \frac{\mathbf{r} \cdot \mathbf{r}'}{rc} \dot{\mathbf{J}}(\mathbf{r}', t') \tag{5.51}$$

using the first terms of the Taylor expansion. Hence from (5.50)

$$\begin{aligned} \mathbf{A} &\approx \int_{\tau'} \frac{\mu_0 [\mathbf{J}]}{4\pi r} \, d\tau' + \int_{\tau'} \frac{\mu_0 [\dot{\mathbf{J}}](\mathbf{r} \cdot \mathbf{r}')}{4\pi rc} \, d\tau' \\ &= \quad \mathbf{A}_0 \quad + \quad \mathbf{A}_1. \end{aligned} \tag{5.52}$$

These are very similar to the first two terms in the expansion of **A** for steady currents (5.32) but with two vital differences.

The first difference is that $[\mathbf{J}]$ can now include non-steady currents so that $\mathbf{A}_0$ is not necessarily zero. In fact, since $J \, dS$ for any element (Fig. 5.3) gives the current I, it also gives the rate of flow of charge from one end to the other, $\dot{Q}$. Since $Q \, d\mathbf{l}$ is the dipole moment of a non-neutral element, **p**, it follows that $\dot{\mathbf{p}} = \dot{Q} \, d\mathbf{l} = \mathbf{J} \, dS \, dl = \mathbf{J} \, d\tau'$.

Hence the $\mathbf{A}_0$ term for non-neutral non-steady currents becomes identical with the electric dipole potential in (4.72) and gives rise to *electric dipole radiation* ($E1$ radiation) with the characteristics given in section 4.7.

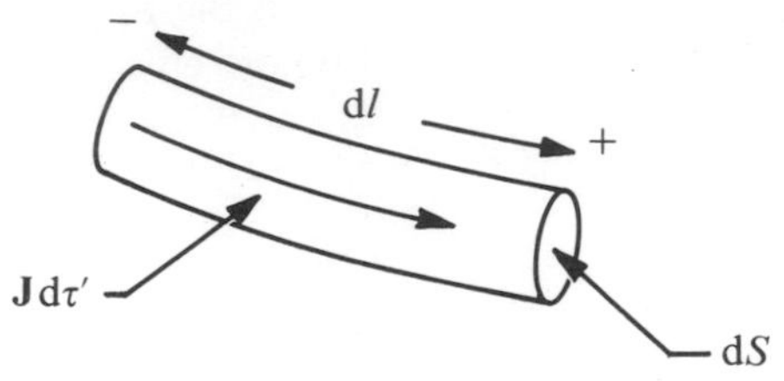

Fig. 5.3 A non-neutral current element forms a time-varying electric dipole

The second difference between (5.52) and (5.32) lies in the $\mathbf{A}_1$ term where $\dot{\mathbf{J}}$ occurs instead of $\mathbf{J}$. However, the same transformation can be made as in (5.35) onwards giving two terms as in (5.38). The second of these two will give a potential $\mu_0(\dot{\mathbf{m}} \times \mathbf{r})/4\pi r^3$ using (5.40) and this clearly gives rise to *magnetic dipole radiation* ($M1$ radiation) as in problem 4.12. The other term, zero in (5.38), can now be shown to be one giving *electric quadrupole* ($E2$) *radiation*. In general, in the full expansion of $\mathbf{A}$ we should find that

$$\mathbf{A}_0 \rightarrow E1 \text{ radiation}$$

$$\mathbf{A}_1 \rightarrow E2 \text{ and } M1 \text{ radiation}$$

$$\mathbf{A}_2 \rightarrow E3 \text{ and } M2 \text{ radiation, etc.}$$

Comparison of $E1$ *and* $M1$ *radiation.* Characteristics of the multipole radiations are best derived from ideal sources. For instance, comparison of section 4.7 with problem 4.12 shows that for dipoles oscillating at the same angular frequency ω, the powers radiated from electric and magnetic dipoles of amplitudes p_0 and m_0 respectively are in the ratio

$$P_{M1}/P_{E1} = (m_0/p_0 c)^2. \tag{5.53}$$

Now consider a system like that of Fig. 5.4a in which both electric and magnetic moments are clearly present. If small enough compared with λ, $I = \dot{Q} = \omega Q$ and hence $p_0 = Q_0\,dx$ while $m_0 = I_0\,dS =$

$\omega Q_0\, \mathrm{d}S$. Thus

$$P_{M1}/P_{E1} = \left(\frac{c\, \mathrm{d}S}{\omega\, \mathrm{d}x}\right)^2 = (2\pi\, \mathrm{d}S/\lambda\, \mathrm{d}x)^2.$$

Assuming that $\mathrm{d}S \sim (\mathrm{d}x)^2$, P_{M1} is a fraction $\sim(\mathrm{d}x/\lambda)^2$ of P_{E1} and hence is very small in the approximation we are using. In the

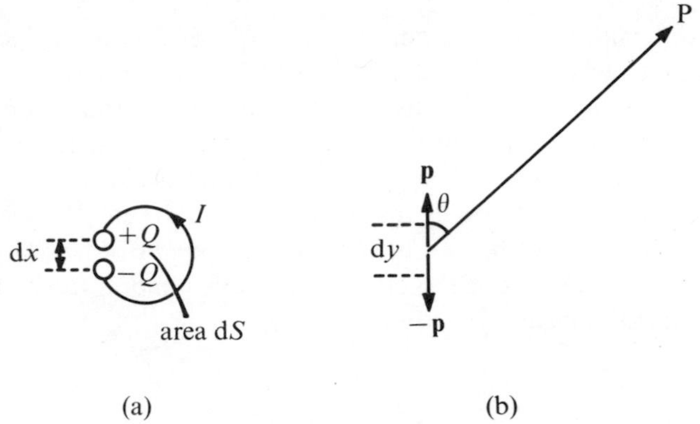

Fig. 5.4 Radiating multipoles: (a) an open loop with both electric and magnetic dipole moments; (b) an electric quadrupole consisting of two dipoles in anti-phase

Hertzian dipole of section 4.7 there will be no $M1$ radiation in the limit $\mathrm{d}x \to 0$.

Comparison of $E1$ and $E2$ radiation. $E2$ radiation can be investigated by means of a quadrupole consisting of two oscillating electric dipoles as in Fig. 5.4b, in anti-phase with each other and displaced by $\mathrm{d}y$. The electric field at P due to one dipole is

$$E_\mathrm{p} = \frac{[\ddot{p}] \sin\theta}{4\pi\varepsilon_0 c^2 r}.$$

The second dipole will produce a field at P, $-(E_\mathrm{p} + (\partial E_\mathrm{p}/\partial y)\, \mathrm{d}y)$, and the resultant field E_q is $-(\partial E_\mathrm{p}/\partial y)\, \mathrm{d}y$. Remembering that $[\ddot{p}]$ is a function of $(t - r/c)$, all terms but one cancel, giving

$$E_\mathrm{q} = \frac{[\dddot{p}] \sin\theta\cos\theta}{4\pi\varepsilon_0 c^3 r}\, \mathrm{d}y = \frac{[\dddot{q}] \sin\theta\cos\theta}{4\pi\varepsilon_0 c^3 r}$$

$$= \left[\frac{\dddot{q}}{\ddot{p}}\right] \frac{\cos\theta}{c} E_\mathrm{p}$$

where q is the quadrupole moment $p\,\mathrm{d}y$. In a general system of linear dimensions $\sim \mathrm{d}y$, $q \sim p\,\mathrm{d}y$, and if both $E1$ and $E2$ radiation of the same angular frequency ω occur, $\ddot{p} = \omega^2 p_0$ and $\dddot{q} = \omega^3 p_0\,\mathrm{d}y$ where p_0 is the dipole amplitude. Thus the power ratio is

$$\frac{P_{E2}}{P_{E1}} = \left(\frac{\omega\,\mathrm{d}y}{c}\right)^2 \sim \left(\frac{\mathrm{d}y}{\lambda}\right)^2.$$

Once again, this is very small in our approximation. In general, we see that where λ is long compared with the dimensions of the radiating system, the $E1$ term completely dominates all others. This is often the situation at radio frequencies (see section 10.7) and in atoms and nuclei. In the last case, γ-radiation has λ of 10^{-10}–10^{-11} cm compared with the nuclear size of 10^{-12}–10^{-13} cm. If, of course, $E1$ radiation should be absent, then the $E2$ or $M1$ radiation dominates and this occurs in the closed loop aerial and in nuclei where dipole transitions are forbidden.

PROBLEMS

5.1 Expand $1/(|\mathbf{r} - \mathbf{r}_i|)$ of equation (5.1) about the origin using Taylor's theorem for three variables x, y, z. Rearrange the terms so as to identify them with those in equation (5.5).

5.2 Using the method of problem 1.9 to generate multipoles at the origin O, show that the potential at P due to an ideal dipole at O is given by $V_1 = -\mathbf{a}\,.\,\mathbf{grad}\,V_0$, where V_0 is the potential at P due to a point charge at O and $\mathbf{a}$ is the vector displacement needed to form the dipole. Show that a quadrupole gives $V_2 = -\mathbf{b}\,.\,\mathbf{grad}\,V_1$ in a similar way and identify the V_1 and V_2 with those in (5.5).

5.3 Show that the quadrupole moment of any system of charges is independent of the origin provided that $\sum Q_i = 0$ and $\mathbf{p} = \sum Q_i\mathbf{r}_i = 0$.

5.4 What are the dipole and quadrupole moments of the following systems: (a) $+Q$ at the point $(a, 0, 0)$; (b) $+Q$ at $(+a, 0, 0)$ and $(-a, 0, 0)$; (c) $+Q$ at each of the six points $(\pm a, 0, 0)$, $(0, \pm a, 0)$, $(0, 0, \pm a)$?

5.5 An ellipsoid of revolution has semi-axes a (along the z-axis) and b (along the x- and y-axes). If it is filled with a total charge Q distributed uniformly throughout its volume, show that its quadrupole moment is $2Q(a^2 - b^2)/5$. (Volume of ellipsoid $= 4\pi ab^2/3$; equation of elliptical cross-section with origin at centre is $z^2/a^2 + x^2/b^2 = 1$.)

5.6 Show that for a spherically symmetrical distribution of charge, all multipole moments are zero except the monopole term.

5.7 Show that $\frac{1}{2}\oint \mathbf{r} \times d\mathbf{r}$ round a closed path C is the vector area enclosed by C.

5.8 Show that the magnetic moment of a system of steady currents defined by (5.40) is independent of the origin.

5.9 The polar diagram of a radiating system gives the power emitted in various directions θ at a constant distance r. Sketch the diagrams in two dimensions for the following: (a) a Hertzian dipole; (b) a magnetic dipole; (c) an electric quadrupole radiator at the origin.

6

Boundary problems

Chapters 1 and 2 gave a general treatment of the effect of conductors, dielectrics, and magnetic materials on electric and magnetic fields, and simple forms of the laws were retained by introducing **D** and **H**. Specific problems, however, usually involve bounded bodies so that the boundary conditions summarized in (4.10) have to be satisfied. To find the fields in such cases, it is better first to solve for an appropriate potential function and to derive **E** or **B** from it, at any rate when conditions are steady (see chapter 7 for time-varying boundary problems). The boundary conditions must then be expressed in terms of V (as in (1.52)), V_m or **A** (see problem 6.15).

A great variety of similar boundary-value problems occurs throughout physics, and numerous methods are available for their solution: we shall restrict ourselves to one special method (the method of images and its extension) and a general method (solution of Laplace's equation) followed by an example of its use. First, however, uniqueness of solution—an important principle guaranteeing the success of many special methods—is discussed in section 6.1, followed by a section showing some simple consequences.

Further methods and many examples are to be found in Smythe (1950).

6.1 Uniqueness theorems

Electrostatic theorem. It is worth considering the uniqueness of the electrostatic potential first because more general cases are embraced than with other potentials. The most general electrostatic problem is one in which there are

(a) given finite distributions of volume charge specified by a volume density ρ (point charges included as vanishingly small volumes),

(b) a set of finite conductors with specified electrostatic potentials V_α, V_β, etc., and surfaces denoted by S_V,

(c) another set of finite conductors with specified *total* charges Q_a, Q_b, etc., over surfaces denoted by S_Q.

Elsewhere there may be finite dielectrics which need not be linear, isotropic, nor homogeneous.

Consider the region of space τ bounded externally (Fig. 6.1) by a

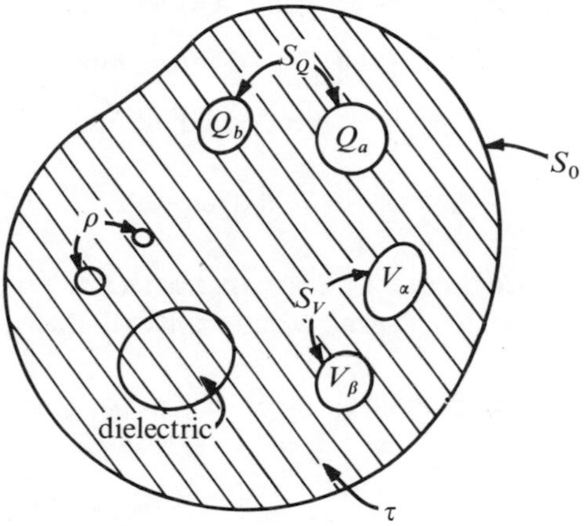

Fig. 6.1 A general electrostatic system. S_0 bounds the whole system and the volume τ (shaded) is bounded externally by S_0 and internally by S_Q and S_V—τ *includes* volumes occupied by dielectrics or volume charges

surface S_0 enclosing the whole system and internally by S_Q and S_V. The volume τ thus excludes that occupied by conductors but includes that occupied by dielectrics and volume charges. S_0 may be allowed to recede to infinity or may be an equipotential surface. Throughout τ the potential V must satisfy the generalized Poisson's equation (see problem 1.17):

$$\text{div}\,(\varepsilon_r\,\textbf{grad}\,V) = -\rho/\varepsilon_0 \qquad (6.1)$$

and must also satisfy

$$V \to 0 \text{ over } S_0 \text{ as } S_0 \to \infty \quad \text{or} \quad V = V_0 \text{ over } S_0 \qquad (6.2)$$

$$V = V_\alpha,\ V_\beta, \text{ etc., over all } S_V. \qquad (6.3)$$

The surface density of charge at any point on a surface S_Q is given by

$\sigma = \varepsilon_r\varepsilon_0 E_n = \varepsilon_r\varepsilon_0\, \partial V/\partial n$, where E_n is the normal component of **E**. Thus a further condition on V is

$$\oint \varepsilon_r\varepsilon_0 \frac{\partial V}{\partial n}\, \mathrm{d}S = Q_a, Q_b, \text{ etc., over all } S_Q. \tag{6.4}$$

There are also boundary conditions to be satisfied at the surfaces of the dielectrics but these do not affect the following argument and merely impose the continuity of V and its first derivative throughout τ.

Suppose now that there are *two* potentials V_1 and V_2 both satisfying (6.1)–(6.4) at every point, and let $(V_1 - V_2) = \phi$. Then

$$\text{div}\,(\varepsilon_r\, \mathbf{grad}\, \phi) = 0 \text{ throughout } \tau \tag{6.5}$$

$$\phi = 0 \text{ over } S_0 \text{ and all } S_V \tag{6.6}$$

$$\oint \varepsilon_r \frac{\partial \phi}{\partial n}\, \mathrm{d}S = 0 \text{ over each } S_Q. \tag{6.7}$$

The divergence theorem (A.35) applies to any vector: if we write it with **A** put equal to $\varepsilon_r\phi\, \mathbf{grad}\, \phi$ and apply it to the volume τ, we get:

$$\int_\tau \text{div}\,(\varepsilon_r\phi\, \mathbf{grad}\, \phi)\, \mathrm{d}\tau = \oint_{S_0, S_V, S_Q} \varepsilon_r\phi\, (\mathbf{grad}\, \phi)\, .\, \mathrm{d}\mathbf{S}$$

or, using identities (A.24) and (A.18),

$$\int_\tau [\phi\, \text{div}\,(\varepsilon_r\, \mathbf{grad}\, \phi) + \varepsilon_r\, (\mathbf{grad}\, \phi)^2]\, \mathrm{d}\tau = \oint_{S_0, S_V, S_Q} \varepsilon_r\phi \frac{\partial \phi}{\partial n}\, \mathrm{d}S. \tag{6.8}$$

From (6.5), the first term on the left is zero. The right-hand side is zero over S_0 and S_V by (6.6). Over each separate S_Q, ϕ is constant and may be taken out of the integral and it is then clear by (6.7) that the right-hand side of (6.8) is also zero over all S_Q. Hence

$$\int_\tau \varepsilon_r\, (\mathbf{grad}\, \phi)^2\, \mathrm{d}\tau = 0. \tag{6.9}$$

Now $\varepsilon_r \geqslant 1$ and $(\mathbf{grad}\, \phi)^2$ is essentially positive. It therefore follows from (6.9) that **grad** ϕ must be everywhere zero and ϕ itself constant throughout τ and over its boundaries. But $\phi = 0$ over S_0 and S_V and so

$$V_1 = V_2 \text{ throughout } \tau. \tag{6.10}$$

The absence of one or more of the conditions (6.2)–(6.4) does not affect the argument materially. If no surface has a specified potential but all, including S_0, have only a specified total charge then from (6.9) it can only be said that V_1 and V_2 may differ by a constant everywhere. Once a zero for V is chosen, however, this arbitrariness disappears and V is unique. In any case, **E** is certainly always unique and so therefore is the surface density of charge σ $(=\varepsilon_r\varepsilon_0 E_n)$ at every point on the surface of a conductor. There is thus only one static distribution of charge which satisfies any given conditions.

Sometimes a uniform field is specified at infinity when

$$V = C - Ez \tag{6.11}$$

where E is the constant field and z its direction. C is a constant depending on the zero chosen for V and represents the quantity $(V + Ez)$. In this case, the condition (6.2) must be replaced by

$$(V + Ez) \to C \quad \text{as} \quad S_0 \to \infty. \tag{6.12}$$

If V_1 and V_2 in the above argument have the same zero, C is the same for both and ϕ is still zero over S_0. If they have different zeros then ϕ is constant $(C_1 - C_2)$ over S_0 and hence once more throughout τ.

Steady currents in resistive media. The most general situation here is one in which there are some electrodes with specified total currents issuing from them, so that over their surfaces, S_I, we have

$$\oint \gamma \frac{\partial V}{\partial n} \, dS = I_c \tag{6.13}$$

because the total current $I_c = \oint \mathbf{J} \cdot d\mathbf{S}$ and $\mathbf{J} = \gamma\mathbf{E}$. Condition (6.13) replaces (6.4). Over other electrodes whose surface are denoted by S_V we have specified potentials giving a condition similar to (6.3), while throughout a volume τ excluding the electrodes we have, from (1.31):

$$\operatorname{div}(\gamma \,\mathbf{grad}\, V) = 0 \tag{6.14}$$

replacing condition (6.1). If we deal with finite distributions of current, then condition (6.2) also holds and all the conditions for the uniqueness of V are present.

Steady magnetic fields. Under conditions in which the scalar potential V_m can be used (section 2.2), we have generally that

$$\nabla^2 V_m = 0 \tag{6.15}$$

corresponding to condition (6.1), and for finite distributions of currents, magnets, and magnetic materials

$$V_m \to 0 \quad \text{as} \quad S_0 \to \infty \tag{6.16}$$

choosing infinity as the zero. There are no conditions corresponding to (6.3) and (6.4) and hence no surfaces corresponding to S_V and S_Q. The conditions for uniqueness of V_m and thus of **B** are therefore present.

A similar theorem exists for the vector potential **A**, provided that its tangential component or that of **B** is specified over any bounding surfaces, but we shall not prove this result (see Stratton, 1941). Problem 6.1 exhibits an important special case of this known as Helmholtz's theorem: if the sources (divergence) and vortices (curl) of any vector field **X** are specified in a finite region and if $\mathbf{X} \to 0$ at infinity, then the vector field is unique.

6.2 Consequences of uniqueness

We should not have spent so much time on uniqueness theorems were they not very important. For we are now quite sure that where a potential function has been found satisfying the conditions specified in a problem, *it is the only solution*. In most cases, we are concerned with less general conditions than (6.1)–(6.4): in particular, V will often satisfy Laplace's equation rather than (6.1), so that solutions of this equation are an important feature of boundary problems. We take this up in section 6.4. In this section, we examine some simple consequences of uniqueness.

As a first example of the power of the uniqueness theorem, consider a hole H inside a conductor charged to a potential V_c. H carries no charge within its boundaries and hence the potential over H satisfies $\nabla^2 V = 0$ throughout its volume and the condition $V = V_c$ over the surface bounding H. It is immediately clear that $V = V_c$ at *all* points within H is *a* solution of the problem and the uniqueness theorem assures us that it is the only solution. There is thus no electric field within H. Compare this proof with the laborious one given in *Electricity and Magnetism*, section 4.1.

Next, consider two conductors remote from others. If a charge Q is taken from one to the other, we are interested in the resulting potentials V_1 and V_2 of the conductors. The uniqueness theorem assures us that there is only one solution for V at any point (apart from an additive constant due to our having specified only the Q's) and consequently $V_1 - V_2$ is unique and so is the quantity

$$C = Q/(V_1 - V_2) \tag{6.17}$$

known as the *capacitance* of the pair of conductors. (The *constancy* of C as Q varies is only guaranteed by superposition and this does not apply when non-linear dielectrics are present—we have only guaranteed the *uniqueness* of C.) C is in farads if Q is in coulombs and V in volts.

If with the same two conductors the potentials are specified instead of the charges, then uniqueness still obtains and the potential everywhere is fixed. This fixes the electric fields and their normal components at the conducting surfaces and hence the surface density of charge at every point on the conductors. Thus the Q's are now fixed.

These results can be extended to any finite set of conductors by using superposition and it is then easy to show that the potentials of any set of N conductors can be expressed in terms of the charges by

$$V_i = \sum_{j=1}^{N} p_{ij} Q_j \tag{6.18}$$

and, conversely, that the charges are given by

$$Q_i = \sum_{j=1}^{N} c_{ij} V_j. \tag{6.19}$$

In these expressions, p_{ij} is a *coefficient of potential*: the potential to which the ith conductor is raised by unit charge on the jth, all other conductors being uncharged. Similarly, c_{ij} are *coefficients of induction* if $i \neq j$, and are called *coefficients of capacitance* if $i = j$ (see *Electricity and Magnetism*, section 5.10 for more detail).

Analogy between current flow and electrostatic field. Consider two electrodes at specified potentials V_1 and V_2 immersed in a medium whose resistivity is much higher than that of the electrode material (in practice, metallic electrodes in an electrolyte satisfy this condition, the ratios of resistivities being $\sim 10^{-6}$). Then problem 1.13 shows that the current entering or leaving the electrodes does so normal to the surfaces, which are thus equipotentials. Throughout the electrolyte, because the conductivity γ is constant, the potential satisfies Laplace's equation by (1.33) and reduces to V_1 and V_2 over the electrode surfaces. The uniqueness theorem tells us that there is only one solution for V throughout the electrolyte, and that it is the same as that for the electrostatic problem of two conductors of the same shape as the electrodes, charged to V_1 and V_2 and immersed in an LIH dielectric medium. Thus Fig. 6.2 represents *both* the lines of

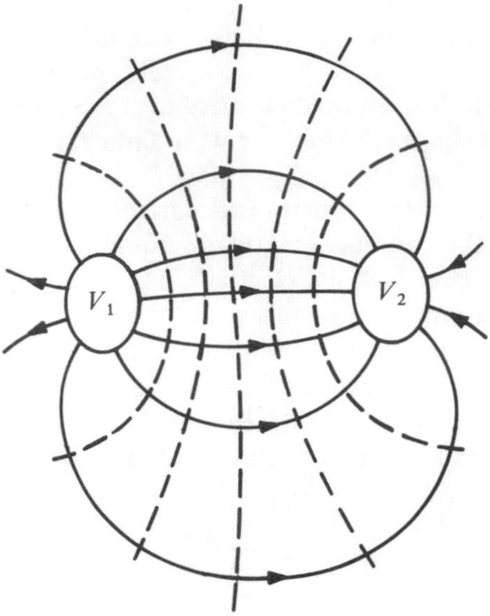

Fig. 6.2 Lines of force (full lines) and equipotentials (broken lines) for either two electrodes in an electrolyte or two charged conductors in a dielectric

E or current flow and the equipotentials in an electrolyte *and* the lines of force and equipotentials in a dielectric.

This has an important practical application, in that equipotential surfaces due to complicated electrode systems in electron lenses may be determined by immersing the system in an electrolytic tank and tracing out the equipotentials by a potentiometric method. If alternating current is used, a probe is connected through a detector to a tapping on a resistor across V_1 and V_2 externally. The probe is dipped into the electrolyte and the detector records a constant value along an equipotential, which can thus be plotted.

Another application is possible because of the relation existing between the capacitance in the electrostatic system and the resistance in the analogous electrolytic system. For a surface enclosing one electrode, the current I crossing it is $\oint \mathbf{J} \cdot d\mathbf{S}$ or $\oint \gamma\mathbf{E} \cdot d\mathbf{S}$. In the electrostatic case, Gauss's theorem gives over the same surface

$$Q = \oint \varepsilon_r \varepsilon_0 \mathbf{E} \cdot d\mathbf{S}.$$

Since **E** is the same in the two cases, we have

$$Q/\varepsilon_r\varepsilon_0 = I/\gamma.$$

But $Q = C(V_1 - V_2)$ and $I = (V_1 - V_2)/R$ so that

$$RC = \varepsilon_r\varepsilon_0/\gamma \tag{6.20}$$

where R is the resistance and C the capacitance. Thus a scale model of the system whose capacitance is required (say an aerial system) can be immersed in an electrolytic tank and the resistance between the conductors measured. Equation (6.20) then enables C to be found and scaled up. The relation is also useful for calculating R in cases where C is easily obtained and R is not.

6.3 The method of images and its extensions

Charges and conductors in vacuo. The class of problem to which the method of images is strictly applicable is that in which certain charge distributions are given together with conductors having given boundaries. It is required to find the electric fields everywhere outside the conductors and hence the distribution of induced charge on the conductors and the forces on the given charges. The simplest example is that of a point charge near an infinite conducting plane considered briefly below and with more detail in *Electricity and Magnetism*, section 4.8. Such problems are not as academic as they appear: for instance, many vacuum electronic devices have electrons or ions moving near metallic electrodes (see Cusack (1958) for the effect of the image force on the work function of a metal).

The method of images is based on the following principle. Any set of charges (no conductors present) yields equipotential surfaces. If a region of space bounded by an equipotential surface V_c is filled with a conductor at the same potential, then the uniqueness theorem ensures that the electric fields and potentials throughout the rest of space are unaffected. Gauss's theorem (1.8) shows that the charges originally within the equipotential surface must equal the total surface charge on the conductor.

In practice, it is the conductor or conductors which are given first and the problem is one of finding the set of charges to give an appropriate equipotential surface fitting the conductor, rather than the other way round. Thus, given a point charge Q a distance d from an infinite plane conducting surface at zero potential, it is clear that the given Q together with a charge $-Q$ a distance d behind the surface (Fig. 6.3a) will give a zero equipotential plane coinciding with that of the conductor so that the field in the left half of the figure is the same in the two cases. The $-Q$ is the required 'image' system,

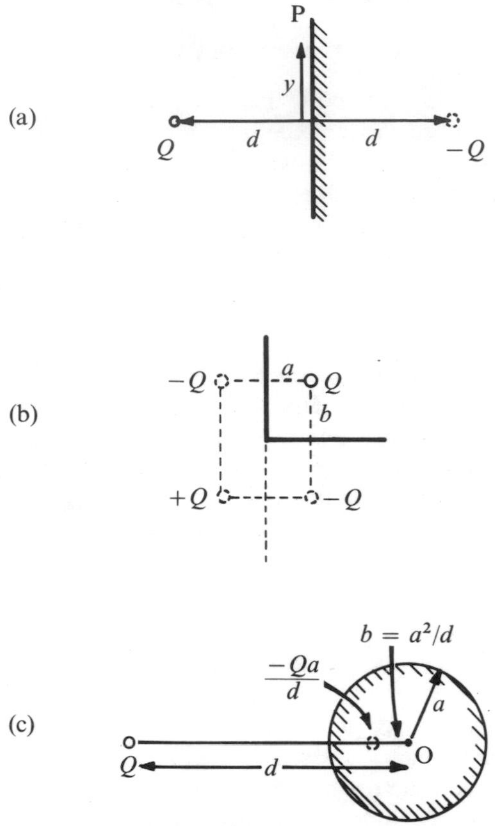

Fig. 6.3 Image systems for (a) point charge and conducting plane; (b) point charge and two intersecting planes; (c) point charge and conducting sphere

the term arising from the optical analogy (which in fact does not extend much beyond this example). The force on Q will be an attractive one of $Q^2/16\pi\varepsilon_0 d^2$ and the distribution of charge on the conductor can be obtained from a knowledge of E_n at a point such as P and using (1.26).

Figure 6.3b shows the image system necessary to make two plane conducting surfaces both equipotentials and Fig. 6.3c the system needed for a sphere. In the case of the sphere, there is a total charge

$-Qa/d$ on its surface so that if the problem were that of an initially uncharged isolated sphere, we should have to add $+Qa/d$ at its centre to preserve both its neutrality and its equipotential spherical surface.

An uncharged conducting sphere in a *uniform* electric field may be dealt with by the same result. The uniform field is produced by two charges, Q at d from the centre on one side and $-Q$ at d on the other, and these are allowed to recede to infinity but with increasing Q in such a way that $E = 2Q/4\pi\varepsilon_0 d^2$ remains constant. The image system is then a dipole at the centre with each charge $\pm Qa/d$ separated by $2b = 2a^2/d$. The dipole moment of a conducting sphere in a uniform field is thus $2Qa^3/d^2$ or

$$p = 4\pi\varepsilon_0 E a^3. \tag{6.21}$$

By using superposition, other problems such as that of a line charge near a conducting plane or a dipole near a conducting sphere may be solved, while the equipotentials of two opposite parallel line charges are useful in two-dimensional problems (see problems 6.8 and 6.9).

Extensions to dielectric and magnetic materials. The surfaces of dielectrics and magnetic materials are not equipotentials, but the method of images is suggestive in obtaining solutions to fit the boundary conditions: the uniqueness theorem ensures that solutions obtained in this way are the required ones.

Consider a point charge Q near a *dielectric* plane (geometry of Fig. 6.3a) whose relative permittivity is ε_r. The boundary conditions to satisfy are the continuity of E_t or V and D_n or $\varepsilon_r \partial V/\partial n$ across the surface and it is clear that in this case there will be a field in the right-hand half to be found as well. Assume (a) the field in the left-hand half is that of Q together with an image Q' at the image point d to the right and (b) that the field in the right-hand half is that of a charge Q'' replacing Q and all space filled with the dielectric (these are the simplest possible assumptions—if they do not work we must make more complicated ones). Equating E_t and D_n on the two sides of the surface at P yields two equations enabling Q' and Q'' to be found. The result gives the fields of Fig. 6.4 and is

$$Q' = -Q\frac{\varepsilon_r - 1}{\varepsilon_r + 1}; \qquad Q'' = Q\frac{2\varepsilon_r}{\varepsilon_r + 1}. \tag{6.22}$$

In a similar way, a sphere of relative permittivity ε_1 situated in an infinite medium of ε_2 in which a uniform electric field E_0 is applied might be expected to behave as a dipole for points outside the sphere by analogy with the conducting sphere. There is now, however, a field inside and the simplest assumption to make about this is that it

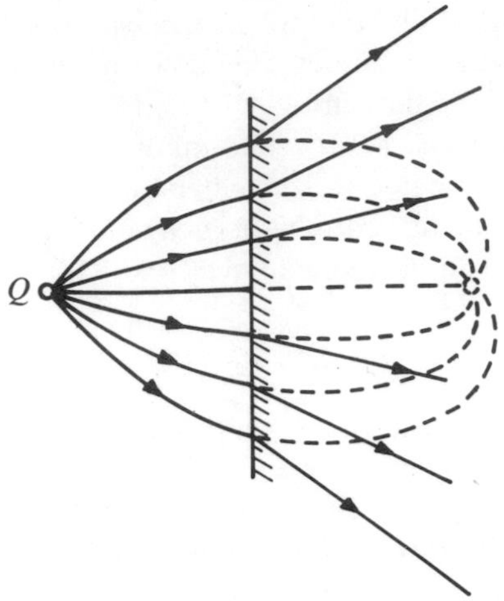

Fig. 6.4 Lines of force due to a point charge and a dielectric with a plane surface

is a uniform field parallel to the applied field. If we make these assumptions and apply the boundary conditions to the spherical surface, we find that they can be satisfied by a dipole moment p' and a uniform field E' given by (problem 6.12):

$$p' = 4\pi\varepsilon_0 a^3 E_0(\varepsilon_1 - \varepsilon_2)/(\varepsilon_1 + 2\varepsilon_2); \qquad E' = 3\varepsilon_2 E_0/(\varepsilon_1 + 2\varepsilon_2). \tag{6.23}$$

For magnetic materials, similar results apply but are less realistic because $\mu_r - 1$ is extremely small for all but ferromagnetic materials, while in these the occurrence of hysteresis means that the theory is inapplicable. However, for very soft ferromagnetics the results would be good approximations.

6.4 Solutions of Laplace's equation

So many problems involve the solution of Laplace's equation that we devote this section to the subject, although the treatment must be far from complete (see Smythe, 1950; Morse and Feshbach, 1953). Any solution of Laplace's equation is known as a *harmonic function* and the particular type of function depends upon the geometry of the boundaries over which certain conditions are specified and upon the symmetry of the system. The geometry and the symmetry together determine which co-ordinate system is most appropriate. Because the equation is linear, superposition applies and any linear combination of solutions is also a solution, a property enabling some complicated problems to be solved as sums of simpler ones.

To solve a particular problem involves the selection of appropriate solutions from those available so as to fit the conditions specified. We now look briefly at solutions in cartesian, spherical, and cylindrical co-ordinates obtained by separation of the variables.

Cartesian co-ordinates. The solution of

$$\frac{\partial^2 V}{\partial x^2} + \frac{\partial^2 V}{\partial y^2} + \frac{\partial^2 V}{\partial z^2} = 0 \tag{6.24}$$

is assumed to be of the form

$$V = X(x)Y(y)Z(z) \tag{6.25}$$

where X is a function only of x, etc. Substitution into (6.24) gives, after division through by XYZ:

$$\frac{1}{X}\frac{\mathrm{d}^2 X}{\mathrm{d}x^2} + \frac{1}{Y}\frac{\mathrm{d}^2 Y}{\mathrm{d}y^2} + \frac{1}{Z}\frac{\mathrm{d}^2 Z}{\mathrm{d}z^2} = 0. \tag{6.26}$$

The first term is a function of x only, the second of y only and the third of z only and if the equation is to be true for all x, y, and z, the only possible conclusion is that each term is separately constant:

$$\frac{1}{X}\frac{\mathrm{d}^2 X}{\mathrm{d}x^2} = k_x^2; \qquad \frac{1}{Y}\frac{\mathrm{d}^2 Y}{\mathrm{d}y^2} = k_y^2; \qquad \frac{1}{Z}\frac{\mathrm{d}^2 Z}{\mathrm{d}z^2} = k_z^2 \tag{6.27}$$

with

$$k_x^2 + k_y^2 + k_z^2 = 0 \tag{6.28}$$

the k^2's being known as *separation constants*. The problem is thus one of solving the three independent equations (6.27) for k^2 positive, negative, or zero. The solutions are typically

k_x^2 positive: $\qquad X = A_1 \sinh k_x x + A_2 \cosh k_x x \qquad$ (6.29)

k_x^2 negative: $\qquad X = A_1 \sin k_x x + A_2 \cos k_x x \qquad$ (6.30)

k_x^2 zero: $\qquad X = A_1 x + A_2 \qquad$ (6.31)

and a possible solution for V is the product of three terms like these, the k^2 satisfying (6.28). To satisfy all the boundary conditions it may be necessary to add an infinite sequence of such terms with the k's all different. The coefficients represented above by A_1 and A_2 are found by techniques similar to those used for finding Fourier coefficients (see problem 6.18).

Spherical polar co-ordinates. We assume the solution of

$$\nabla^2 V \equiv \frac{1}{r^2}\frac{\partial}{\partial r}\left(r^2 \frac{\partial V}{\partial r}\right) + \frac{1}{r^2 \sin\theta}\frac{\partial}{\partial\theta}\left(\sin\theta \frac{\partial V}{\partial\theta}\right) + \frac{1}{r^2 \sin^2\theta}\frac{\partial^2 V}{\partial\phi^2} = 0 \tag{6.32}$$

to be of the form

$$V = R(r)\Theta(\theta)\Phi(\phi). \tag{6.33}$$

Substituting this in (6.32) and multiplying through by $(r^2 \sin^2\theta)/R\Theta\Phi$:

$$\frac{\sin^2\theta}{R}\frac{\mathrm{d}}{\mathrm{d}r}\left(r^2 \frac{\mathrm{d}R}{\mathrm{d}r}\right) + \frac{\sin\theta}{\Theta}\frac{\mathrm{d}}{\mathrm{d}\theta}\left(\sin\theta \frac{\mathrm{d}\Theta}{\mathrm{d}\theta}\right) + \frac{1}{\Phi}\frac{\mathrm{d}^2\Phi}{\mathrm{d}\phi^2} = 0. \tag{6.34}$$

The last term is a function of ϕ only and the rest is a function of r and θ only so that the two parts must be separately constant. Using m^2 as a separation constant, we have

$$\frac{\mathrm{d}^2\Phi}{\mathrm{d}\phi^2} + m^2\Phi = 0 \tag{6.35}$$

and because V must be single-valued, m must be an integer so that $\Phi(0) = \Phi(2\pi)$, etc.; the solutions are usually written in the form

$$\Phi = A\,\mathrm{e}^{\pm im\phi} \tag{6.36}$$

rather than (6.30) which it resembles. The rest of (6.34) can then be written as a separate r and a θ term so that a further separation constant k can be used. If we write $k = l(l+1)$, we get for the radial part

$$\frac{\mathrm{d}}{\mathrm{d}r}\left(r^2 \frac{\mathrm{d}R}{\mathrm{d}r}\right) - l(l+1)R = 0 \tag{6.37}$$

of which solutions are of the form

$$R = Ar^l + B/r^{l+1}. \tag{6.38}$$

The θ part becomes

$$\frac{\mathrm{d}}{\mathrm{d}\theta}\left(\sin\theta\,\frac{\mathrm{d}\Theta}{\mathrm{d}\theta}\right) + \left[l(l+1) - \frac{m^2}{\sin^2\theta}\right]\Theta\sin\theta = 0 \tag{6.39}$$

and this can be written, using a new variable $x = \cos\theta$, as

$$\frac{\mathrm{d}}{\mathrm{d}x}\left[(1-x^2)\frac{\mathrm{d}\Theta}{\mathrm{d}x}\right] + \left[l(l+1) - \frac{m^2}{(1-x^2)}\right]\Theta = 0. \tag{6.40}$$

The solutions of (6.39) or (6.40) are known as *associated Legendre functions* denoted by $P_l^m(x)$ or $P_l^m(\cos\theta)$ for specific values of l and m. (Functions of the second order $Q_l^m(x)$ also exist but have singularities along the axis $\theta = 0$ or π and so do not normally form solutions of interest in a physical problem.) Values of $P_l^m(x)$ can be found in mathematical texts. The angular part of the complete solution, when normalized, is known as a *spherical* or *tesseral* harmonic $Y_l^m(\theta, \phi)$ so that, in general,

$$V = \sum_{l=0}^{\infty}\sum_{m=-l}^{+l} RY_l^m(\theta,\phi) \tag{6.41}$$

where the coefficients once again are determined by the boundary conditions. It should be noted that convergent solutions only exist for integral values of l and values of m ranging from $-l$ to $+l$.

In many cases of interest, problems have an axial symmetry about an axis so chosen that there is no dependence on ϕ. In these cases, $m = 0$ and $\Phi = 1$ and solutions are of the form

$$V = R(r)\Theta(\theta) \tag{6.42}$$

where R is still given by (6.38) and Θ is the solution of (6.40) with $m = 0$:

$$(1-x^2)\frac{\mathrm{d}^2\Theta}{\mathrm{d}x^2} - 2x\frac{\mathrm{d}\Theta}{\mathrm{d}x} + l(l+1)\Theta = 0 \tag{6.43}$$

known as Legendre's equation. Convergent solutions are polynomials in x or $\cos\theta$ known as *Legendre polynomials* and denoted by $P_l(\cos\theta)$. The first few terms for integral l's are

$$P_0(x) = 1; \quad P_1(x) = x; \quad P_2(x) = \tfrac{1}{2}(3x^2 - 1);$$
$$P_3(x) = \tfrac{1}{2}(5x^3 - 3x). \tag{6.44}$$

These will be recognized as identical with the terms in the expansion (5.3). The general solution will be of the form

$$V = \sum_{l=0}^{\infty} A_l r^l P_l(\cos\theta) + \sum_{l=0}^{\infty} B_l P_l(\cos\theta)/r^{l+1} \tag{6.45}$$

where the coefficients A_l and B_l have to be found for each l.

It is an extremely useful device where axial symmetry exists to see whether the solution along the axis of symmetry $\theta = 0$ is known by elementary methods. For if it is, its expansion in powers of r or $1/r$ must be identical with (6.45) with $\theta = 0$. This is, since $P_l(1) = 1$:

$$V_{\text{axis}} = (A_l z^l + B_l/z^{l+1}) \tag{6.46}$$

where z is the distance along the axis of symmetry from the origin. This yields the coefficients A_l and B_l for the general solution (6.45) (see problem 6.13).

Cylindrical polar co-ordinates. Laplace's equation here is

$$\frac{1}{r}\frac{\partial}{\partial r}\left(r\frac{\partial V}{\partial r}\right) + \frac{1}{r^2}\frac{\partial^2 V}{\partial \theta^2} + \frac{\partial^2 V}{\partial z^2} = 0 \tag{6.47}$$

and similar separation of the variables leads to a solution in cylindrical harmonics:

$$V = R(r)\Theta(\theta)Z(z) \tag{6.48}$$

in which R, Θ, and Z satisfy

$$\frac{\mathrm{d}^2 Z}{\mathrm{d}z^2} - k^2 Z = 0; \qquad \frac{\mathrm{d}^2\Theta}{\mathrm{d}\theta^2} + m^2\Theta = 0 \tag{6.49}$$

$$r\frac{\mathrm{d}}{\mathrm{d}r}\left(r\frac{\mathrm{d}R}{\mathrm{d}r}\right) + (k^2r^2 - m^2)R = 0 \tag{6.50}$$

in which k and m are separation constants and m must be integral if V is to be single-valued. Equation (6.50) is Bessel's equation whose solutions are *Bessel functions* of the mth order denoted by $J_m(kr)$, and $N_m(kr)$, the latter becoming infinite at the origin. Thus the complete cylindrical harmonic is of the form

$$\begin{matrix} J_m(kr)\cos m\theta \\ N_m(kr)\sin m\theta \end{matrix}\; \mathrm{e}^{\pm kz} \tag{6.51}$$

If there is no dependence on z, we have a two-dimensional problem only, in the r, θ-plane, and Laplace's equation lacks the final term. The solution is then

$$V = R(r)\Theta(\theta) \tag{6.52}$$

where Θ and R satisfy

$$\frac{d^2\Theta}{d\theta^2} + n^2\Theta = 0 \tag{6.53}$$

$$r\frac{d}{dr}\left(r\frac{dR}{dr}\right) - n^2R = 0 \tag{6.54}$$

where n^2 is the separation constant and n is restricted to integral values as before. The solutions for $n > 0$ of (6.53) and (6.54) give

$$\begin{matrix}\sin n\theta \\ \cos n\theta\end{matrix}\,(A_n r^n + B_n/r^n)$$

while for $n = 0$, $R = A_0 + B_0 \log_e r$ and $\Theta = C + D\theta$. For single-valued V, however, the latter is inadmissible and $D = 0$. Thus

$$V = A_0 + B_0 \log_e r + \sum_{n=1}^{\infty} \left[r^n(A_n \sin n\theta + A_n' \cos n\theta) + r^{-n}(B_n \sin n\theta + B_n' \cos n\theta)\right]. \tag{6.55}$$

If, in addition to the lack of dependence on z, there is axial symmetry as well, then dependence on θ disappears and cylindrical symmetry is complete. Laplace's equation reduces to

$$\frac{d}{dr}\left(r\frac{dV}{dr}\right) = 0 \tag{6.56}$$

giving

$$V = C + k \log_e r \tag{6.57}$$

where C and k are constants of the problem. This is the solution, for instance, for an infinite cylinder of charge outside which the electric field ($E_r = -\partial V/\partial r = -k/r$) can be obtained by elementary methods using Gauss's theorem.

6.5 Magnetic shielding—An example

We choose as an example of the above methods a calculation of the magnetic shielding afforded by a soft iron barrier, using a two-dimensional case to simplify the computation a little while retaining the main features.

Take a very long (effectively infinite) soft iron tube of relative permeability μ_r with an annular cross-section of internal and external radii a and b respectively (Fig. 6.5a). It is situated in an applied uniform magnetic field of flux density B_0 such that the axis of the

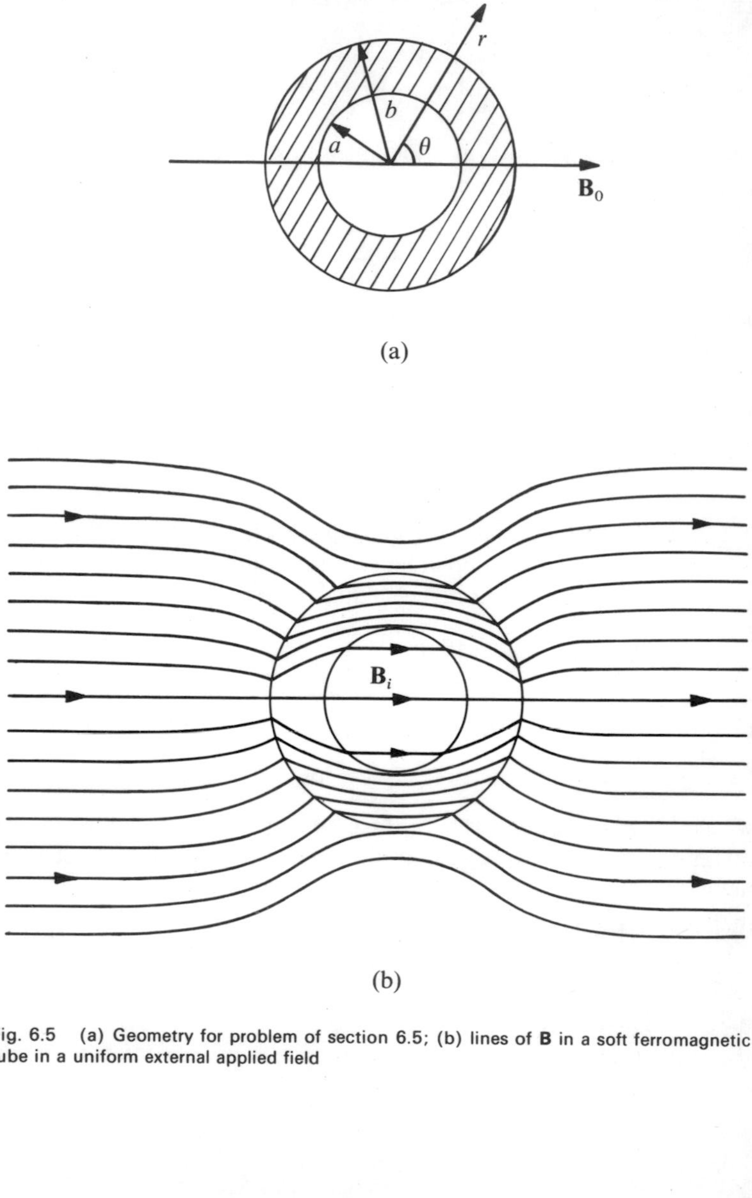

Fig. 6.5 (a) Geometry for problem of section 6.5; (b) lines of **B** in a soft ferromagnetic tube in a uniform external applied field

tube is perpendicular to B_0. The problem, to find the flux density inside the tube, is a two-dimensional one in which cylindrical coordinates are appropriate and scalar potentials solutions take the form of (6.55).

For points outside the tube, call the scalar magnetic potential V_0; for $a \leqslant r \leqslant b$, let it be V_m; and for $r \leqslant a$, V_i. Now V_0 must yield a uniform B_0 as $r \to \infty$ and since $r \cos \theta$ is the appropriate form for a uniform field, the solutions with $n = 1$ must be used if the boundary conditions are to be satisfied for all θ. Moreover the field must be finite at $r = 0$ and so we try the following:

$$r \geqslant b \qquad V_0 = -B_0 r \cos \theta + (C \cos \theta)/r \tag{6.58}$$

$$b \geqslant r \geqslant a \qquad V_m = Dr \cos \theta + (E \cos \theta)/r \tag{6.59}$$

$$a \geqslant r \qquad V_i = -B_i r \cos \theta \tag{6.60}$$

where B_i is the required field and C, D, E are constants.

The boundary conditions (2.44) and (2.45) imply the continuity of V (from that of H_t) and of $\mu_r\, \partial V/\partial r$ (from that of B_n) across both boundaries. At the boundary $r = b$, we obtain

$$-B_0 b + C/b = Db + E/b; \qquad -B_0 - C/b^2 = \mu_r D - \mu_r E/b^2$$

and at $r = a$:

$$Da + E/a = -B_i a; \qquad \mu_r D - \mu_r E/a^2 = -B_i.$$

These four equations are sufficient to determine the unknown constants. Since we only require B_i, eliminate C between the first two equations and use the resulting equation to eliminate E from the last two. The remaining relations then show that $D = -B_i(\mu_r + 1)/2\mu_r$ and hence that

$$B_i = \frac{4B_0 \mu_r p}{(\mu_r^2 + 1)(p - 1) + 2\mu_r(p + 1)} \tag{6.61}$$

where p stands for the ratio b^2/a^2. For $\mu_r \gg 1$, as is usual,

$$B_i = \frac{4B_0 p}{\mu_r(p - 1) + 2(p + 1)}. \tag{6.62}$$

Hence, unless the tube is extremely thin, the first term in the denominator will predominate and the internal flux density will be only a small fraction of the applied flux density. This is in contrast to electrostatic shielding in which the internal field in a similar case is strictly zero. The lines of **B** are shown in Fig. 6.5b.

PROBLEMS

6.1 The divergence and curl of a vector field are specified by div $\mathbf{A} = s$, **curl** $\mathbf{A} = \mathbf{v}$, where s and $\mathbf{v}$ are finite systems of sources and vortices, and where $\mathbf{A}$ tends to zero towards infinity. If $\mathbf{A}_1$ and $\mathbf{A}_2$ are two vector fields satisfying these conditions, show that $\mathbf{A}_1 = \mathbf{A}_2$ (Helmholtz's theorem).

6.2 Find the mutual electric energy associated with charges Q_i and Q_j on the ith and jth conductors of a system and thus show that $p_{ij} = p_{ji}$. To what potential is an uncharged conducting sphere of radius a raised by a point charge Q at a distance r from its centre? ($r > a$).

6.3 Calculate the coefficients of potential for three thin concentric conducting spherical shells of radii a, b, and c such that $a < b < c$. Find the coefficient of capacitance c_{bb} and hence the capacitance of the system if the smallest and largest spheres are earthed to the surroundings.

6.4 The two plates of a condenser have coefficients of capacitance c_{11} and c_{22} and a coefficient of induction c_{12}. Find its capacitance.

6.5 Current flows in a very large bath of electrolyte between two very long parallel rod electrodes of negligible cross-section and a distance d apart. If the conductivity of the electrolyte is γ, what is the resistance per unit length between the electrodes?

6.6 Leakage currents flow radially outwards between the inner and outer conductors of a coaxial cable whose radii are a and b. If the conductivity of the 'insulator' is γ, find the leakage conductance per unit length of the cable.

6.7 Show that the system of charges in Fig. 6.3b does in fact produce a zero equipotential coincident with the spherical surface. Find the ratio between the maximum and minimum surface densities of charge induced on the sphere.

6.8 Find the capacitance per unit length of a thin horizontal telegraph wire of radius a at a height h above the earth ($h \gg a$).

6.9 Use problem 1.4 to find the capacitance per unit length between two long parallel wires of radii a whose axes are separated by a distance h. Do not now assume that $h \gg a$.

6.10 An electric dipole of moment $\mathbf{p}$ is a distance r from a semi-infinite conducting plane, and $\mathbf{p}$ is perpendicular to the plane. Find the force on the dipole.

6.11 Find the potential due to a conducting sphere of radius a placed in an applied uniform field $\mathbf{E}_0$ using the axially symmetric solutions of Laplace's equation.

6.12 Derive equations (6.23) giving the effective fields due to a dielectric sphere of radius a embedded in an infinite dielectric medium of different permittivity carrying an applied uniform field $\mathbf{E}_0$.

6.13 Find the magnetic field at a point off the axis of a circular coil of radius a carrying a current I in terms of the spherical co-ordinates (r, θ), where r is measured from the centre of the coil and $\theta = 0$ along the axis of the coil. Take $r > a$ and keep terms only up to $1/r^5$.

6.14 A semi-infinite medium of relative permeability μ_r occupies the region $z > 0$ and steady currents I are located *in vacuo* ($z < 0$). Show that the magnetic field for $z < 0$ is given by I together with an image in the plane $z = 0$ of magnitude $(\mu_r - 1)I/(\mu_r + 1)$; and the field for $z > 0$ is given by currents of magnitude $2\mu_r I/(\mu_r + 1)$ replacing the original currents in an infinite medium of relative permeability μ_r.

6.15 What boundary conditions on the vector potential **A** are imposed by those on **B** and **H**?

6.16 Show that when all currents flow everywhere in the z direction the vector potential satisfies a scalar Poisson's equation. Find the vector potential for an infinitely long cylindrical conductor of radius a carrying a current I distributed uniformly over its cross-section. The relative permeability of the conductor is μ_r. Find also **B** and **H**.

6.17 A conducting material fills the region of space in which $z > 0$. If it is raised to a steady electric potential V_0, find the potential everywhere by solving Laplace's equation.

6.18 A very long tube along the z-axis has a square cross-section with conducting walls at $x = 0$ and $x = a$, $y = 0$ and $y = a$. The wall at $y = a$ is at an electrostatic potential V_0 and the rest are at zero potential. Find the potential at any point (x, y) in a cross-section.

Part 3

Electromagnetic Waves in Matter

The greatest success of electromagnetic theory lies in its ability to account for optical phenomena. These are, however, part of a broader field of study which covers the general interaction of electromagnetic radiation with matter. The next two chapters deal with non-quantum aspects of this interaction.

We first see, in chapter 7, how the simplest model for materials—the continuum model—permits us to account both for the well-known laws of optics and for some more special properties, like the reflecting powers of metals, which only electromagnetic theory satisfactorily explains. All this needs only the assumption that electromagnetic waves are simply propagated in continuous media characterized only by their relative permittivity and electric conductivity.

Clearly, however, this is not entirely satisfactory when we are aware of the atomic and molecular structure of materials and in chapter 8, therefore, a different view is taken. The events are now assumed to take place *in vacuo* and involve the interaction of the wave with atomic particles, reradiation from which gives rise to scattering and in certain circumstances to refraction. We are thus able finally to show how the continuum model gives results consistent with the microscopic treatment.

7

Macro-media: optical properties of dielectrics and conductors

It is not the intention in this chapter to deal with the complete range of optical phenomena, but rather to show how some fundamental laws of optics and properties of light follow naturally from the electromagnetic theory of chapter 4 without the need of special assumptions. We saw there how some of the properties of light coincided exactly with those of electromagnetic waves, and we now wish to go further along the same path by introducing media other than vacuum.

Now it is certainly true that many optical phenomena do not need the full electromagnetic theory for their explanation: the broad features of interference and diffraction phenomena, for instance, are explicable on any scalar wave theory and some polarization effects on any vector wave theory. In other words, it is not necessary in these instances to specify anything about the quantity whose fluctuating amplitude forms the wave. For that reason we do not touch on those topics. But many features of reflection and refraction at boundaries and of propagation within media of various types need an *electromagnetic* wave theory and these are the features which concern us here.

We deal first with ideal dielectrics containing no conduction charges or currents and then with conducting and absorbing materials. In both cases, the propagation in the body of the material is first examined and then followed by a look at boundary effects.

7.1 Propagation in isotropic dielectrics

Maxwell's equations in unbounded LIH dielectrics are those of (4.6) with $\rho = 0$, $\mathbf{J} = 0$, $\mathbf{D} = \varepsilon_r\varepsilon_0\mathbf{E}$, and $\mathbf{H} = \mathbf{B}/\mu_r\mu_0$, ε_r and μ_r being constant scalars. The wave equation can be derived exactly as in section 4.3 and now gives a phase velocity

$$v_p = \frac{1}{(\varepsilon_r\varepsilon_0\mu_r\mu_0)^{1/2}} = \frac{c}{(\varepsilon_r\mu_r)^{1/2}}. \tag{7.1}$$

The *refractive index* of a material is in general defined by

$$n = c/v_p \tag{7.2}$$

and (7.1) thus shows that

$$n^2 = \varepsilon_r\mu_r \approx \varepsilon_r \tag{7.3}$$

the approximation applying for non-ferromagnetic materials. It is known from experimental measurements that both n and ε_r vary with frequency so that (7.3) would only be expected to apply when both quantities refer to the same frequency. This variation, leading to *dispersion*, cannot be explained on a strictly macroscopic theory and must be taken as given. There may of course be wide ranges over which no dispersion occurs and in some cases (7.3) may even apply when ε_r is the static permittivity and n the optical refractive index (e.g., for diamond, $\varepsilon_s = 5{\cdot}66$, $n_D{}^2 = 5{\cdot}68$). We shall in this chapter deal with the propagation of monochromatic radiation and leave details of the cause and effects of dispersion until chapter 8.

It should be noted that since $\varepsilon_r > 1$, the velocity of light in a medium, c/n, is always less than c. It is therefore possible for high energy particles to possess velocities in excess of v_p. When such particles pass through an insulator, a bluish light known as *Čerenkov radiation* is emitted. This was first noticed by Mallet (1926) and by Čerenkov in 1934 in transparent bodies placed near sources of γ-radiation. It was early discovered that the radiation must be attributed to secondary electrons produced by the γ-radiation and not to the γ-rays themselves.

The phenomenon does not depend on the acceleration of the electrons (which causes bremsstrahlung) but is purely a property of the fast *uniformly moving* charge interacting with the medium. Examination of the method of deriving the retarded potentials (4.84) and (4.85) reveals that, in a dielectric of refractive index n, the denominators would become $r - n\mathbf{v}\,.\,\mathbf{r}/c$ or $r(1 - nv_r/c)$ and this would replace the s occurring in (4.86). So even without acceleration, a particle velocity such that $v_r = c/n$ makes the induction fields infinite and we expect the solution to break down. A similar phenomenon is familiar in acoustics where the solution is known to be that of a shock wave: in the present case, it is also found that a wave results from the motion. The following explanation is based on that of Jelley (1958) to whom the reader is referred for further details.

A charge traversing a dielectric first increases and then decreases the electric polarization **P** in the surrounding medium as it passes any given point. We have seen already (equation (4.8)) that $\partial \mathbf{P}/\partial t$ can be equivalent to a current in generating fields and so we expect a series of pulses of radiation from successive points on an electron or proton track. For slow particles, **P** has time to reach its equilibrium

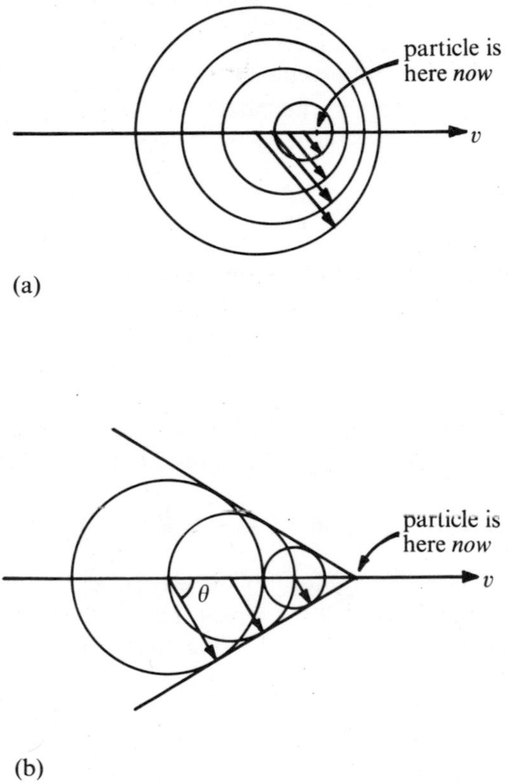

Fig. 7.1 A few of the wave pulses from a particle with (a) a velocity $v = \frac{1}{2}v_p$; (b) $v = 2v_p$

value at all points so that $\partial \mathbf{P}/\partial t$ is spherically symmetrical and the resultant radiation is zero (problem 7.1). For fast particles, the polarization ahead of any one is less than that behind it and there is emitted radiation, but as long as $v < c/n$ there is no coherence in any direction (Fig. 7.1a). As soon as $v = c/n$, however, there is coherence along the direction of travel and for velocities in excess of c/n (Fig. 7.1b) coherence occurs in a direction θ given by $\cos\theta = c/nv$ or, using $\beta = v/c$:

$$\cos\theta = 1/n\beta. \tag{7.4}$$

This result has been confirmed experimentally, but it must be remembered that, in practice, interactions between the charged particles and the medium is sure to cause a spread of β's and thus of θ's. Nevertheless, the angle θ is a measure of the energy of the particles and is used as such in some Čerenkov counters.

7.2 Propagation in anisotropic dielectrics

In anisotropic materials, the relative permittivity is no longer a scalar and to deal with wave propagation we refer all fields to the principal axes so that

$$D_x = \varepsilon_x \varepsilon_0 E_x; \qquad D_y = \varepsilon_y \varepsilon_0 E_y; \qquad D_z = \varepsilon_z \varepsilon_0 E_z. \tag{7.5}$$

Thus Maxwell's equations become, with $\rho = 0$, $\mathbf{J} = 0$, and $\mu_r = 1$:

$$\mathbf{curl\,E} = -\partial \mathbf{B}/\partial t; \qquad \text{div}\,\mathbf{B} = 0 \tag{7.6a, b}$$

$$\mathbf{curl\,B} = \mu_0\,\partial \mathbf{D}/\partial t; \qquad \text{div}\,\mathbf{D} = 0 \tag{7.7a, b}$$

while $\text{div}\,\mathbf{E} \neq 0$ because of (7.5). The wave equation for $\mathbf{E}$ is obtained as usual by taking the **curl** of (7.6a) and using (7.7a):

$$\mathbf{curl\,curl\,E} \equiv \mathbf{grad}\,\text{div}\,\mathbf{E} - \nabla^2\mathbf{E} = -\mu_0\,\partial^2\mathbf{D}/\partial t^2. \tag{7.8}$$

To find the phase velocity for a plane wave obeying this wave equation, we use the form (4.38) in which the wave vector $\mathbf{k}$ is given by $k\hat{\mathbf{s}}$, $\hat{\mathbf{s}}$ being a unit vector normal to the wave front:

$$\mathbf{E} = \mathbf{E}_0\,e^{i(\mathbf{k}\cdot\mathbf{r}-\omega t)} \tag{7.9}$$

although now we have, not $v_p = c$, but

$$v_p = \frac{\omega}{k} = \frac{c}{n} \tag{7.10}$$

where n is the refractive index. We can now substitute (7.9) in (7.8) and use (4.40). This gives

$$\mathbf{k}(\mathbf{k}\cdot\mathbf{E}) - k^2\mathbf{E} = -\mu_0\omega^2\mathbf{D} \tag{7.11}$$

or, dividing through by k^2:

$$\hat{\mathbf{s}}(\hat{\mathbf{s}}\cdot\mathbf{E}) - \mathbf{E} = -\mu_0 v_p{}^2\mathbf{D}. \tag{7.12}$$

In order to express this solely in terms of **E**, we must write down the three components separately, the x component being

$$s_x(\hat{\mathbf{s}}\cdot\mathbf{E}) - E_x = -\frac{v_p{}^2\varepsilon_x E_x}{c^2} \tag{7.13}$$

using $c^2 = 1/\varepsilon_0\mu_0$.

We now define three quantities which are purely properties of the medium and have the dimensions of velocities. They are v_x, v_y, v_z defined by

$$v_x{}^2 = c^2/\varepsilon_x; \qquad v_y{}^2 = c^2/\varepsilon_y; \qquad v_z{}^2 = c^2/\varepsilon_z \tag{7.14}$$

so that if we solve (7.13) for E_x, we get

$$E_x = \frac{s_x(\hat{\mathbf{s}}\cdot\mathbf{E})}{(1 - v_p{}^2/v_x{}^2)} \tag{7.15}$$

with similar expressions for E_y and E_z. The three components of **E** are, however, related through the fact that div **D** or **k . D** is zero. Since

$$\mathbf{k}\cdot\mathbf{D} = k(s_x\varepsilon_x E_x + s_y\varepsilon_y E_y + s_z\varepsilon_z E_z) = 0$$

we have that

$$\frac{s_x{}^2}{(v_p{}^2 - v_x{}^2)} + \frac{s_y{}^2}{(v_p{}^2 - v_y{}^2)} + \frac{s_z{}^2}{(v_p{}^2 - v_z{}^2)} = 0 \tag{7.16}$$

an equation, known as *Fresnel's equation*, connecting the direction of propagation of the wave with the phase velocity in that direction. To see the meaning of (7.16) it is better written in the form

$$s_x{}^2(v_p{}^2 - v_y{}^2)(v_p{}^2 - v_z{}^2) + s_y{}^2(v_p{}^2 - v_z{}^2)(v_p{}^2 - v_x{}^2)$$
$$+ s_z{}^2(v_p{}^2 - v_x{}^2)(v_p{}^2 - v_y{}^2) = 0 \tag{7.17}$$

for here we now see that the equation is a quadratic in $v_p{}^2$, giving four roots, two each of the same magnitude but opposite sign. That is, there are two phase velocities in a general direction and *double refraction* occurs. Wave surfaces can be drawn using (7.16), giving the values of v_p in any direction in (x, y, z) space. Figure 7.2 shows sections through such surfaces for ε's so chosen that $v_x > v_y > v_z$.

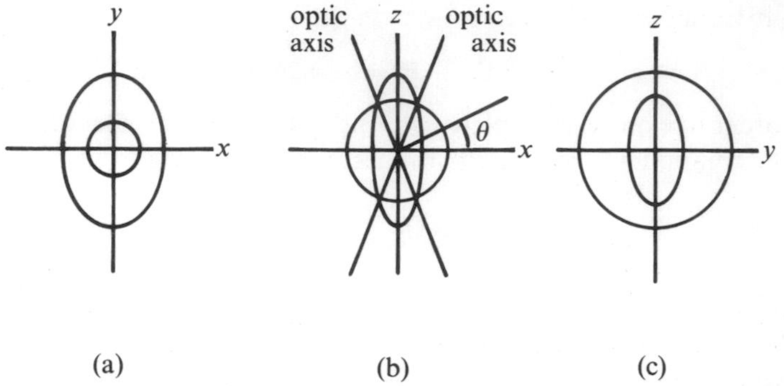

Fig. 7.2 Wave-surface cross-sections in a biaxial material with $v_x > v_y > v_z$. In (b) for instance, $s_x = \cos\theta$, $s_y = 0$, $s_z = \sin\theta$ and from (7.17), $v_p^2 = v_y^2$ or $v_p^2 = v_z^2 \cos^2\theta + v_x^2 \sin^2\theta$

It can be seen that there are two directions in the xz-plane for which only one value of v_p exists (of magnitude v_y). These directions are called *optic axes* and a material exhibiting this property is *biaxial*.

In all three sections, one wave is seen to propagate isotropically: this is the *ordinary* wave while the other is the *extraordinary*. Both waves can be shown to be transverse since from (7.6b) and (7.7b)

$$\mathbf{k}\,.\,\mathbf{B} = \mathbf{k}\,.\,\mathbf{H} = 0; \qquad \mathbf{k}\,.\,\mathbf{D} = 0 \tag{7.18}$$

while problem 7.3 shows that if $\mathbf{D}'$ is the displacement vector in the ordinary ray and $\mathbf{D}''$ in the extraordinary,

$$\mathbf{D}'\,.\,\mathbf{D}'' = 0 \tag{7.19}$$

i.e., the two waves are polarized in perpendicular planes.

However, because $\mathbf{k}\,.\,\mathbf{E} \neq 0$, $\mathbf{E}$ is not in the plane perpendicular to $\mathbf{k}$ and thus the Poynting vector $\mathbf{E} \times \mathbf{H}$ (defining the *ray* direction) will not be in the direction of $\mathbf{k}$ (normal to the wave front). Rays are not, in general, perpendicular to wave fronts.

When any two of the $\varepsilon_x, \varepsilon_y, \varepsilon_z$ are equal, we have *uniaxial* materials with one optic axis only, while if all three are equal, the material is isotropic. Further properties connected with birefringence are brought out in problems 7.2–7.4. It only remains to say that biaxial materials are crystals with orthorhombic symmetry or lower;

uniaxial materials include crystals with tetragonal or hexagonal symmetry, isotropic materials strained in one direction, and isotropic materials in an applied electric or magnetic field (Kerr and Cotton-Mouton effects respectively).

7.3 Reflection and refraction at a boundary between dielectrics

Throughout this section we use the geometry of Fig. 7.3 in which the xy-plane constitutes the boundary between LIH dielectrics of refractive indices n_1 and n_2. The normals to the wave-fronts (rays) are drawn for the incident, reflected, and transmitted waves, but we do not assume initially that all three are coplanar even though they are so drawn in the figure.

Frequency and direction of reflected and transmitted waves. We take an incident plane wave whose wave vector $\mathbf{k}_i$ makes an angle θ_i with the z-axis: $\mathbf{k}_i$ and the z-axis between them then define the plane of incidence. The incident electric vector may then be written

$$\mathbf{E}_i = \mathbf{E}_{i0}\, e^{i(\mathbf{k}_i \,.\, \mathbf{r} - \omega_i t)} \tag{7.20}$$

where ω_i is the angular frequency, so that ω_i/k_i is the phase velocity in medium 1. Hence, because this is c/n_1:

$$k_i = n_1\omega_i/c. \tag{7.21}$$

Similarly for the other two beams, with appropriate subscripts:

$$\mathbf{E}_r = \mathbf{E}_{r0}\, e^{i(\mathbf{k}_r \,.\, \mathbf{r} - \omega_r t)}; \qquad \mathbf{E}_t = \mathbf{E}_{t0}\, e^{i(\mathbf{k}_t \,.\, \mathbf{r} - \omega_t t)} \tag{7.22}$$

and

$$k_r = n_1\omega_r/c; \qquad k_t = n_2\omega_t/c. \tag{7.23}$$

At the boundary, the tangential component of $\mathbf{E}$ is continuous and so for instance the x-components of (7.20) and (7.22) must obey

$$E_{i0x}\, e^{i(\mathbf{k}_i \,.\, \mathbf{r} - \omega_i t)} + E_{r0x}\, e^{i(\mathbf{k}_r \,.\, \mathbf{r} - \omega_r t)} = E_{t0x}\, e^{i(\mathbf{k}_t \,.\, \mathbf{r} - \omega_t t)} \tag{7.24}$$

for all x, y, and t. This condition can only be satisfied if the coefficients of x, y, and t in the exponentials are equal and so we have immediately that

$$\omega_i = \omega_r = \omega_t = \omega \text{ say} \tag{7.25}$$

i.e., the frequency of the waves is unchanged by reflection or refraction. It follows that the different phase velocities in the two media imply different wave-lengths.

We also have from (7.24) that

$$\mathbf{k}_i \cdot \mathbf{r} = \mathbf{k}_r \cdot \mathbf{r} = \mathbf{k}_t \cdot \mathbf{r} \tag{7.26}$$

for all x, y. Each wave-vector $\mathbf{k}$ can be written as $k\hat{\mathbf{s}}$, where k is given by (7.21) or (7.23) and $\hat{\mathbf{s}}$ is the unit vector along the wave normal whose components s_x, s_y, s_z give the direction cosines of the ray with respect to the x-, y-, z- axes. Thus

$$\mathbf{k}_i \cdot \mathbf{r} = k_i\hat{\mathbf{s}}_i \cdot \mathbf{r} = \frac{n_1\omega}{c} x \sin\theta_i + \frac{n_1\omega}{c} z \cos\theta_i \tag{7.27}$$

because s_y is zero for the incident beam which is in the xz-plane. It follows that the y terms in the other expressions of (7.26) are also zero, and therefore that s_y for the reflected and transmitted beams is zero. Thus *the reflected and transmitted rays are in the same plane as the incident ray and the normal*—often known as the first law of reflection and refraction. Because of this, s_x for the reflected ray can be written $\sin\theta_r$ and similarly for the other direction cosines. Hence

$$\mathbf{k}_r \cdot \mathbf{r} = \frac{n_1\omega}{c}(x \sin\theta_r + z \cos\theta_r) \tag{7.28}$$

$$\mathbf{k}_t \cdot \mathbf{r} = \frac{n_2\omega}{c}(x \sin\theta_t + z \cos\theta_t). \tag{7.29}$$

Equating coefficients of x in (7.27), (7.28), and (7.29) gives

$$\theta_i = \theta_r \tag{7.30}$$

$$n_1 \sin\theta_i = n_2 \sin\theta_t. \tag{7.31}$$

Equation (7.30) embodies the second law of reflection and (7.31) the second law of refraction or *Snell's law*.

These laws will follow from any wave theory since the phases of (7.24) must match at the boundary irrespective of the nature of the amplitudes. We must now investigate these amplitudes to find phenomena needing a specifically electromagnetic theory.

Amplitudes of reflected and transmitted waves, $n_2 > n_1$. First consider incidence from the less dense medium. Although there are four boundary conditions on the field vectors given by (4.10), only two are independent with plane waves because E and B are related by $E = v_p B$. We shall use only the conditions

$$E_{tan} \text{ is continuous;} \qquad H_{tan} \text{ is continuous} \tag{7.32}$$

and note that in either medium, $H = B/\mu_0 = E/\mu_0 v_p$ or

$$H = nE/\mu_0 c \tag{7.33}$$

where n is the refractive index.

First, consider a plane polarized wave whose incident **E** vector is *parallel* to the plane of incidence as in Fig. 7.3. The incident **H** vector

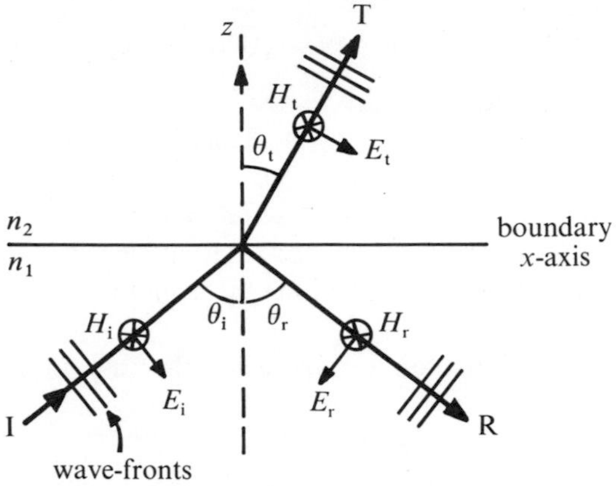

Fig. 7.3 Geometry for reflection and refraction at a dielectric boundary. The directions of **E** and **H** are those for plane waves with the **E** vector parallel to the plane of incidence

will be directed into the diagram and the directions of the fields in the reflected and transmitted waves are as shown. Thus the continuity of E_{tan} across the boundary gives

$$E_i \cos \theta_i - E_r \cos \theta_i = E_t \cos \theta_t \tag{7.34}$$

and the continuity of H_{tan} gives

$$H_i + H_r = H_t \tag{7.35}$$

or, using (7.33):

$$n_1 E_i + n_1 E_r = n_2 E_t. \tag{7.36}$$

In the last three equations we have omitted the zero subscripts on E and H, it being understood that the phases now cancel and the equations are relations between amplitudes.

The interest lies in the fractions of the incident amplitude which are reflected and transmitted. First, E_t is eliminated between (7.34) and (7.36) giving a reflection coefficient $r_{\parallel}$:

$$r_{\parallel} = E_r/E_i = \frac{n_2 \cos \theta_i - n_1 \cos \theta_t}{n_2 \cos \theta_i + n_1 \cos \theta_t}$$

or, using Snell's law (7.31):

$$r_{\parallel} = \frac{(n_2/n_1)\cos\theta_i - \cos\theta_t}{(n_2/n_1)\cos\theta_i + \cos\theta_t} = \frac{\tan(\theta_i - \theta_t)}{\tan(\theta_i + \theta_t)}. \tag{7.37}$$

Similarly, a transmission coefficient $t_{\parallel}$ is obtained:

$$t_{\parallel} = E_t/E_i = \frac{2\cos\theta_i}{(n_2/n_1)\cos\theta_i + \cos\theta_t} = \frac{2\cos\theta_i \sin\theta_t}{\sin(\theta_i + \theta_t)}. \tag{7.38}$$

Equations (7.37) and (7.38) are *Fresnel relations* for waves whose **E** vector is parallel to the plane of incidence. The *reflecting power* or *reflectivity* $R_{\parallel}$ is the ratio of the *intensities* of reflected and incident beams per unit area of the interface and is clearly just $r_{\parallel}^2$. The *transmissivity* $T_{\parallel}$ is similarly defined, but will depend on the refractive indices and angles in a way different from that of $t_{\parallel}^2$ (see problems 7.6 and 7.8).

Similar calculations can be made for the case in which the **E**

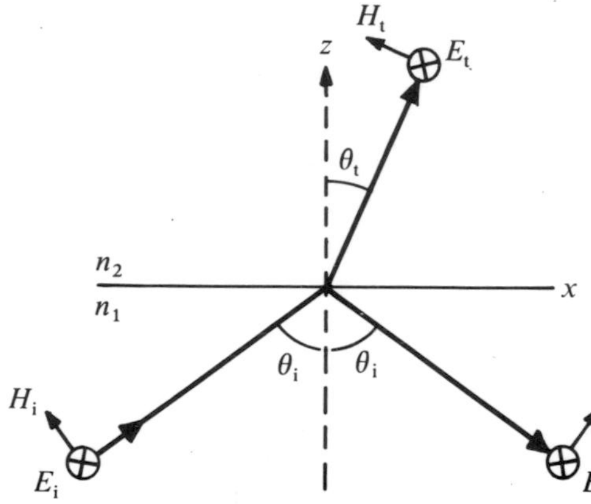

Fig. 7.4 Reflection and refraction of a plane wave with the **E** vector perpendicular to the plane of incidence

vector is perpendicular to the plane of incidence as in Fig. 7.4. The boundary conditions now give

$$E_i + E_r = E_t \tag{7.39}$$

$$H_i \cos\theta_i - H_r \cos\theta_i = H_t \cos\theta_t \tag{7.40}$$

or, by (7.33),

$$n_1 E_i \cos\theta_i - n_1 E_r \cos\theta_i = n_2 E_t \cos\theta_t. \tag{7.41}$$

Equations (7.39) and (7.41) give two more Fresnel relations:

$$r_\perp = \frac{\cos\theta_i - (n_2/n_1)\cos\theta_t}{\cos\theta_i + (n_2/n_1)\cos\theta_t} = -\frac{\sin(\theta_i - \theta_t)}{\sin(\theta_i + \theta_t)} \tag{7.42}$$

$$t_\perp = \frac{2\cos\theta_i}{\cos\theta_i + (n_2/n_1)\cos\theta_t} = \frac{2\cos\theta_i \sin\theta_t}{\sin(\theta_i + \theta_t)}. \tag{7.43}$$

The interesting coefficients are $r_\parallel$ and $r_\perp$, plotted in Fig. 7.5a

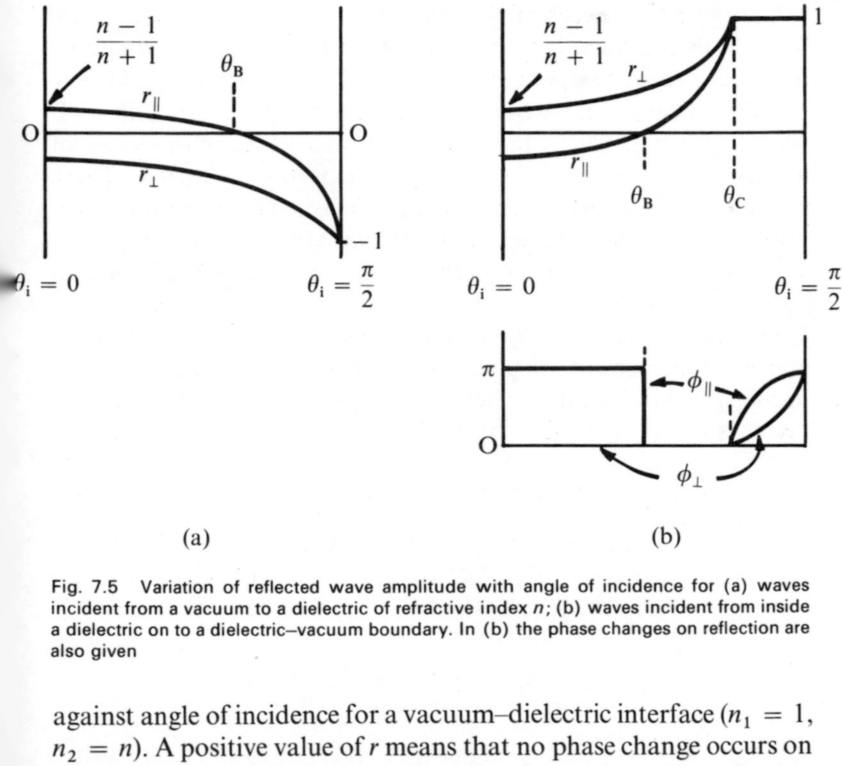

Fig. 7.5 Variation of reflected wave amplitude with angle of incidence for (a) waves incident from a vacuum to a dielectric of refractive index n; (b) waves incident from inside a dielectric on to a dielectric–vacuum boundary. In (b) the phase changes on reflection are also given

against angle of incidence for a vacuum–dielectric interface ($n_1 = 1$, $n_2 = n$). A positive value of r means that no phase change occurs on reflection, a negative value that the phase changes by π. The reflecting power at normal incidence is seen to be

$$R_n = \left(\frac{n-1}{n+1}\right)^2 \tag{7.44}$$

while for grazing incidence the reflecting power approaches unity, a phenomenon easily observed with most surfaces.

At a particular angle of incidence, Fig. 7.5a and equation (7.37) show that $r_{\parallel}$ becomes zero. This is a result of $(\theta_i + \theta_t)$ being $\pi/2$: the reflected and transmitted rays are perpendicular for this angle of incidence, known as the *Brewster angle*, θ_B. For reflection at a vacuum–dielectric interface, we shall have the refractive index n given in general by $\sin\theta_i/\sin\theta_t$ and at the Brewster angle by $\sin\theta_B/\sin(\pi/2 - \theta_B)$. Thus

$$\tan\theta_B = n_2/n_1 = n. \tag{7.45}$$

Any incident light can be resolved into two plane-polarized components (not necessarily with any constant phase relationship between them). Such light incident at the Brewster angle would be reflected with no component of **E** parallel to the plane of incidence, i.e., the reflected light would always be plane-polarized with its **E** vector perpendicular to the plane of incidence. At other angles of incidence the reflected light is only partially polarized. These phenomena are easily observed in light reflected from the surface of water or glass, and indeed the general variation shown in Fig. 7.5a accords well with experimental measurements up to and including optical frequencies.

Incidence in the optically denser medium, $n_1 > n_2$. Although the above theory does not depend on the relative values of n_1 and n_2, Snell's law shows us that when $n_1 > n_2$, $\sin\theta_t$ exceeds $\sin\theta_i$ and θ_t becomes $\pi/2$ at an angle θ_c of incidence known as the *critical angle*,

$$\sin\theta_c = n_2/n_1. \tag{7.46}$$

For greater angles of incidence, θ_t does not exist as a solution to the Snell's law equation (7.31). We can retain the form of the reflection and transmission coefficients, however, by writing

$$\cos\theta_t = (1 - \sin^2\theta_t)^{1/2} = \left(1 - \frac{n_1^{\,2}}{n_2^{\,2}}\sin^2\theta_i\right)^{1/2}.$$

The expression in the bracket is negative if $\theta_i > \theta_c$ and $\cos\theta_t$ is then imaginary. Let us therefore write it as

$$\cos\theta_t = i\left(\frac{n_1^{\,2}}{n_2^{\,2}}\sin^2\theta_i - 1\right)^{1/2} = ib, \text{ say.} \tag{7.47}$$

Then the relation (7.42) for instance becomes

$$r_{\perp} = \frac{(n_1/n_2)\cos\theta_i - \cos\theta_t}{(n_1/n_2)\cos\theta_i + \cos\theta_t} = \frac{a - ib}{a + ib} \tag{7.48}$$

where both $a\ (=(n_1 \cos \theta_i)/n_2)$ and b are real. This is a complex quantity whose magnitude is 1 and whose phase angle $\phi_\perp$ varies between 0 and π as shown in Fig. 7.5b. The variation of $r_\parallel$ and its phase $\phi_\parallel$ is also shown. Thus at angles of incidence exceeding the critical angle θ_c, both reflection coefficients are 1 and we always have *total internal reflection.*

Although all the energy is reflected and none transmitted when total internal reflection occurs, there is nevertheless some disturbance in the second medium. From (7.22) the transmitted **E** vector is

$$\mathbf{E}_t = \mathbf{E}_{t0}\ e^{i(\mathbf{k}_t \cdot \mathbf{r} - \omega t)}$$

and by using (7.29) and substituting $\cos \theta_t = ib$ from (7.47) and $\sin \theta_t = (n_1 \sin \theta_i)/n_2$:

$$\mathbf{E}_t = \mathbf{E}_{t0}\ e^{-n_2 \omega b z/c}\ e^{i(x k_i \sin \theta_i - \omega t)}. \tag{7.49}$$

This represents a wave travelling *along the interface* (in the x-direction) but with an amplitude decaying in the z-direction. The penetration depth into the second medium is $c/n_2\omega b$, which is of the order of the wave-length in the medium of the radiation involved. Such a wave is known as an *evanescent wave* and once established it carries no energy away into the second medium.

General reflection at a dielectric boundary. Although we have dealt above with waves polarized in planes parallel and perpendicular to the plane of incidence, any form of incident light can be resolved into two components and the resultant reflected amplitude obtained by superposition. It should be noted that, in general, the two components suffer different phase changes so that the state of

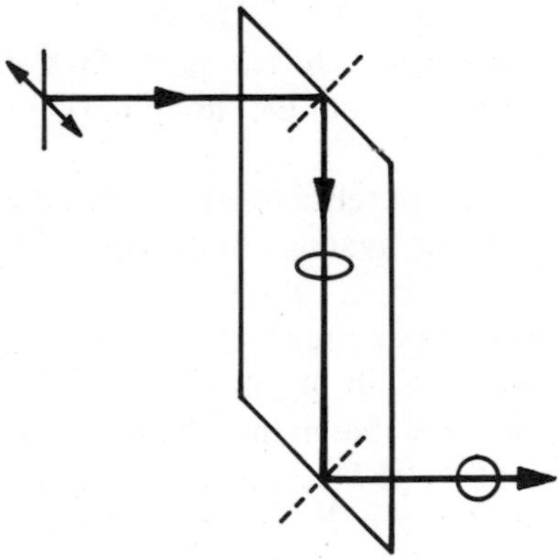

Fig. 7.6 The Fresnel rhomb

polarization is affected. An example of this is afforded by the Fresnel rhomb (Fig. 7.6), in which light is incident internally at an angle greater than θ_c and such that the difference between $\phi_{\parallel}$ and $\phi_{\perp}$ in Fig. 7.5b is exactly $\pi/4$ (this occurs in glass at about 53°). If the incident light has its plane of polarization at 45° to the plane of incidence, $E_{\parallel}$ and $E_{\perp}$ are equal in amplitude and on reflection are still so but with a phase difference now of $\pi/4$. A second reflection as shown introduces a further phase difference of $\pi/4$, making a total of $\pi/2$ and producing circularly polarized light.

7.4 Propagation in absorbing media

The **E** vector in a monochromatic plane wave takes the form $\mathbf{E}_0 \exp \{i(\mathbf{k} \cdot \mathbf{r} - \omega t)\}$ in an ideal dielectric, where $\mathbf{E}_0$ is a real constant and no diminution in amplitude occurs. In a medium where absorption takes place, the decay can be described by assuming that the wave number k is complex or, in view of (7.21), that the refractive index is complex. For if we take

$$\mathbf{n} = n + i\kappa \tag{7.50}$$

the wave now becomes, if propagation is in the z-direction

$$\begin{aligned} \mathbf{E} = \mathbf{E}_0 \, \mathrm{e}^{i(\mathbf{k}z - \omega t)} &= \mathbf{E}_0 \, \mathrm{e}^{i(\omega \mathbf{n} z/c - \omega t)} \\ &= \mathbf{E}_0 \, \mathrm{e}^{-\omega \kappa z/c} \, \mathrm{e}^{i(\omega n z/c - \omega t)} \end{aligned} \tag{7.51}$$

a wave whose amplitude decays in such a way that it falls to 1/e of its initial value in a distance

$$\alpha = c/\omega\kappa \tag{7.52}$$

known as the *penetration depth*. The real part of **n** thus behaves as an observable refractive index and the imaginary part defines the absorption.

The above description is purely a formal one and we now see how it corresponds to behaviour in actual materials, first dielectrics and then conductors.

Real dielectrics. Over certain ranges of frequency, the polarization in a dielectric does not remain in phase with the applied electric field. (It must be emphasized that in this chapter we have to take this as a given experimental fact.) This effect can be taken care of by a complex relative permittivity in $\mathbf{P} = \varepsilon_0(\boldsymbol{\varepsilon}_r - 1)\mathbf{E}$ such that

$$\boldsymbol{\varepsilon}_r = \varepsilon' + i\varepsilon'' \tag{7.53}$$

where both ε' and ε'' can be measured experimentally, at least from radio to microwave frequencies.

The complex permittivity inserted into Maxwell's equations would yield a wave equation as in section 7.1 in which the phase velocity would again be given by $c/(\boldsymbol{\varepsilon}_r\mu_r)^{1/2} \sim c/\boldsymbol{\varepsilon}_r^{\,1/2}$ and the refractive index by $\boldsymbol{\varepsilon}_r^{\,1/2}$, now complex. Thus from (7.50)

$$\mathbf{n}^2 = \boldsymbol{\varepsilon}_r \tag{7.54}$$

or

$$(n^2 - \kappa^2) + i2n\kappa = \varepsilon' + i\varepsilon''.$$

Thus

$$\varepsilon' = n^2 - \kappa^2; \qquad \varepsilon'' = 2n\kappa. \tag{7.55}$$

It is true to say, therefore, that ε'' (like κ) is responsible for absorption in that when it is zero no absorption occurs. There is, however, no simple relation between the absorption coefficient κ and ε''.

A dielectric behaving in this way is called *lossy* and the ratio

$$\varepsilon''/\varepsilon' = \tan\delta \tag{7.56}$$

where δ is the loss angle of the material. If an alternating potential difference $V_0\,e^{j\omega t}$ is applied to a condenser of capacitance C with vacuum between its plates, the current I across it is given by

$$I = j\omega C V_0\,e^{j\omega t} \tag{7.57}$$

so that I and V are in quadrature and no loss of energy occurs. (Note that here we have reverted to standard a.c. practice and used a time variation $e^{j\omega t}$ instead of $e^{-i\omega t}$, so that $-j$ replaces i in our normal treatment.) When an imperfect dielectric is introduced, the capacitance becomes $\varepsilon_r C$ so that by (7.53) with $i = -j$:

$$I = j\omega\varepsilon' C V_0\,e^{j\omega t} + \omega\varepsilon'' C V_0\,e^{j\omega t}. \tag{7.58}$$

The dielectric loss thus introduces an *in-phase* potential difference akin to a resistive term. A lossy condenser can thus be made equivalent *at a given frequency* to an ideal condenser in series with a resistance.

Conductors, especially metals. We now turn to conducting media in which, excluding ferromagnetics, Maxwell's equations become

(ε_r now being real):

$$\operatorname{div} \mathbf{B} = 0; \qquad \mathbf{curl\ B} = \mu_0 \gamma \mathbf{E} + \frac{\varepsilon_r}{c^2}\frac{\partial \mathbf{E}}{\partial t} \tag{7.59a, b}$$

$$\operatorname{div} \mathbf{E} = 0; \qquad \mathbf{curl\ E} = -\frac{\partial \mathbf{B}}{\partial t}. \tag{7.60a, b}$$

To derive the wave equation, take the **curl** of (7.60b) in the usual way and use (7.59b):

$$\mathbf{curl\ curl\ E} = -\frac{\partial}{\partial t}(\mathbf{curl\ B}) = -\mu_0 \gamma \frac{\partial \mathbf{E}}{\partial t} - \frac{\varepsilon_r}{c^2}\frac{\partial^2 \mathbf{E}}{\partial t^2}$$

so that, by (A.34) and (7.60a):

$$\nabla^2 \mathbf{E} = \frac{\varepsilon_r}{c^2}\frac{\partial^2 \mathbf{E}}{\partial t^2} + \mu_0 \gamma \frac{\partial \mathbf{E}}{\partial t}. \tag{7.61}$$

The same equation also applies to **B**.

If conduction current is negligible, (7.61) degenerates into the wave equation of section 7.1 as is otherwise clear by putting $\gamma = 0$ in (7.59b). If, on the other hand, displacement current can be neglected, then (7.61) is no longer a wave equation but one describing a diffusion process. In metallic conductors particularly, as discussed in section 4.1, the conduction current will normally predominate so that on physical grounds we do not expect waves to penetrate very far below the surface.

To investigate the form of wave which can be propagated, consider a monochromatic plane wave whose fields are

$$\mathbf{E} = \mathbf{E}_0\, e^{i(\mathbf{k}\,.\,\mathbf{r} - \omega t)}; \qquad \mathbf{B} = \mathbf{B}_0\, e^{i(\mathbf{k}\,.\,\mathbf{r} - \omega t)}. \tag{7.62}$$

Using the substitution (4.40) in Maxwell's equations above, we find

$$\mathbf{k}\,.\,\mathbf{B}_0 = 0; \qquad \mathbf{k}\,.\,\mathbf{E}_0 = 0 \tag{7.63}$$

$$\mathbf{k} \times \mathbf{E}_0 = \omega \mathbf{B}_0 \tag{7.64}$$

$$i\mathbf{k} \times \mathbf{B}_0 = \mu_0 \gamma \mathbf{E}_0 - \omega \varepsilon_r \mathbf{E}_0 / c^2. \tag{7.65}$$

Thus, *spatially*, **E** and **B** are both transverse to **k** by (7.63) and are perpendicular to each other by (7.64), with amplitudes related by $E = v_p B$. All this is apparently as in a plane wave in a dielectric. (In fact, it is possible for a spatially constant *longitudinal* **E** to exist but it decays in time with a relaxation time $\tau = \varepsilon_r \varepsilon_0 / \gamma$ and does not affect the wave fields—see problem 7.11.) Equation (7.65), however, shows that the matter is not so simple because one of the components must be complex. Using either (7.64) and (7.65) to eliminate **E** and **B** or, what is the same, using substitution (4.40) in the wave equation (7.61) we have

$$\mathbf{k}^2 = \omega^2\varepsilon_r/c^2 + i\mu_0\gamma\omega \tag{7.66}$$

where **k** is the complex magnitude of **k**. The refractive index, from (7.10), is therefore $\mathbf{k}c/\omega$ and so

$$\mathbf{n}^2 = \mathbf{k}^2c^2/\omega^2 = \varepsilon_r + i\mu_0\gamma c^2/\omega.$$

Using $c^2 = 1/\varepsilon_0\mu_0$ and $\tau = \varepsilon_r\varepsilon_0/\gamma$, the relaxation time for the medium:

$$\mathbf{n}^2 = \varepsilon_r + i\varepsilon_r/\omega\tau. \tag{7.67}$$

It is clear that absorption will occur just as it did in the lossy dielectric and indeed conduction is one possible contribution to the ε'' of (7.53). From (7.50) and (7.67) we have, equating real and imaginary parts,

$$n^2 - \kappa^2 = \varepsilon_r; \qquad 2n\kappa = \varepsilon_r/\omega\tau.$$

Solving for n and κ:

$$n^2 = \frac{\varepsilon_r}{2}\left[1 + \left(1 + \frac{1}{\omega^2\tau^2}\right)^{1/2}\right] \tag{7.68}$$

$$\kappa^2 = \frac{\varepsilon_r}{2}\left[-1 + \left(1 + \frac{1}{\omega^2\tau^2}\right)^{1/2}\right]. \tag{7.69}$$

The expressions simplify considerably if $\omega\tau$ is either very large or very small.

If $\omega\tau \gg 1$, then $n^2 \approx \varepsilon_r$ and $\kappa \approx \varepsilon_r^{1/2}/2\omega\tau$ or $n/2\omega\tau$ giving a penetration depth, from (7.52), of

$$\alpha = 2c\tau/n. \tag{7.70}$$

This condition may apply well to very poor conductors, but even for moderately good conductors such high frequencies are needed to make $\omega\tau \gg 1$, that absorptive effects other than conduction can easily affect the results. In any case, the static value of γ is no longer a good guide to its high-frequency value.

If $\omega\tau \ll 1$, (7.68) and (7.69) give both n^2 and κ^2 approximately equal to $\varepsilon_r/2\omega\tau$ or

$$n^2 \approx \kappa^2 \approx \gamma/2\varepsilon_0\omega. \tag{7.71}$$

It follows that

$$\mathbf{n} = (1 + i)(\gamma/2\varepsilon_0\omega)^{1/2} \tag{7.72}$$

and that, from (7.52), the penetration depth is

$$\alpha = (2/\mu_0\gamma\omega)^{1/2} \tag{7.73}$$

as in (3.27) with $\mu_r = 1$. These values are likely to hold with metals at least up to infra-red frequencies, and with other conductors up to radio frequencies where the static conductivity is still likely to be a valid substitution for γ. For copper, the penetration depth given by (7.73) is about $7/\nu^{1/2}$ cm at a frequency ν, and this is about 10^{-4} cm in the microwave region. The wave and its associated currents are thus confined to a very thin layer near the surface in a good conductor. This is the *skin effect*, already met in section 3.4.

The complex $\mathbf{n}$ of (7.72) means that $\mathbf{k}$ is also complex and has equal real and imaginary parts. By (7.64) this means that **E** and **B** differ in phase by $\pi/4$, unlike the situation in a dielectric where they are in phase. However, the small penetration depth in good conductors makes very difficult any experimental verification of the results of this section. For this, we look to reflection from the surface.

7.5 Reflection at metallic surfaces

This can be treated in the same way as reflection at dielectric surfaces and leads to broadly similar variations. However, because of the complex refractive index there are phase changes between 0 and π for reflection at any angle of incidence ($\cos\theta_t$ is imaginary as in total internal reflection in a dielectric). Plane polarized light is, in general, elliptically polarized on reflection and examination of the state of polarization enables n and κ to be determined.

The important feature in strongly absorbing materials is their reflecting power and we now derive an expression for this at normal incidence. In Fig. 7.7, let the field vectors be oriented as shown and let us apply the usual conditions of continuity giving

$$E_i + E_r = E_t \tag{7.74}$$

$$H_i - H_r = H_t. \tag{7.75}$$

To convert (7.75) into a relation involving E, we must use (7.33) with the complex index so that

$$H = \mathbf{n}E/\mu_0 c \tag{7.76}$$

and so

$$E_i - E_r = \mathbf{n}E_t. \tag{7.77}$$

Equations (7.74) and (7.77) yield for the reflection coefficient

$$\mathbf{r} = E_r/E_i = \frac{1 - \mathbf{n}}{1 + \mathbf{n}} \tag{7.78}$$

and the reflecting power at normal incidence is therefore

$$R_n = |\mathbf{r}|^2 = \frac{(1 - n)^2 + \kappa^2}{(1 + n)^2 + \kappa^2}. \tag{7.79}$$

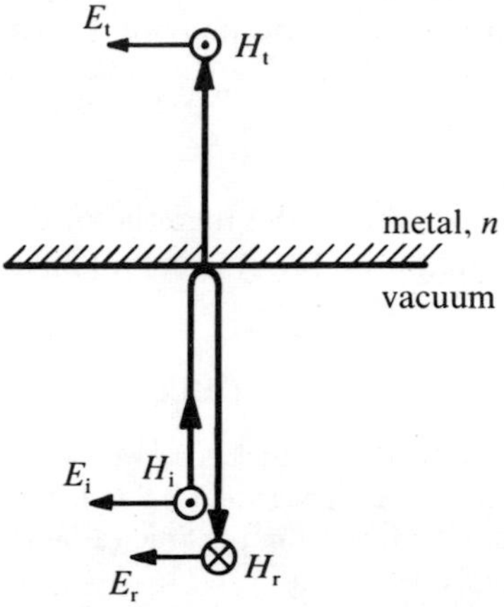

Fig. 7.7 Reflection of a wave at a metal surface

In section 7.4, we saw that for metals up to infra-red frequencies $\omega\tau \ll 1$ and n^2 and κ^2 are both approximately $\gamma/2\varepsilon_0\omega$ and much greater than 1. Hence (7.79) would become

$$R_n \approx \frac{n^2 + \kappa^2 - 2n}{n^2 + \kappa^2 + 2n} \approx \frac{n^2 - n}{n^2 + n}$$

$$= \frac{1 - 1/n}{1 + 1/n}$$

$$\approx 1 - 2n.$$

That is,

$$R_n \approx 1 - 2(2\varepsilon_0\omega/\gamma)^{1/2}. \tag{7.80}$$

The reflecting power is thus very high, differing only by a small quantity from 1. A perfect conductor ($\gamma = \infty$) would be a perfect reflector. These formulae give good agreement with experiment for metals in the infra-red region—Hagen and Rubens (1903) showed that $(1 - R_n)\gamma^{1/2}$ at a given frequency was the same for a variety of metals—but often fail in the visible region. Metals (in common with other strongly absorbent materials) *are* good reflectors, but the conductivity cannot be regarded as a simple constant at all frequencies, particularly where electrons other than conduction electrons begin to play their part in the absorption process. Measurements in the visible region sometimes show $n < 1$, and the colour of many metals indicates that selective absorption is occurring: these phenomena cannot be accounted for by the above macroscopic theory.

References

A standard work covering the material of this chapter is Born and Wolf (1965). Ditchburn (1962) is comprehensive on double refraction.

PROBLEMS

7.1 The polarization **P** in a dielectric varies sinusoidally in time and is spherically symmetrical in space so that **P** is always radial. Why would you expect no radiation to arise from the time variations? Generalize the result to any variation of **P** with time.

7.2 Show that the **E** vector of a plane wave propagated in an anisotropic dielectric is not perpendicular to the wave normal $\hat{\mathbf{s}}$ but does lie in the plane containing $\hat{\mathbf{s}}$ and **D**. If the direction of propagation of energy (the ray direction) is defined by a unit vector $\hat{\mathbf{t}}$, draw a diagram showing the relationship in space between $\hat{\mathbf{s}}$, $\hat{\mathbf{t}}$, **D**, **E**, **B**, and **H**.

7.3 Show that the two displacement vectors $\mathbf{D}'$ and $\mathbf{D}''$ associated with the phase velocities v_p' and v_p'' in double refraction are perpendicular to each other for any given direction of propagation.

7.4 A uniaxial crystal has $v_x = v_y = v_0$ and $v_z = v_e$. Show that the wave surfaces consist of a sphere given by $v_p^2 = v_0^2$ and an ellipsoid of revolution given by $v_p^2 = v_e^2(s_x^2 + s_y^2) + v_0^2 s_z^2$. Show that the optic axis lies in the z-direction.

7.5 If the continuity of D_n across a boundary is used instead of that of $H_{\tan}$, show that equation (7.36) is still obtained.

7.6 A plane electromagnetic wave is incident on the boundary between two LIH dielectric media. Find expressions for the incident, reflected, and transmitted power per unit area *of the boundary* and show that there is energy balance at the interface, i.e., that the sum of reflected and transmitted power is equal to the incident power.

7.7 An electromagnetic wave of unit amplitude is incident on one side of a plane boundary between two media and the amplitudes of the reflected and transmitted waves are r and t respectively. If the rays are all reversed in direction, then r and t should recombine to give the unit amplitude once more. Use this to show that $r' = -r$ and $r^2 + tt' = 1$, where r' and t' are the values of r and t for incidence on the other side of the boundary. Show that the coefficients (7.37), (7.38), (7.42), and (7.43) obey these relations.

7.8 Derive expressions for the reflectivities and transmissivities of light at a plane dielectric surface where the angle of incidence is θ_i and the angle of refraction is θ_t. Consider, separately, the cases with **E** parallel and perpendicular to the plane of incidence.

7.9 Discuss the phase changes at normal incidence as shown in Fig. 7.5.

7.10 If α is the angle between the **E** vector and the plane of incidence of a plane-polarized wave incident on a dielectric boundary, show that the reflectivity is given by $R = R_{\parallel} \cos^2 \alpha + R_{\perp} \sin^2 \alpha$, where $R_{\parallel}$ and $R_{\perp}$ are the reflectivities of problem 7.8.

7.11 Show that a spatially uniform electric field in any direction may exist in a conductor, but that if it does it decays in time according to $\mathbf{E} = \mathbf{E}_0 \exp(-t/\tau)$ where τ is the relaxation time defined in problem 1.11.

8

Micro-media: scattering and dispersion

In the last chapter, the propagation of waves in media was treated as a macroscopic problem in which relative permittivity and electric conductivity were taken as given for materials regarded as continua. This approach cannot account for variations with frequency known to occur, and we must therefore look to the atomic and molecular structure of matter for explanations. The simplest system, a single free charge interacting with an incident plane wave, is considered first, followed in turn by more complicated arrangements until metals, dielectrics, etc., themselves are reached. Where possible, we shall want to see when a macroscopic treatment might be valid and we should expect this to be so when wave-lengths become long compared with the distance between scattering centres.

8.1 Scattering by a single free charge

A particle of mass m and charge Q (typically an electron with charge $-e$) is in the path of a plane monochromatic wave *in vacuo*. Both the **E** and **B** vectors will exert a force on Q given by the Lorentz formula $\mathbf{F} = Q(\mathbf{E} + \mathbf{v} \times \mathbf{B})$, where $\mathbf{v}$ is the velocity of the particle itself produced by the wave, and assumed throughout this treatment to be non-relativistic so that $v \ll c$. Because $B = E/c$ in the wave, the force exerted by B on the charge is $\sim v/c$ of that exerted by E and may be neglected.

Thus only the action of the electric field on the charge need be considered. The equation of motion is therefore

$$m\ddot{\mathbf{r}} = Q\mathbf{E} \tag{8.1}$$

and because $\mathbf{E} = \mathbf{E}_0\, e^{i(\mathbf{k}\,.\,\mathbf{r} - \omega t)}$ in the plane wave

$$\ddot{\mathbf{r}} = \frac{Q\mathbf{E}_0}{m}\, e^{i(\mathbf{k}\,.\,\mathbf{r} - \omega t)} \tag{8.2}$$

and so the acceleration, velocity, and displacement of the particle are all in the same direction as $\mathbf{E}_0$ which is constant. Let us use the

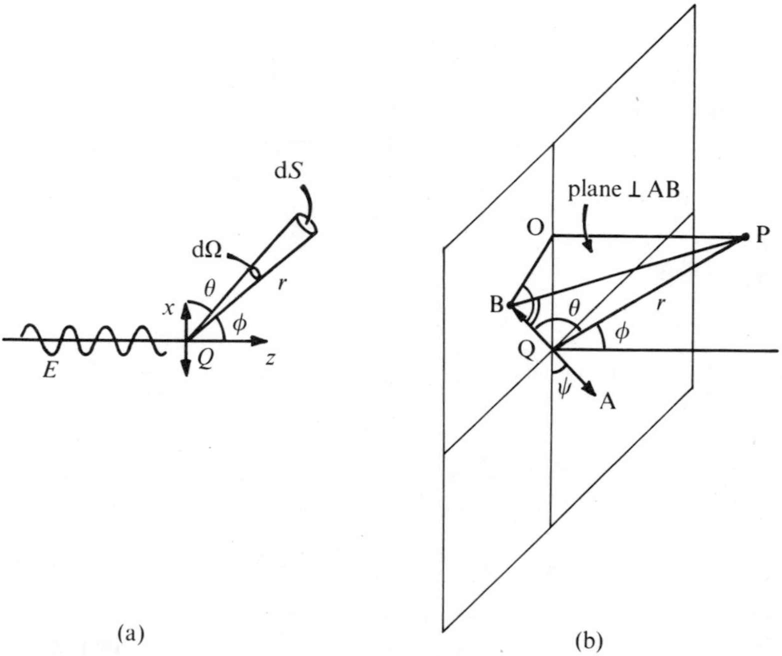

Fig. 8.1 (a) Geometry for scattering of plane-polarized electromagnetic wave by a charged particle; (b) a plane of polarization turned through ψ with respect to that in (a)

geometry of Fig. 8.1a so that the displacement in the x-direction is given by

$$\ddot{x} = \frac{QE_0}{m}\, e^{i(kz - \omega t)}. \tag{8.3}$$

The charge oscillates sinusoidally and will behave like the radiating dipole of section 4.8, Fig. 4.6b, with a dipole moment

$$p = Qx. \tag{8.4}$$

It follows from (8.3) that

$$\ddot{p} = \frac{Q^2 E_0}{m} e^{i(kz-\omega t)}. \tag{8.5}$$

We showed in section 4.8 that this type of dipole radiated in the same way as the Hertzian dipole of section 4.7, so that equations (4.77)–(4.79) apply. From (4.79), the mean power radiated in all directions is

$$\bar{P} = \frac{\overline{(\ddot{p})^2}}{6\pi\varepsilon_0 c^3} = \frac{Q^4 {E_0}^2}{12\pi\varepsilon_0 m^2 c^3}. \tag{8.6}$$

This radiation is said to be *scattered* by the charge and the *total scattering cross-section* σ_T is given by the ratio of $\bar{P}$ to the incident energy flux given by (4.47) as $\varepsilon_0 c {E_0}^2/2$. Thus

$$\sigma_T = \frac{8\pi Q^4}{3(4\pi\varepsilon_0)^2 m^2 c^4}. \tag{8.7}$$

The quantity

$$R^2 = Q^4/(4\pi\varepsilon_0)^2 m^2 c^4 \tag{8.8}$$

has the dimensions of a length squared and σ_T can be written

$$\sigma_T = 8\pi R^2/3. \tag{8.9}$$

This gives the area in the incident beam containing as much energy as is scattered by the particle. For an electron, R takes the value

$$R_e = e^2/4\pi\varepsilon_0 mc^2 \tag{8.10}$$

known as the *classical electron radius* of magnitude $\sim 2{\cdot}8 \times 10^{-13}$ cm and giving σ_T a value of about $0{\cdot}66 \times 10^{-24}$ cm^2. This type of scattering is known as *Thomson scattering*.

The *differential scattering cross-section* is defined as the power scattered into unit solid angle per unit incident energy flux. If a solid angle $\mathrm{d}\Omega$ is subtended at the particle by an area $\mathrm{d}S$, the mean power over $\mathrm{d}S$ is $\bar{N}\,\mathrm{d}S$, where N is the Poynting vector. The mean power per unit solid angle is thus $\bar{N}\,\mathrm{d}S/\mathrm{d}\Omega = \bar{N}r^2$ (Fig. 8.1a). The differential scattering cross-section is therefore

$$\mathrm{d}\sigma_T/\mathrm{d}\Omega = 2\bar{N}r^2/\varepsilon_0 c {E_0}^2$$

where $\bar{N}$ for the scattered radiation is obtained from (4.78) with $\overline{\ddot{p}^2}$

given by $Q^4E_0^{\,2}/2m^2$ so that

$$\frac{d\sigma_T}{d\Omega} = R^2 \sin^2 \theta. \tag{8.11}$$

The incident radiation here has been plane-polarized. For unpolarized waves an average must be taken over all orientations of the plane of **E**. Suppose in Fig. 8.1b, that AB is the direction of **E** in another wave incident on the particle of Fig. 8.1a, so that the angle between AB and the plane of Fig. 8.1a containing the field point is ψ. P is the original field point and the angle θ appearing in (8.11) is shown. It is now preferable to express the scattering in terms of the angle ϕ which is common to all azimuths. In Fig. 8.1b, the plane POB perpendicular to AB is drawn in so that we can see that the length of BQ is given both by $r \cos \theta$ and by $r \sin \phi \cos \psi$. (The marked angles at B are right angles.) Hence,

$$\sin^2 \theta = 1 - \cos^2 \theta = 1 - \sin^2 \phi \cos^2 \psi.$$

Averaging over all azimuths ψ and using the fact that the mean value of $\cos^2 \psi$ will be $\frac{1}{2}$, (8.11) becomes

$$\frac{d\sigma_T}{d\Omega} = R^2(1 + \cos^2 \phi)/2 \tag{8.12}$$

the $\frac{1}{2}(1 + \cos^2 \phi)$ being known as the *polarization factor*.

8.2 Scattering by a single elastically-bound charge

Consider now the same charge as in the previous section but elastically bound so that a restoring force $-m\omega_0^{\,2}x$ is brought into play when it is displaced. We also assume that there is a small amount of damping proportional to $\dot{x}$ (see section 12.3) which may be produced in practice by collisions or radiation. The equation of motion now becomes

$$m\ddot{x} = QE - m\omega_0^{\,2}x - mb\dot{x} \tag{8.13}$$

where b is the damping constant per unit mass. Thus

$$\ddot{x} + b\dot{x} + \omega_0^{\,2}x = \frac{QE_0}{m}\,e^{i(kz-\omega t)}. \tag{8.14}$$

This the well-known equation of forced motion of a damped harmonic oscillator and the solution

$$x = \frac{QE_0\,e^{i(kz-\omega t)}}{m[(\omega_0^{\,2} - \omega^2) - i\omega b]} \tag{8.15}$$

shows that the displacement is, in general, out of phase with E. The dipole moment $p = Qx$ and we may write the solution from (8.15) in the form

$$p = \frac{Q^2 E_0 \, e^{i(kz - \omega t + \delta)}}{m[(\omega_0{}^2 - \omega^2)^2 + \omega^2 b^2]^{1/2}} \tag{8.16}$$

where

$$\tan \delta = \omega b/(\omega_0{}^2 - \omega^2). \tag{8.17}$$

Equation (8.16) allows us to calculate the cross-sections for scattering as before. We note that $\overline{p^2}$ will differ from its value in section 8.1 by the addition of a factor ω^4 in the numerator and the bracketed factor in the denominator: the phase δ makes no difference to the mean values. We shall thus have for the total scattering cross-section, using (8.8):

$$\sigma_R = \frac{8\pi R^2 \omega^4}{3[(\omega_0{}^2 - \omega^2)^2 + \omega^2 b^2]} \tag{8.18}$$

with corresponding expressions for the differential cross-sections.

In any material, by far the largest proportion of scattering is by electrons because of the effect of the m^2 factor in the denominator of the expressions for the cross-sections. Restricting ourselves now to electrons, we distinguish three possibilities: the incident frequency much smaller than ω_0, much greater than ω_0, or approximately the same.

At long wave-lengths, $\omega \ll \omega_0$ and (8.18) becomes

$$\sigma_R = 8\pi R_e{}^2 \omega^4 / 3\omega_0{}^4 \tag{8.19}$$

assuming b is small. The amount of scattered energy is thus proportional to $1/\lambda^4$ where λ is the wave-length, a form known as *Rayleigh scattering*.

When $\omega \sim \omega_0$, the amount of scattering becomes very large and the damping term cannot be ignored. The scattering is known as *resonance radiation*.

At short wave-lengths, $\omega \gg \omega_0$ and

$$\sigma_R \to \sigma_T$$

i.e., Thomson scattering occurs and the charge behaves as if it were free. This is likely to occur at the X-ray end of the electromagnetic spectrum, but it is just here that specifically quantum mechanical effects become significant. We shall touch on these matters in section

12.2, only noting here that a predominant process at high energies is *Compton scattering* by electrons which, unlike any of the above, involves a change of frequency in the scattered radiation.

For the differential scattering cross-sections, the same angular factors come into play as in section 8.1. Thus, in terms of the scattering angle ϕ, scattering from a plane-polarized incident beam depends upon $\cos^2 \phi$ from (8.11) so that there is no scattering in the direction of oscillation of the particle for which $\phi = \pi/2$. With unpolarized incident radiation, the factor $\frac{1}{2}(1 + \cos^2 \phi)$ replaces the $\cos^2 \phi$ so that scattering occurs in all directions but is a minimum for $\phi = \pi/2$.

The state of polarization of the scattered radiation can be obtained by examining the direction of the **E** vector. With a Hertzian dipole, **E** in the wave zone lies always in the plane containing the dipole axis and the radius vector **r** (see equation (4.77) and Fig. 4.4) and is at right angles to **r**. Thus, even when the incident radiation is unpolarized, the scattered radiation has a degree of polarization unless

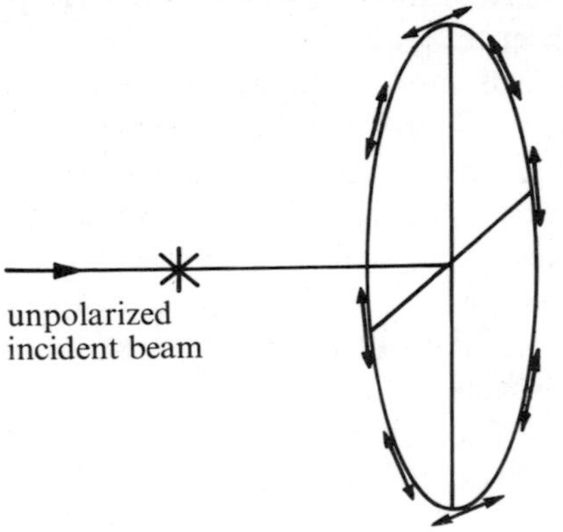

Fig. 8.2 Radiation scattered through $\pi/2$ from an unpolarized incident beam is plane-polarized

$\phi = 0$, while in the plane $\phi = \pi/2$ the radiation is always plane-polarized (Fig. 8.2).

8.3 Distributions of scattering centres

Scattering from real materials does not always exhibit the simple features of sections 8.1 and 8.2 because the total mean intensity is the result of adding contributions from large numbers of particles. The resultant intensity of a number of waves is always found by adding the amplitudes, taking due account of the phases, and squaring the resultant (or, if complex, finding the square of the modulus). If the phase difference between any two waves at a point in space is constant for all time, they are said to be *coherent*, while if the phase difference varies in a completely random way they are *incoherent*. In practice, a state somewhere between the two extremes is common and the two waves are then *partially coherent*.

Partial or complete coherence can arise in several ways. In optical interferometers, a degree of self-coherence is usually produced between two waves originating from the same point in the source but pursuing different paths. The addition of amplitudes to give the resultant intensity shows that there is a spatial variation producing interference fringes. This type of coherence is limited by the fact that ordinary sources consist of atomic radiators whose life-time is finite (10^{-8}–10^{-9} s) so that wave trains are of finite length. As the path difference between them increases, the wave trains get more and more out of step and the degree of coherence decreases. This results in a smaller visibility of the fringes and, for large path differences, their complete absence.

We are concerned more with waves from different radiating particles. In a normal source of light, there is no coherence between waves from different parts of the source (although laser beams are highly monochromatic and therefore nearly coherent). In our case, the scattered waves originate from particles all excited by the same incident radiation so that we might expect some degree of coherence. In general (as shown in problem 8.1), the resultant *intensity* of a set of incoherent waves at any point is obtained by adding the constituent intensities. Thus, if A_1, A_2, etc., are the amplitudes of the waves from a set of sources, the intensity I is

$$I = (A_1 + A_2 + A_3 + \cdots)^2 \text{ for coherent sources}$$

$$I = A_1{}^2 + A_2{}^2 + A_3{}^2 + \cdots \text{ for incoherent sources}$$

or, for N identical sources of amplitude A:

$$I = N^2A^2 \text{ for coherent sources}$$

$$I = NA^2 \text{ for incoherent sources.}$$

For further discussion of coherence, see Garbuny (1965), Born and Wolf (1965).

The relative phases of scattered electromagnetic waves depend upon (a) the phase difference δ between the incident radiation and the oscillations of the particle as given, for instance, by (8.17) and

(b) the path length traversed by the incident wave *to* the particle and the scattered wave *from* the particle. One general point is clear: that the scattering in a forward direction (that of the incident beam) will always be coherent because the path lengths are virtually the same for all particles in a collection and so, for identical particles, are the phase shifts δ. The forward scattering is not only very intense but is coherent with the incident beam and we shall see in the next section that the combination forms a resultant with a new phase velocity. This essentially explains *refraction* and gives a physical reality to the Huygens constructions with secondary wavelets used in elementary optics.

In this section, we deal with the total sideways scattering which, for identical centres, is entirely dependent on (b) above. Two considerations arise here. The first is the wave-length of the incident radiation λ compared with the size a of the region containing scattering centres; the second is the geometrical arrangement of the centres. If $\lambda \gg a$, the phase of the incident radiation is the same at all centres and the scattered radiation is emitted from points in a region small compared with λ: the path lengths are the same and the scattering is coherent. If $\lambda \ll a$, complete incoherence normally occurs, while if $\lambda \sim a$ the geometrical arrangement must be examined, for it may lead to angular factors where a slight or considerable degree of order exists.

Atoms with Z electrons. The electrons in an atom are responsible for most of the scattering because of the comparatively great mass of the nuclei which diminishes the cross-sections (see equation (8.7)). The electrons are distributed over a volume for which a above is ~ 1 Å. Thus for $\lambda \gg 1$ Å we can expect the cross-sections for a single atom to be Z^2 times greater than that for a single electron and for $\lambda \ll 1$ Å only Z times greater. X-ray wave-lengths span this range and we must remember that when $\lambda \ll 1$ Å, quantum effects like Compton scattering and the photo-electric effect are likely to be prominent. Where $\lambda \sim 1$ Å, which is an important region from the point of view of X-ray diffraction by crystals, the average arrangement of electrons within the atom must be taken into account. This is, of course, only ascertainable from quantum theory. The natural way of expressing the result is in terms of the Thomson cross-sections since we are in the region where the frequencies are much higher than natural frequencies (or, in quantum terms, where the X-ray photon energies are much higher than the binding energies of the electrons). Thus, the differential cross-section for X-ray scattering from a single atom is expressed as

$$\frac{d\sigma_a}{d\Omega} = \frac{d\sigma_T}{d\Omega}|f|^2 \tag{8.20}$$

where f is the *atomic scattering factor*. Assuming a spherically symmetrical atom, f takes the form

$$f = \int_0^\infty 4\pi r^2 \rho(r) \frac{\sin(\mu r)}{\mu r} \, dr \tag{8.21}$$

where $\rho(r)\,d\tau$ is the probability that an electron lies in a volume element $d\tau$ at a distance r from the centre of the atom and $\mu = 4\pi(\sin\phi)/\lambda$. For $\phi = 0$, we must have that $f = Z$ and $d\sigma_a/d\Omega = Z^2\, d\sigma_T/d\Omega$.

Molecules, crystals, and amorphous materials. We can now treat each atom as a scattering centre rather than each individual electron and ask how materials as collections of atoms behave, restricting ourselves to sideways scattering.

In *gases*, the scattering centres are randomly distributed so that scattering is incoherent, while the low density of centres means that it is also quite small. At long wave-lengths, including the visible region, Rayleigh scattering occurs, particularly because of small statistical fluctuations in density in regions of size $\sim\lambda$. This gives a greater sideways scattering of the shorter wave-lengths, an effect most noticeable in the blue of the sky (polarized as in Fig. 8.2) and the redness of some sunsets and sunrises. In these last two, the sunlight traverses a long path in the atmosphere and becomes deficient in the short wave-lengths, an effect enhanced by *small* dust and vapour particles. Much larger particles merely produce scattering by diffuse reflection and diffraction of light and the general dependence on wave-length disappears (as in white clouds).

When gases are composed of poly-atomic molecules, the identical nature of each molecule on the scale of a few Å imposes a small amount of regularity, enough to produce a slight angular factor in X-ray scattering different from that of (8.20). If the molecule has an anisotropic polarizability, the direction of induced dipole moments will not be that of the incident **E** vector and the scattered radiation at $\phi = \pi/2$ will not then be plane-polarized as in Fig. 8.2.

In *molecular liquids and amorphous solids*, there is often sufficient order to give, in the scattered radiation, diffraction haloes which become more pronounced as the degree of order increases. Ordering on an atomic scale produces the greatest effect in the X-ray region once more. In the extreme case, a *perfectly crystalline solid* gives rise to so-called *X-ray diffraction*, in which the scattering is very intense in certain directions given by the Bragg law, and zero in all others. The intensities of the radiation in these directions is a function of the atomic scattering factors above and of the geometrical arrangement of the atoms in the repeating unit cell, a function known as the *structure factor*. Departure from perfect symmetry leads to an increase in the scattering in directions other than those obeying the Bragg law. It follows that X-ray diffraction and scattering can give information not only about the ideal arrangements of atoms in a crystalline array but also about imperfections such as lattice defects.

At longer wave-lengths, sideways scattering in a transparent solid with no inhomogeneity is small compared with that in a gas in spite of the greater density because there are no statistical fluctuations in the numbers of centres in volumes comparable with λ^3.

8.4 Refraction and reflection as scattering processes

It has already been noted that scattering in the line of the incident beam produces coherent radiation, and we now look at the result of this coherence in a dense medium, i.e., one in which the number of scattering centres in a volume λ^3 is large. We shall show that the refraction described macroscopically by a single quantity n or ε_r is the result of processes on an atomic scale *in vacuo*, but the problem is such a complicated one that we make drastic simplifying assumptions to display the physical ideas more clearly. In carrying out the exercise, we shall also justify our future procedure in investigating dispersion through properties of the *medium* rather than going through the difficult calculations involved in looking at the refracted wave itself.

Consider a plane monochromatic wave *in vacuo* incident normally on the surface of a dielectric whose absorption is small, the **E** vector being

$$\mathbf{E}_i = \mathbf{E}_{i0}\, e^{i(k_0 z - \omega t)}. \tag{8.22}$$

If we can show that the wave in the medium can be described by

$$\mathbf{E}_m = \mathbf{E}_{m0}\, e^{i(kz - \omega t)} \tag{8.23}$$

then the medium can be regarded as a continuum with refractive index $n = k/k_0$. Now this new wave in the medium differs in phase from what $\mathbf{E}_i$ *would have been* at z by an amount $(k - k_0)z$ or by

$$\beta = (n - 1)k_0 z. \tag{8.24}$$

Hence we have to show that the coherent scattering adds to the $\mathbf{E}_i$ of (8.22) in such a way that a phase shift *proportional to z* is produced: the constant of proportionality will give us n.

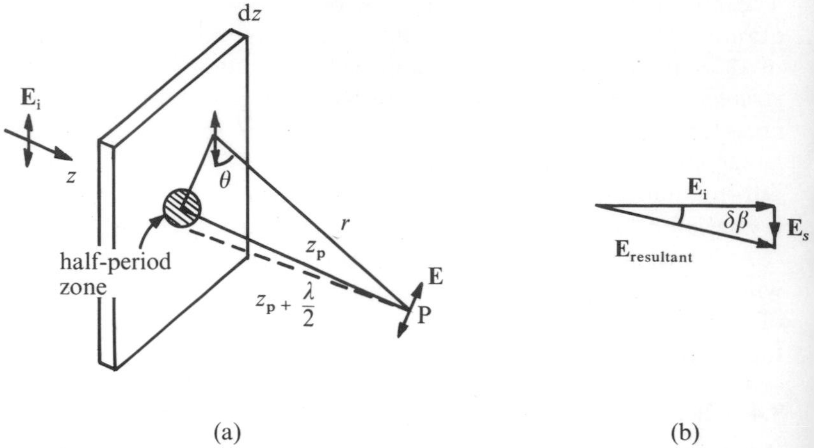

Fig. 8.3 (a) Scattering in a forward direction by a sheet of dielectric; (b) combination of incident and scattered wave with phase difference $\pi/2$ to give resultant phase shift $d\beta$ with respect to the incident wave

Consider a plane sheet of the dielectric (Fig. 8.3a), effectively infinite in the x and y directions and of thickness dz. The incident wave (8.22) sets the charges into oscillation and a typical one has a moment given by

$$\mathbf{p} = \alpha_0 \mathbf{E}_i \, e^{i\delta} \tag{8.25}$$

where α_0 is the amplitude of the polarizability. These dipoles produce fields at P whose components other than those parallel to $\mathbf{E}_i$ will cancel. Hence the effective scattered field from a typical dipole is parallel to $\mathbf{E}_i$ and in magnitude and direction is given by

$$\mathbf{E}_s = \frac{\omega^2 \alpha_0 \mathbf{E}_i \, e^{i\delta}}{4\pi\varepsilon_0 c^2 r} \sin^2\theta \tag{8.26}$$

using (4.77). The whole sheet of dipoles contains n_v per unit volume say, so that unit area contains $n_v \, dz$. Thus the field from a small region of the sheet will be, per unit area, $n_v \, dz$ greater than (8.26).

To add the contributions from the whole plane, we assume that λ is large compared with z_P so that the method of half-period zones can be used. This is a method familiar in Fresnel diffraction problems in optics. It shows that when amplitudes are proportional to $1/r$ and fall off with increasing obliquity (as in (8.26)), the resultant disturbance at P is the same as $1/\pi$ of those from the first half-period zone acting all in phase; but that the phase of the resultant is $\pi/2$ behind that of the incident wave. Since the area of the first zone (Fig. 8.3a) is $\pi z_P\lambda$, the whole plane gives a scattered field at P of

$$\delta \mathbf{E}_s = \frac{\lambda n_v \omega^2 \alpha_0 \mathbf{E}_i}{4\pi\varepsilon_0 c^2} e^{i(\delta - \pi/2)} dz$$

$$= \frac{\pi n_v \alpha_0}{\varepsilon_0 \lambda} \mathbf{E}_i e^{i(\delta - \pi/2)} dz. \tag{8.27}$$

For negligible δ, this lags behind $\mathbf{E}_i$ by a phase angle of about $\pi/2$ and Fig. 8.3b shows that the phase shift produced by this layer alone would be

$$\delta\beta = \frac{\pi n_v \alpha_0}{\varepsilon_0 \lambda} dz. \tag{8.28}$$

In the steady state, we should have to take into account the scattering from layers both before and after P since in a backward direction there is also a contribution (8.27) from each layer. Were P a point in the space in front of the dielectric the backward wave from all layers would give rise to a resultant *reflected* wave. With P inside the material, the scattered wave from all layers combines with the remaining incident wave to give a phase shifted wave. The reader is referred to Rossi (1959) for a complete account of the way contributions like (8.27) from all layers give rise to a new phase velocity. It is sufficient for us to see that the scattered waves will produce a phase shift depending linearly on the distance z_P through the material as required by (8.24) and that, therefore, the value of n is legitimately obtained from calculations of the electric polarizability α_0 of the material, as is clear from (8.28).

Since the dipoles in the medium are oscillating in the direction of the transmitted **E** vector, reference to Fig. 7.3 will show that when **E** is in the plane of incidence no radiation will take place along the reflected ray should that be perpendicular to the transmitted ray. This is just the situation, however, at the Brewster angle and explains the effect in terms of scattering.

8.5 Molecular theory of dielectrics

Since we have established that dispersion may be investigated in terms of the polarizability of the medium, we now wish to see how this arises as a result of atomic and molecular properties. This will enable us in succeeding sections to find how we expect the refractive index to vary with frequency.

The polarizability α of a single molecule (using the term molecule in a wide sense to include even a formula unit in ionic crystals) is its mean dipole moment per unit local electric field $\mathbf{E}_b$. If there are n_v molecules per unit volume, then the electric polarization is

$$\mathbf{P} = n_v \alpha \mathbf{E}_b = \frac{N_A \rho_m \alpha \mathbf{E}_b}{M} \tag{8.29}$$

where ρ_m is the density, N_A is Avogadro's number and M the molecular weight. But $\mathbf{P} = \varepsilon_0(\varepsilon_r - 1)\mathbf{E}$ where $\mathbf{E}$ is the macroscopic field and so

$$\varepsilon_r - 1 = \frac{n_v \alpha}{\varepsilon_0} \frac{\mathbf{E}_b}{\mathbf{E}}. \tag{8.30}$$

The molecular theory of dielectrics is concerned with the ratio $\mathbf{E}_b/\mathbf{E}$ and with the way the molecular arrangements contribute to α.

Polar and non-polar materials. If the molecule has a permanent electric dipole moment p_0 because the centroids of the positive and negative charges do not on the average coincide, the material is *polar* and one contribution to α arises because of the alignment of the dipoles in the electric field. This is an orientation effect and we denote the contribution to α by α_o.

In addition, whether polar or non-polar, all molecules are distorted in a field some by relative displacement of electrons and nuclei, some by relative displacement of ions. The former effect can occur even in atoms and is often called atomic polarizability, α_a, or electronic polarizability. The latter is molecular or ionic polarizability, α_i. Orders of magnitude for α_a and α_i can be obtained from simple models (see problems 8.3 and 8.5).

The contribution of polar molecules is determined by the temperature because the dipoles in the absence of the electric field are randomly oriented due to thermal interaction. When a field is applied, any one dipole has a potential energy $-p_0 E_b \cos\theta$ by (1.62) and will contribute $p_0 \cos\theta$ towards the total polarization along E_b. Thus the statistical mechanical probability of finding the dipole making an angle between θ and $\theta + d\theta$ with E_b is

$$e^{-(p_0 E_b \cos\theta)/kT} 2\pi \sin\theta \, d\theta$$

where $2\pi \sin\theta\, d\theta$ is the elementary solid angle at the centre of the dipole. Thus the average contribution of the dipole to α_o is

$$\overline{p_0 \cos\theta} = \frac{\int_0^\pi p_0 \cos\theta\, e^{-(p_0 E_b \cos\theta)/kT} \sin\theta\, d\theta}{\int_0^\pi e^{-(p_0 E_b \cos\theta)/kT} \sin\theta\, d\theta}$$

$$= p_0 \, \mathrm{L}\left(\frac{p_0 E_b}{kT}\right) \tag{8.31}$$

where $\mathrm{L}(x)$ is the Langevin function, $(\coth x - 1/x)$, which tends to $x/3$ as $x \to 0$. In practice, electric fields which can be produced are such that $p_0 E_b \ll kT$ so that

$$\overline{p_0 \cos\theta} = p_0^2 E_b / 3kT$$

and

$$\alpha_o = p_0^2 / 3kT. \tag{8.32}$$

Thus, from (8.30),

$$\varepsilon_r - 1 = \frac{n_v}{\varepsilon_0}\left(\alpha_a + \alpha_i + \frac{p_0^2}{3kT}\right)\frac{\mathbf{E}_b}{\mathbf{E}}. \tag{8.33}$$

For static fields, it is therefore possible to distinguish between polar and non-polar dielectrics by the temperature dependence of ε_r and to determine p_0 where it exists. Such information is valuable in ascertaining the atomic arrangement within molecules.

The local field. The calculation of $\mathbf{E}_b$ from molecular models is a difficult problem only made amenable by treating special cases. In a very dilute gas at low pressure, we might expect $\mathbf{E}_b \sim \mathbf{E}$ so that by (8.33) and (8.29) the quantity $(\varepsilon_r - 1)/\rho_m$ should be constant at constant temperature. This is not so for even moderate pressures.

The classical approach to the problem is that of Lorentz. The local field is obtained by imagining a spherical cavity round the molecule scooped out, the sphere being large enough to contain many molecules but small enough for variations of the macroscopic $\mathbf{P}$ to be negligible across its diameter. The field at the centre is then the sum of three parts: $\mathbf{E}_0$, the applied external field; $\mathbf{E}_1$, the field due to polarization charges in the dielectric generally given by (1.39); $\mathbf{E}_2$, the field produced by the polarization charges on the inner surface of the cavity. The molecules in the sphere are then replaced and the field $\mathbf{E}_3$ due to these must be calculated microscopically, treating them as discrete sources.

The fields $\mathbf{E}_0$ and $\mathbf{E}_1$ together are just the macroscopic field $\mathbf{E}$, $\mathbf{E}_2$ is given by $\mathbf{P}/3\varepsilon_0$ (problem 8.6) while $\mathbf{E}_3$ cannot be calculated generally but, at any rate for isotropic polarizability and non-polar molecules, will be proportional to $\mathbf{P}$ itself. Thus we may write

$$\mathbf{E}_b = \mathbf{E} + \frac{\mathbf{P}}{3\varepsilon_0} + \frac{\lambda\mathbf{P}}{\varepsilon_0}. \tag{8.34}$$

For random distributions as in a gas or for a cubic array, λ is zero or very small and in these cases (8.30) becomes

$$\frac{\varepsilon_r - 1}{\varepsilon_r + 2} = \frac{n_v\alpha}{3\varepsilon_0} = \frac{N_A\rho_m\alpha}{3\varepsilon_0 M}. \tag{8.35}$$

This is known as the *Clausius–Mossotti* formula. It applies well to gases for which the expression $(\varepsilon_r - 1)/\rho_m(\varepsilon_r + 2)$ is found to be independent of pressure at constant temperature.

The Lorentz approach assumes all dipoles to be aligned and this would not occur in polar substances. Moreover, the Clausius–Mossotti formula is only applicable when nearby molecules can be ignored. A more realistic approach by Onsager considers the molecule in a real cavity in the dielectric and finds the cavity field as in (6.23). In addition, the fact that a polar molecule induces further polarization in the cavity walls giving both an extra electric field and a further distortion of the molecule is also taken into account. This yields, instead of (8.35):

$$(\varepsilon_r - 1)(2\varepsilon_r + 1)/3\varepsilon_r = n_v\alpha/3\varepsilon_0 \tag{8.36}$$

and is found to give better results in polar gases than (8.35). For further details and methods of dealing with liquids and solids, the reader is referred to Anderson (1964) and Fröhlich (1958).

8.6 Dispersion in polar dielectrics

The above treatment was confined to steady fields for which ε_r takes its static value denoted by ε_s. We now consider the application of electric fields varying with time, in this section in a polar dielectric with $\alpha = \alpha_a + \alpha_i + \alpha_o$. The response of the polarization $\mathbf{P}$ to a change in electric field $\mathbf{E}$ depends on the type of polarizability. Distortion effects leading to α_a and α_i are associated with characteristic frequencies of vibration in the atoms and molecules and these lead to resonance effects considered in the next section. The characteristic frequencies are high enough for the response to be instantaneous in the radio-frequency region.

The orientation effects leading to α_o are associated with a relaxation time τ. If, for instance, a steady field is suddenly applied at $t = 0$, the polarization $\mathbf{P}_1$ will often rise exponentially to an equilibrium value $\mathbf{P}_\infty = n_v\alpha_o\mathbf{E}_b$ as in

$$\mathbf{P}_1 = \mathbf{P}_\infty(1 - e^{-t/\tau})$$

and at any instant $\mathbf{P}_1$ obeys

$$\tau \frac{d\mathbf{P}_1}{dt} + \mathbf{P}_1 = \mathbf{P}_\infty \tag{8.37}$$

a characteristic equation for relaxation processes (see problem 8.7). When the field and $\mathbf{P}_1$ both vary in time with an angular frequency ω, then $\mathbf{P}_\infty$ is changing all the time and is, in general, given by $n_v\alpha_o\mathbf{E}_{b0}\,e^{-i\omega t} = n_v\alpha_o\mathbf{E}_{b0}\,e^{j\omega t}$. $\mathbf{P}_1$ has the same time variation and so from (8.37)

$$\mathbf{P}_1 = \frac{n_v\alpha_0\mathbf{E}_{b0}\,e^{j\omega t}}{1 + j\omega\tau}.$$

There is also a contribution from α_a and α_i which we assume follows the field in phase at these frequencies:

$$\mathbf{P}_2 = n_v(\alpha_a + \alpha_i)\mathbf{E}_{b0}\,e^{j\omega t}.$$

Hence

$$\boldsymbol{\varepsilon}_r - 1 = \frac{\mathbf{P}_1 + \mathbf{P}_2}{\varepsilon_0\mathbf{E}} = \left(\frac{\alpha_o}{1 + j\omega\tau} + \alpha_a + \alpha_i\right)n_v\frac{\mathbf{E}_{b0}}{\mathbf{E}_0}. \tag{8.38}$$

Let the value of ε_r at frequencies high enough for only α_a and α_i to be effective be ε_∞. Then

$$\varepsilon_\infty - 1 = (\alpha_a + \alpha_i)n_v\mathbf{E}_{b0}/\mathbf{E}_0$$

while the static permittivity is given by

$$\varepsilon_s - 1 = \frac{n_v\alpha_o\mathbf{E}_{b0}}{\mathbf{E}_0} + \varepsilon_\infty - 1. \tag{8.39}$$

From (8.38) and (8.39):

$$\boldsymbol{\varepsilon}_r = \frac{\varepsilon_s - \varepsilon_\infty}{1 + j\omega\tau} + \varepsilon_\infty = \frac{\varepsilon_s - \varepsilon_\infty}{1 - i\omega\tau} + \varepsilon_\infty. \tag{8.40}$$

From (7.53) we write $\boldsymbol{\varepsilon}_r = \varepsilon' - j\varepsilon''$ and equate real and imaginary parts:

$$\varepsilon' = \varepsilon_\infty + \frac{\varepsilon_s - \varepsilon_\infty}{1 + \omega^2\tau^2} \tag{8.41}$$

$$\varepsilon'' = \frac{(\varepsilon_s - \varepsilon_\infty)\omega\tau}{1 + \omega^2\tau^2}. \tag{8.42}$$

These are known as the *Debye equations*. They give variations in $\boldsymbol{\varepsilon}_r$, and hence in the refractive index and absorption, as shown at low frequencies in Fig. 8.4. The quantity $\omega\tau$ can be eliminated between

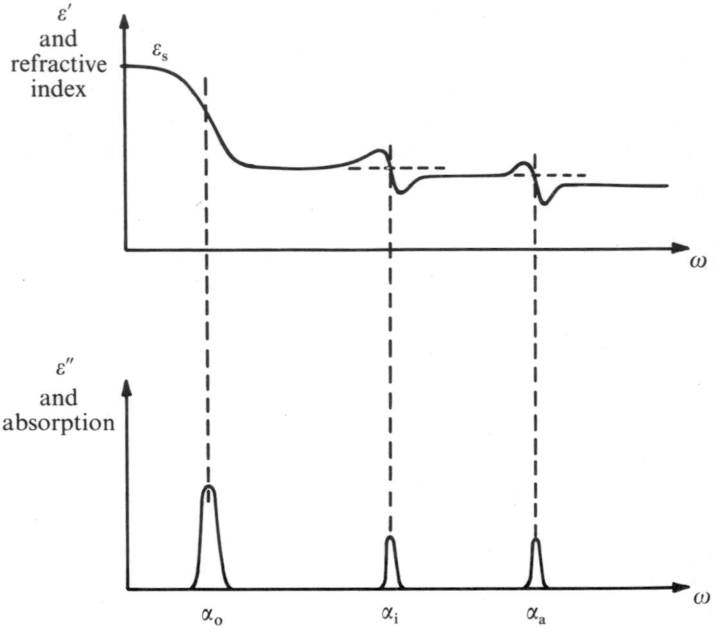

Fig. 8.4 Variation with frequency of relative permittivity and refractive index

(8.41) and (8.42) to give a relation between ε' and ε'':

$$\varepsilon''^2 + \left[\varepsilon' - \tfrac{1}{2}(\varepsilon_s - \varepsilon_\infty)\right]^2 = \left[\tfrac{1}{2}(\varepsilon_s + \varepsilon_\infty)\right]^2. \tag{8.43}$$

If ε'' is plotted as ordinate and ε' as abscissa for various frequencies, (8.43) predicts that the points lie on a circle whose highest point gives the relaxation time τ (see problem 8.8). The graph is known as a *Cole–Cole* plot. In practice, although the general variation indicated in Fig. 8.4 is found to occur in polar materials at radio frequencies, Cole–Cole plots reveal that they are often characterized by a set of relaxation times rather than by a single one.

The relaxation process is thus, in general, more complicated than we have assumed. Nevertheless, the main conclusions remain valid: that with increase in frequency the polar molecules lag further out of phase with the applied field and eventually do not follow the variations at all. In the region where $\omega \sim 1/\tau$ there is absorption, but away from this region ε'' is small and the refractive index is given by $n^2 \sim \varepsilon'$.

8.7 Dispersion in non-polar dielectrics

We now assume that frequencies will be high enough to neglect any contribution to α from polar molecules but that, as in section 8.2, the electrons responsible for refraction are bound by an elastic force $-m\omega_0{}^2\mathbf{x}$ where $\mathbf{x}$ is the displacement, and are subject to radiation damping $b\dot{\mathbf{x}}$. We thus arrive at the same equation of motion as in (8.13) where $\mathbf{E}$ is now the local field $\mathbf{E}_{b0}\, e^{-i\omega t}$. The solution for $\mathbf{x}$ is again given by (8.15) so that we have the polarization $\mathbf{P}$ given by $n_v e\mathbf{x}$. Thus the polarizability $\boldsymbol{\alpha}$ is complex and is given by

$$\boldsymbol{\alpha} = \frac{e^2}{m}\frac{1}{(\omega_0{}^2 - \omega^2) - i\omega b}$$

and so, using (8.30), we have

$$\boldsymbol{\varepsilon}_r - 1 = \frac{n_v e^2}{\varepsilon_0 m}\frac{\mathbf{E}_{b0}}{\mathbf{E}_0}\frac{1}{(\omega_0{}^2 - \omega^2) - i\omega b}. \tag{8.44}$$

It follows that

$$\varepsilon' = 1 + \frac{n_v e^2}{\varepsilon_0 m}\frac{\omega_0{}^2 - \omega^2}{(\omega_0{}^2 - \omega^2)^2 + \omega^2 b^2}\frac{\mathbf{E}_{b0}}{\mathbf{E}_0} \tag{8.45}$$

$$\varepsilon'' = \frac{\omega b}{(\omega_0{}^2 - \omega^2)^2 + \omega^2 b^2}\frac{n_v e^2}{\varepsilon_0 m}\frac{\mathbf{E}_{b0}}{\mathbf{E}_0}. \tag{8.46}$$

If $\mathbf{E}_{b0} \sim \mathbf{E}_0$, the variations of ε' and ε'' with frequency are of the type shown in Fig. 8.4 and labelled α_i and α_a. For many gases the local field is again given by the Lorentz method leading once more to the Clausius–Mossotti formula

$$\frac{\boldsymbol{\varepsilon}_r - 1}{\boldsymbol{\varepsilon}_r + 2} = \frac{n_v e^2}{3\varepsilon_0 m}\frac{1}{(\omega_0{}^2 - \omega^2) - i\omega b} \tag{8.47}$$

and here the variations are similar but algebraically more complex. Replacement of $\boldsymbol{\varepsilon}_r$ by $\mathbf{n}^2$ in (8.47) gives the Lorentz–Lorenz formula for refractive index.

Resonance absorption occurs over regions where $\omega \sim \omega_0$ and the refractive index here is given in terms of ε' and ε'' by (7.55). Outside these regions, ε'' can be neglected and we have the simple relation $n^2 = \varepsilon'$. The absorption regions are narrower in gases, where damping is smaller, than in solids or liquids, and are responsible for absorption spectra of which the Fraunhofer lines in the sun's spectrum are good examples.

If we use the approximation $\mathbf{E}_{b0} \sim \mathbf{E}_0$, then

$$\mathbf{n}^2 = 1 + \frac{n_v e^2}{\varepsilon_0 m} \frac{1}{(\omega_0{}^2 - \omega^2) - i\omega b}. \tag{8.48}$$

The real and imaginary parts of $\mathbf{n}$ (n and κ) have variations similar to those of ε' and ε'' as shown in Fig. 8.4. It will be seen that over most of the spectral range, n will increase with increase of frequency. But in the narrow regions of resonance absorption, n decreases sharply as ω increases and this is known as *anomalous dispersion*.

In practice, there are for a given substance several frequencies ω_0, some in the infra-red due to ionic oscillations or to molecular vibrations and rotations, and some in the visible and ultra-violet due to electronic transitions. The total refractive index becomes the sum of a number of terms each like (8.48) and each with its ω_0. It is easily shown (problem 8.11) that the value of ε' at frequencies well below a particular resonance ω_p is greater than that at frequencies well above it. The fall in ε' through each resonance is $K/\omega_p{}^2$ where K is $n_v e^2 \mathbf{E}_{b0}/\varepsilon_0 m \mathbf{E}_0$. Thus each resonance can be thought of as contributing an amount $K/\omega_p{}^2$ to ε' as the frequency progressively decreases (Fig. 8.4a). For any one resonance, the value of ε' given by (8.45) is then altered so that the unity on the right-hand side is replaced by ε_∞, this denoting the contributions of all the resonances at higher frequencies.

Quantum theory yields a dispersion formula similar to the above but of the form

$$\mathbf{n}^2 = 1 + \frac{n_v e^2}{\varepsilon_0 m} \sum_p \frac{f_p}{(\omega_p{}^2 - \omega^2) - i\omega b} \tag{8.49}$$

where f_p is called the *oscillator strength* of the particular transition and is related to the transition probability. It is found experimentally that f_p is generally less than 1 and that frequently $\sum f_p \sim 1$. This corresponds to the fact that the electrons may all suffer the same set of transitions from one state to others, with emission or absorption of quanta $\hbar\omega_p$, but that the relative probabilities are not all equal. Classically, f_p would normally be interpreted as the number of oscillators in a molecule with frequency ω_p but this would make the f_p integers and is untenable. We thus regard the molecule as composed of a number of oscillators each of strength f_p less than 1.

Crystalline dielectrics are non-conductors because of the energy gap between the full valence band of electronic levels and the empty conduction band. Any incident radiation can only cause electronic transitions (and thus be absorbed) when the quantum energy $\hbar\omega$ is at least as large as the energy gap. If the gap is wide enough, as in diamond (5.5 eV), the absorbed quanta lie well above the visible region and the crystal is transparent and colourless. Where the gap is smaller or where impurity levels occur between the valence and conduction bands, selective absorption of quanta over the visible region can give rise to colours. Details of these processes may be found in texts on solid state physics (e.g. Kittel (1966)).

8.8 Dispersion in metals and plasmas

It might be thought that the refractive indices of metals could be obtained from a model similar to that of the last section but with the assumption that the electrons were free so that all $\omega_0 = 0$. This would give, from (8.44)

$$\mathbf{n}^2 = \boldsymbol{\varepsilon}_r = 1 - \frac{n_v e^2}{\varepsilon_0 m\omega(\omega + ib)} \tag{8.50}$$

assuming that $\mathbf{E}_{b0} \sim \mathbf{E}_0$. This simple assumption by no means explains all the phenomena observed in metals and it is found that the contributions of bound electrons must be taken into account. Moreover, b cannot be calculated except on a quantum mechanical basis. Nevertheless, one feature is accounted for as follows. The real part of (8.50) gives

$$\varepsilon' = 1 - \frac{n_v e^2}{\varepsilon_0 m(\omega^2 + b^2)} \tag{8.51}$$

while the imaginary part is equivalent to a conductivity (from (7.67))

$$\gamma = \frac{n_v e^2 b}{\varepsilon_0 m(\omega^2 + b^2)}. \tag{8.52}$$

It is clear from (8.51) that there should be a critical frequency below which ε' is negative so that high absorption and reflectivity occur as we expect in a metal (sections 7.4, 7.5). Above this frequency, however, ε' is positive ($\kappa^2 < n^2$) and the absorption and reflectivity should fall to quite a small value. This is in fact observed, for instance in the alkali metals: above frequencies corresponding to wave-lengths of about 2000 Å, metallic sodium becomes fairly transparent and behaves like a dielectric.

If ω is very high or b very small, then it may be possible that a material containing free electrons would have, from (8.50)

$$\mathbf{n}^2 = \varepsilon_r = 1 - \frac{n_v e^2}{\varepsilon_0 m \omega^2}. \tag{8.53}$$

This occurs in two important cases. In the X-ray region, frequencies are greatly in excess of ω_0 and are much greater than b, so that (8.53) should give the refractive index of a material for X-rays. It predicts that n should be less than 1 but only by a few parts in a million, so that total external reflection should be possible at glancing angles. This has been verified by Compton (1922).

The second case in which (8.53) applies is that of a tenuous plasma or highly ionized gas. Here we define a frequency ω_p such that

$$\omega_p{}^2 = n_v e^2/\varepsilon_0 m \tag{8.54}$$

so that

$$\mathbf{n} = (1 - \omega_p{}^2/\omega^2)^{1/2}. \tag{8.55}$$

For high frequencies, $\omega > \omega_p$ and $\mathbf{n}$ is real but less than 1. If $\omega < \omega_p$, then $\mathbf{n}$ becomes imaginary and strong attenuation with no propagation occurs. ω_p is known as the *plasma frequency* and clearly both it and $\mathbf{n}$ depend on n_v, the density of charges.

The ionosphere consists of several layers of plasma in each of which n_v increases with height up to a certain point and then decreases. A given frequency ω propagated from the earth will be greater than ω_p at the bottom of a layer and will propagate with little or no attenuation. As n_v and ω_p increase, however, there may come a point at which $\omega = \omega_p$. The layer then becomes strongly absorbent and, as a consequence, highly reflecting. Pulses thus reflected can be used to investigate the variation of n_v with height. Short-wave radio propagation takes place at frequencies ω which are high enough to be always greater than ω_p. Here, oblique propagation with n less than 1 produces refraction which may bend the beam back to the earth.

Gyrotropic media. Magnetic properties have not concerned us because most transparent materials have such small magnetic susceptibilities, $\mu_r - 1$, that there is no noticeable effect on wave propagation. Ferromagnetic materials are mostly metals opaque to electromagnetic waves, the only exception being a class known as *ferrites*. These have a high resistivity and a μ_r which considerably alters the phase velocity from its vacuum value. Of interest to us is the propagation of an electromagnetic wave in a ferrite to which a magnetic flux density **B** is applied. The propagation of a plane-polarized wave along **B** is best studied by splitting it into two circularly polarized components of opposite helicity (see problem 4.5), for it can be shown that the effect of electron spins precessing about **B** is to cause the right-and left-handed components to travel with different phase velocities. On emergence, therefore, the plane of polarization has been rotated, a phenomenon known as the *Faraday effect*. Unlike the effect of an optically active material, the Faraday effect is not reciprocal—it is dextro-rotatory for propagation along the direction of **B** and laevo-rotatory in the opposite direction—and a material behaving in this way is called *gyrotropic*. (See section 10.5 for an application.)

Another such medium is a plasma subjected similarly to a magnetic flux density. Here, the electrons and ions perform helical paths with opposite senses about the direction of **B** and with the electron cyclotron frequency (ω_{ce}) and ion cyclotron frequency (ω_{ci}) respectively, where $\omega_{ce} \ll \omega_{ci}$. At frequencies much above ω_{ci}, the ionic motion becomes ineffective in interacting with the electromagnetic wave and only the effect of the gyrating electrons remains. It is then possible to show that the refractive indices for right- and left-handed circularly polarized waves propagated parallel to **B** are

$$n^2 = 1 - \frac{\omega_p{}^2}{\omega(\omega \pm \omega_{ce})} \tag{8.56}$$

where the positive sign corresponds to positive helicity or left-handed polarization. In some frequency ranges, the two components of opposite helicity will both be propagated but with different velocities and the medium is thus gyrotropic. At the highest frequencies, $\omega \gg \omega_{ce}$ and (8.55) is recovered. (For more details of propagation in plasmas, see Spitzer (1962).)

8.9 Dispersion relations

We have encountered above several examples of dispersive media whose properties have been specified by giving the dependence of n or ε_r on the angular frequency ω. An expression of that type, showing how the velocity of propagation varies with frequency, is sometimes known as a dispersion relation and may take several forms, depending on the variables—occasionally a relation between ω and k is given. In recent literature, however, the term *dispersion relation* has a slightly different and more important meaning which we now briefly explore.

When we examine the various expressions for the complex permittivities, such as (8.40) or (8.44), there are certain features which have a deeper significance than might appear from the relatively naive models used, features which are in fact independent of the model. The most important of these is the evident connection between the real and imaginary parts of $\boldsymbol{\varepsilon}_r$, i.e., between the disper-

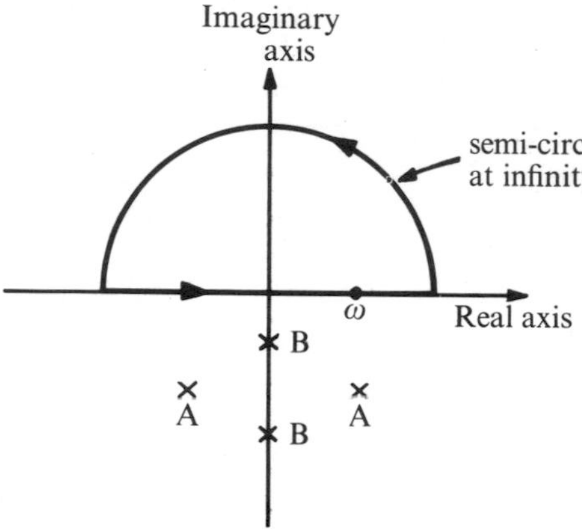

Fig. 8.5 The complex frequency plane. AA are poles of $\varepsilon_r - 1$ in (8.44) for $4\omega_0^2 - b^2 > 0$. BB are poles for $4\omega_0^2 - b^2 < 0$. The contour in the upper half-plane (representing a semi-circle at infinity) thus contains no poles.

sion and the absorption. This connection is not fortuitous, but can be shown to result from a mathematical property of $\boldsymbol{\varepsilon}_r$ regarded as a function of ω. This property, seemingly quite remote from physics, is a result of allowing ω to take complex values which may be plotted on an Argand diagram or complex plane as in Fig. 8.5 (note that i and not j is consistently used in this section, so that time variations take the form $A\,e^{-i\omega t}$). The *poles* of a function like $\boldsymbol{\varepsilon}_r - 1$ are briefly the values of ω making the denominators zero, so that in (8.40) there is a pole at $\omega = -i/\tau$ and in (8.44) the poles are at $[-ib \pm (4\omega_0^2 - b^2)^{1/2}]/2$. Now these always lie in the lower half-plane of Fig. 8.5—*there are no poles in the upper half-plane.*

As a direct consequence of this, we can carry out a contour integration of the function $[\varepsilon_r(\omega') - 1]/(\omega' - \omega)$ along the path shown in the figure, ω being a fixed real frequency and ω' taking the values along the contour. Cauchy's theorem (see Morse and Feshbach, chapter 4) then gives us that

$$\mathrm{P}\int_{-\infty}^{+\infty} \frac{\varepsilon_r(\omega') - 1}{(\omega' - \omega)}\, d\omega' = \pi i \varepsilon_r(\omega) \tag{8.57}$$

where the symbol P indicates the principal value defined by

$$\mathrm{P}\int_{-\infty}^{+\infty} \frac{f(\omega')}{(\omega' - \omega)}\, d\omega' = \lim_{\delta \to 0}\left[\int_{-\infty}^{\omega-\delta} \frac{f(\omega')}{(\omega' - \omega)}\, d\omega' + \int_{\omega+\delta}^{\infty} \frac{f(\omega')}{(\omega' - \omega)}\, d\omega'\right].$$

Equating real and imaginary parts of (8.57) gives

$$\varepsilon' - 1 = \frac{1}{\pi}\mathrm{P}\int_{-\infty}^{\infty} \frac{\varepsilon''}{(\omega' - \omega)}\, d\omega' \tag{8.58}$$

$$\varepsilon'' = -\frac{1}{\pi}\mathrm{P}\int_{-\infty}^{\infty} \frac{(\varepsilon' - 1)}{(\omega' - \omega)}\, d\omega'. \tag{8.59}$$

These are known as dispersion relations and show that the real part of the relative permittivity depends on the variation of the imaginary part over the whole range of frequencies and vice versa.

Causality. That such relations exist depends on the fact that the poles of $\varepsilon_r - 1$ lie in the lower half of the complex plane and this at first sight seems to depend on the model. It can, however, be proved that the same applies in any causal system. Thus, if an excitation $E(t)$ gives rise to a response $R(t)$, suppose that they are connected through a response function $A(\omega)$:

$$R(t) = A(\omega)E(t).$$

Then it can be shown that $A(\omega)$ has no poles in the upper half of the complex plane provided that (1) $E(t) = 0$ for $t < 0$ at any point implies that $R(t) = 0$ for $t < 0$, (2) $A(\omega) \to 0$ as $\omega \to \infty$. Condition

(1) is that of causality, so that dispersion relations are possible in widely differing physical systems. In this chapter, the electric field **E** is the excitation, the polarization **P** is the response and the function $A(\omega)$ is $\varepsilon_r - 1$.

The importance of dispersion relations lies in the possibility of determining the complete response function by measuring the absorption over all frequencies. We shall meet a further example in the next chapter and for more details and applications refer the reader to the excellent article by Hamilton (1960).

Crossing relations. The integrals in (8.58) and (8.59) extend over negative values of ω, which have no physical meaning. These can be eliminated by using what are known as *crossing relations*:

$$\varepsilon'(-\omega) = \varepsilon'(\omega)$$

$$\varepsilon''(-\omega) = -\varepsilon''(\omega).$$

In other words, ε' is an even function of ω and ε'' an odd function, as is clear from all the particular examples we have encountered. With these,

$$\varepsilon' - 1 = \frac{2}{\pi} \mathrm{P} \int_0^\infty \frac{\omega' \varepsilon''}{(\omega'^2 - \omega^2)} \mathrm{d}\omega' \qquad (8.60)$$

$$\varepsilon'' = -\frac{2\omega}{\pi} \mathrm{P} \int_0^\infty \frac{\varepsilon' - 1}{(\omega'^2 - \omega^2)} \mathrm{d}\omega'. \qquad (8.61)$$

PROBLEMS

8.1 The electric fields of two waves at a point *in vacuo* are given by $E_1 \cos \omega t$ and $E_2 \cos(\omega t + \delta)$. Find the resultant intensity at the point averaged over a long period of time. Show that for completely incoherent waves the resultant intensity is the sum of the component intensities.

8.2 Carry out the same calculation as in problem 8.1 using the complex representations $E_1 \,\mathrm{e}^{-i\omega t}$ and $E_2 \,\mathrm{e}^{-i(\omega t + \delta)}$.

8.3 Find the static polarizability of the Bohr hydrogen atom in terms of the Bohr radius a_0. Assume that any displacement of the proton is small compared with a_0 and takes place perpendicular to the plane of the orbit.

8.4 Find the polarizability of an electron bound in an atom with a natural frequency ω_0 and no damping.

8.5 Find the static polarizability of a one-dimensional lattice of the type occurring in problem 1.20, assuming that the displacements x are small compared with the lattice constant r_0 and take place along the line of ionic centres.

8.6 Find the electric field strength in a spherical cavity cut in a dielectric with a uniform polarization **P**, assuming that **P** is unaffected by the presence of the cavity.

8.7 Find the linear displacement x of a particle of mass m subjected to an exciting force $F_0\,\mathrm{e}^{-i\omega t}$, a damping force $k\dot{x}$ and a restoring force $\omega_0{}^2 x$, when the inertial term $m\ddot{x}$ can be neglected. Plot x against ω and show that the response displays the characteristics of a relaxation type of oscillation as in section 8.6.

8.8 Show that the highest point of the Cole–Cole plot (8.43) will yield the relaxation time τ.

8.9 In most expressions for dispersion, the refractive index is obtained as a function of ω. Find an appropriate expression for the group velocity $v_\mathrm{g} = \mathrm{d}\omega/\mathrm{d}k$.

8.10 Find the group velocity for plasma waves of refractive index given by (8.55) and show that $v_\mathrm{p} v_\mathrm{g} = c^2$.

8.11 Several well-separated electronic resonances occur in a dielectric at frequencies $\omega_1, \omega_2 \ldots \omega_\mathrm{p} \ldots$ Show that ε' falls by an amount $K/\omega_\mathrm{p}{}^2$ as it passes through each resonance from frequencies well below ω_p to those well above it. K is a constant.

8.12 Find how ε_r varies with the polarizability under the Lorentz and Onsager assumptions about the local field. Show that the former leads to a critical value for $n_\mathrm{v}\alpha$ of $3\varepsilon_0$, at which ε_r becomes infinite.

Part 4

Hardware

The subject-matter of the following two chapters is very much the domain of the practical physicist or engineer who is concerned with the conversion of other forms of energy into electrical energy carrying information and power and with the transfer of that energy from one point to another. Where such transfer takes place over short distances, material devices such as networks of conductors or waveguides are used. Over large distances, the amount of material needed becomes too great and propagation through a space is effected by transmitting and receiving aerials or antennae.

In chapter 9, we deal entirely in the approximation known as network theory which is sufficiently accurate at lower frequencies and very convenient mathematically in that the differential field equations often reduce to algebraic equations. At frequencies approaching and within the micro-wave region we revert to field theory (chapter 10), although some concepts from network theory are retained.

9

Linear networks

Simple networks are often the physicist's first introduction to electricity in school courses but their importance tends to diminish with more advanced studies, which concentrate on field theory as exemplified by previous chapters of this book. It seems desirable, however, that such an everyday and practical branch of the subject should be seen in its relation to field theory, and in the first section of this chapter we see why and under what conditions network theory is valid.

The rest of the chapter deals with various aspects of linear networks of which physicists should be aware. The *design* of a circuit to possess given properties (network *synthesis*) is normally the province of the electrical or electronic engineer and no attempt is made to enter this field of study. We touch rather on the behaviour of given networks under various conditions (network *analysis*), because the reader will see analogies with other physical systems throughout, and also because the physicist should know something of the way the hardware provided by engineers is likely to behave. This last point may involve the reading of literature needing a knowledge of the terminology and methods developed in this chapter.

It must be emphasized that modern network theory, both linear and non-linear, extends far beyond what we have space to describe. For further details, reference should be made to the texts listed at the end of the chapter.

9.1 Relation of network theory to field theory

Any attempt to solve some elementary network problems using Maxwell's equations directly would meet with great difficulties.

Even a simple series LCR circuit would involve the most complicated boundary conditions. Yet network theory reduces the problem to a straightforward algebraic exercise and if a problem can be so reduced it is considerably simplified. We ask, first, why this simplification occurs and, second, by seeing how the network theory follows from Maxwell's equations, what its range of application is.

In a network-type problem and solution no field quantities such as **E**, **B**, **D**, or **H** appear at all. Instead, the situations are described entirely in terms of current I and potential difference or voltage V. The use of current and not current density implies that there is a fixed area across which charge flows, i.e., that conducting wires or their equivalent carry the currents. Moreover, the potential difference between two *points* is in reality that between cross-sections of conducting wire assumed to be equipotential surfaces. The conducting wires or *leads* connect together certain *elements* into the network, but *it is I and V in the wires which are the concern of the network problem and not what happens to I and V within the elements*. It is this feature, principally, which accounts for much of the simplicity of network theory, for the complexities within an element are replaced by a relation between I and V at its terminals. These relations lead to differential and integral equations which easily reduce to algebraic equations as we see in section 9.3.

The solution of network problems depends on the use of two laws, known as Kirchhoff's laws, summarized by

K1 $$\sum I = 0 \tag{9.1}$$

over any closed surface, particularly around any junction of leads, and

K2 $$\sum V = 0 \tag{9.2}$$

round any closed path. Provided certain conditions are fulfilled, K1 and K2 can be shown to follow from Maxwell's equations in spite of the apparent remoteness. We now examine this connection.

For completely steady conditions, we have from (4.6):

$$\mathbf{curl\ H} = \mathbf{J}; \qquad \mathbf{curl\ E} = 0 \tag{9.3}$$

from which it follows that div $\mathbf{J} = 0$ and $\mathbf{curl\ E} = 0$, whose integral forms are (using Gauss's divergence and Stokes's theorems)

$$\oint_S \mathbf{J} \,.\, \mathrm{d}\mathbf{S} = 0; \qquad \oint_C \mathbf{E} \,.\, \mathrm{d}\mathbf{s} = 0 \tag{9.4}$$

for any closed surface S or closed path C. These are effectively (9.1) and (9.2) and they express the conservation of charge and the path-independence of potential difference. They enable us to say, for any element with only two external connections as in Fig. 9.1a, that the

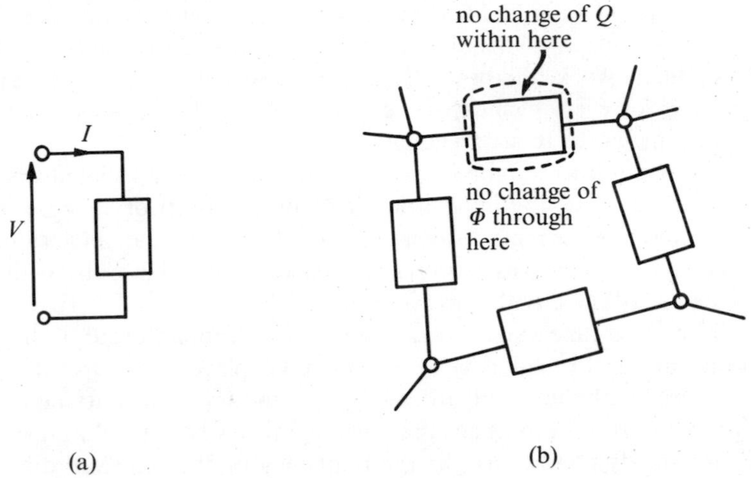

Fig. 9.1 (a) Two-terminal element or network; (b) one mesh of a network

current I entering by one lead is the same as that leaving by the other and that the potential difference V across the terminals is a unique quantity. Thus if the relation between I and V is known for every element, K1 and K2 enable equations to be set up and solved. In linear networks, V/I is constant for every element (its resistance R) and the solution of steady current networks of this type is familiar in elementary work.

When time variations occur, (9.3) becomes

$$\mathbf{curl\ H} = \mathbf{J} + \partial \mathbf{D}/\partial t; \qquad \mathbf{curl\ E} = -\partial \mathbf{B}/\partial t \tag{9.5}$$

and instead of (9.4) we have

$$\oint_S \mathbf{J} \cdot \mathrm{d}\mathbf{S} = -\partial Q/\partial t; \qquad \oint_C \mathbf{E} \cdot \mathrm{d}\mathbf{s} = -\partial \Phi/\partial t \tag{9.6}$$

where Q is the charge within S and Φ the magnetic flux through C. Thus (9.4) and hence K1 and K2 do not strictly hold at all. Suppose, however, that we could so arrange matters that there was (a) no accumulation of charge along the leads, (b) negligible change of magnetic flux associated with the currents in the leads and (c) no leakage of magnetic flux from the interior of any element. Then a surface such as the dotted one in Fig. 9.1b would contain a constant Q, and the mesh would have no changes in Φ across it. In these circumstances, (9.6) would reduce to (9.4) and K1 and K2 would again apply to I and V *in the leads* so that, for instance, the same current would enter and leave any element. All changes in Q and Φ would be confined to the interior of the elements which are excluded from the network equations. If we then know the relations between I and V for every element, we can use K1 and K2 as with steady current networks to set up equations.

The breakdown of conditions (a), (b), and (c) is associated with two effects: first, the finite velocity of propagation of changes in fields and the currents associated with them, i.e., the velocity of electromagnetic waves; second, the leakage of fields outside the elements. We deal with these in turn.

If periodic time variations are slow enough (quasi-steady), their propagation through a network can take place in a time short compared with the period and we can assume at any instant that the distributions of current are the same as those which would prevail under steady conditions. As the frequency of the time variations increases, the corresponding wave-length shortens until it becomes comparable with the linear size of the network. The current entering an element might then well be different from that leaving it at the same instant because of the different values of I at different points along the leads and the resultant accumulation of charge. K1 thus breaks down. Similarly, it becomes impossible to assign a unique value to V across an element and K2 also breaks down. The size of the network and the elements is thus crucial, and network theory with *lumped* or localized elements becomes inapplicable to normal laboratory circuits for wave-lengths of about a metre or so. Basically, the connecting wires cannot be disregarded and must be treated as *distributed* elements like the transmission lines of section 9.6, and the same effect occurs in inductors and resistors which at lower frequencies are satisfactorily treated as lumped.

We now turn to flux leakage. To prevent this, the construction of elements is usually such as to confine electric and magnetic fields to their interiors. At low frequencies, any stray fields can be taken into account by assuming further lumped elements (e.g., stray capacitance to earth). But even a small unconfined time-varying field leads to radiation of power which, as (4.81) shows, will increase as the wave-length decreases and will become appreciable when λ is comparable with the linear size of the element. This sets a practical limit to the use of conventional elements and open leads and explains the use of waveguides and cavities so that the fields are better confined.

In spite of this, network theory is broadly applicable with properly constructed elements up to micro-wave frequencies and we devote the next few sections to some aspects of it. Some detailed applications are to be found in chapters 6 and 10 of *Electricity and Magnetism*.

9.2 Lumped network elements

In order to make calculations manageable, several idealizations have to be made about network elements. Fortunately, it is usually quite easy to approach the ideal very closely, and in some cases exactly, by careful construction and choice of operating conditions.

We assume first that our elements are *lumped*: they occupy regions between terminals and determine the relation between I and V at those terminals. *Passive* elements contain no sources of electrical energy while *active* elements may inject into a network energy from an external source. Some elements have only two accessible terminals while others have four or even more: the commonest are summarized in table 9.1. Networks can also be classified according to the number of accessible *terminal-pairs* or *ports*.

Table 9.1 Lumped Network Elements

	Passive	*Active*
2-terminal	R, L, C	$-R$ (e.g., tunnel diode) Independent sources of I and V (ideal)
4-terminal	M	Controlled sources (valves, transistors, generators)

The second assumption is that the elements are *linear*: the relations connecting I and V and their derivatives, characteristic of the element, contain no powers other than unity. Thus the relations assumed for R, L, and C are those familiar from elementary work:

$$V = RI \qquad \text{or} \qquad I = GV = V/R \tag{9.7}$$

$$V = L\frac{dI}{dt} \qquad \text{or} \qquad I = \frac{1}{L}\int_0^t V\,dt + I(0) \tag{9.8}$$

$$V = \frac{1}{C}\int_0^t I\,dt + V(0) \qquad \text{or} \qquad I = C\frac{dV}{dt} \tag{9.9}$$

in which R, L, and C are constant and $I(0)$ and $V(0)$ are initial values of current and voltage. In practice, non-linearity occurs in all elements, but if the amplitudes of variation in I and V are kept small, such non-linearity can be made negligible in most cases. Gross non-linearity is sometimes unavoidable and in fact is utilized in many devices. Much of the rest of this chapter does not apply in these instances.

9.3 Passive 2-terminal networks: impedance and admittance functions

Consider a passive network of resistors, capacitors, and inductors with two accessible terminals as in Fig. 9.1a. Both I and V are varying with time due to some external excitation which is for the moment immaterial. The variations are not restricted to sinusoidal ones so that $V(t)$ and $I(t)$ are quite general functions of time. If we apply (9.7)–(9.9) to each element of the network and use K1 and K2 throughout it we should obtain a number of integro-differential equations from which a relation between V and I could, often with some difficulty, be obtained. For instance, for a series LCR combination, we should have

$$V(t) = L\frac{\mathrm{d}I}{\mathrm{d}t} + RI + \frac{1}{C}\int_0^t I\,\mathrm{d}t + V_C(0). \tag{9.10}$$

Such equations can be expressed more concisely by using the operator $\mathrm{p} = \mathrm{d}/\mathrm{d}t$, with the properties

$$\mathrm{p}^n = \mathrm{d}^n/\mathrm{d}t^n \quad \text{and} \quad \frac{1}{\mathrm{p}}\,\mathrm{f}(t) = \int_0^t \mathrm{f}(t)\,\mathrm{d}t. \tag{9.11}$$

The operator D used in the solution of differential equations differs only in that p denotes differentiation specifically with respect to time. These operators obey most of the rules of algebra and this allows them to be treated as algebraic quantities, the exceptions being that p does not always commute with variables nor do powers of p always commute with each other if either is a negative power. Using p, (9.7)–(9.9) become:

For R: $V = RI$ or $I = V/R$ (9.12)

For L: $V = \mathrm{p}LI$ or $I = V/\mathrm{p}L + I(0)$ (9.13)

For C: $V = \dfrac{I}{\mathrm{p}C} + V(0)$ or $I = \mathrm{p}CV$ (9.14) and equations for networks can be obtained using these and K1 and K2. Thus for the series *LCR* circuit, (9.10) becomes

$$V(t) = (\mathrm{p}L + R + 1/\mathrm{p}C)I(t) + V_C(0) \tag{9.15}$$

and for more complicated networks the relation is in general

$$V(t) = Z(\mathrm{p})I(t) + \text{terms in } I(0) \text{ and } V(0) \tag{9.16}$$

the extra terms representing the initial conditions. The function $Z(\mathrm{p})$ is known as the *impedance function* of the network and it can be found by using the same rules as those for obtaining the complex impedance in an a.c. network, except that $\mathrm{p}L$ takes the place of $j\omega L$ and $1/\mathrm{p}C$ that of $1/j\omega C$ (but p^2 is not put equal to -1). In a similar way, the relation can also be obtained in the form

$$I(t) = Y(\mathrm{p})V(t) + \text{terms in } V(0) \text{ and } I(0) \tag{9.17}$$

where $Y(\mathrm{p})$ is the *admittance function* and equals $1/Z(\mathrm{p})$. We now look at the uses of such functions.

Transient behaviour. Here we are interested in the behaviour of the network when there is no external excitation, so that the terminals will be either short-circuited or open-circuited. The integro-differential equations are now homogeneous with solutions normally of the form $A_0\,\mathrm{e}^{st}$ where the s's are discovered by substitution in the equations and the A_0's are given by the initial conditions. The general solution is a superposition of enough terms to give the same number of constants A_0 as the order of the original equations.

Now a solution of the form $I = I_0\,\mathrm{e}^{st}$, $V = V_0\,\mathrm{e}^{st}$ in the relations (9.8) and (9.9) lead to the same relations as (9.13) and (9.14) except that (a) the *operator* p is replaced by the *number s*, and (b) because of this the initial values disappear, as can be checked by integration. Thus we now have

$$\text{For } L\colon V = sLI; \qquad \text{For } C\colon V = I/sC \tag{9.18}$$

and using K1 and K2 gives, instead of (9.16) and (9.17):

$$\mathbf{V}(t) = \mathbf{Z}(s)\mathbf{I}(t) \quad \text{or} \quad \mathbf{I}(t) = \mathbf{Y}(s)\mathbf{V}(t) \tag{9.19}$$

where $\mathbf{V}$, $\mathbf{I}$, $\mathbf{Z}$, and $\mathbf{Y}$ may be complex.

For a short-circuited network, $\mathbf{V}(t)$ is permanently zero and so

$$\mathbf{Z}(s)\mathbf{I}(t) = 0 \tag{9.20}$$

for all t. The solution is thus given by

$$\mathbf{Z}(s) = 0 \quad \text{(S.C.)} \tag{9.21}$$

while for an open-circuited network, $\mathbf{I}(t)$ is zero and hence

$$\mathbf{Y}(s) = 1/\mathbf{Z}(s) = 0 \quad \text{(O.C.).} \tag{9.22}$$

The values of s are thus the roots of the polynomial equation obtained by equating the numerator (short-circuit) or the denominator (open-circuit) of the impedance function to zero. If all values of s are real, the solution is thus the sum of exponential terms which decay to zero as t tends to infinity. If all values of s are imaginary, the solution is oscillatory with no damping. If the values are complex such that

$$\mathbf{s} = \sigma + j\omega \tag{9.23}$$

the real part, always negative, represents damping while the imaginary part gives the natural (angular) frequencies. In practical cases, damping always occurs so that all solutions tend to zero as t tends to infinity, giving rise to the term *transient*.

The determination of natural frequencies of a system has thus been

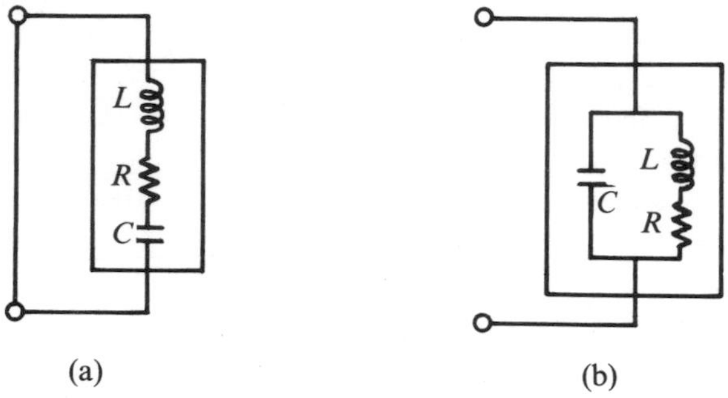

Fig. 9.2 The natural frequencies of an *LCR* circuit can be obtained by treating it as either (a) a short-circuited network or (b) an open-circuited network

reduced to algebra. As an example, consider a series *LCR* network first as a short-circuited network as in Fig. 9.2a. Here

$$\mathbf{Z}(\mathbf{s}) = \mathbf{s}L + R + 1/\mathbf{s}C \tag{9.24}$$

and the roots of $\mathbf{Z}(\mathbf{s}) = 0$ are

$$\mathbf{s}_1, \mathbf{s}_2 = -\frac{R}{2L} \pm \left(\frac{R^2}{4L^2} - \frac{1}{LC}\right)^{1/2} \tag{9.25}$$

so that if the circuit is under-damped the second term is imaginary and the natural angular frequencies come to the single value

$$\omega_N = \left(\frac{1}{LC} - \frac{R^2}{4L^2}\right)^{1/2} \tag{9.26}$$

On the other hand, the same network could be treated as an open-circuited network as in Fig. 9.2b in which

$$\mathbf{Y}(\mathbf{s}) = 1/\mathbf{Z}(\mathbf{s}) = \mathbf{s}C + 1/(R + \mathbf{s}L) = \frac{\mathbf{s}^2LC + \mathbf{s}RC + 1}{R + \mathbf{s}L}$$

and equating the numerator to zero gives the same roots as in (9.25).

Where roots are equal, some modification must be made to the above analysis, but we shall not pursue these cases.

Sinusoidal excitation (*a.c.*). If the excitation from an external source is sinusoidal with an angular frequency ω, the steady state solution is one for which the variations of V and I take the form

$$\mathbf{V} = \mathbf{V}_0\, e^{j\omega t}; \qquad \mathbf{I} = \mathbf{I}_0\, e^{j\omega t} \tag{9.27}$$

(using j for $-i$ to conform with normal a.c. usage). We assume that we are now only interested in times long enough for transients to have become negligible. Once again, the relations (9.13) and (9.14) simplify by the disappearance of the initial $I(0)$ and $V(0)$ terms and we have

$$\text{For } L\colon \mathbf{V} = j\omega L\mathbf{I}; \qquad \text{For } C\colon \mathbf{V} = I/j\omega\mathbf{C} \tag{9.28}$$

so that the network equations (9.16) and (9.17) become

$$\mathbf{V}(t) = \mathbf{Z}(j\omega)\mathbf{I}(t) \quad \text{or} \quad \mathbf{I}(t) = \mathbf{Y}(j\omega)\mathbf{V}(t) \tag{9.29}$$

where $\mathbf{Z} = 1/\mathbf{Y}$, and $\mathbf{Z}(j\omega)$ and $\mathbf{Y}(j\omega)$ are the complex impedance and admittance respectively of the network between its terminals. They have real and imaginary parts:

$$\mathbf{Z} = R + jX; \qquad \mathbf{Y} = G + jB = \frac{R - jX}{|Z|^2} \tag{9.30}$$

where R is the resistance of the network, G its conductance, X its reactance, and B its susceptance.

Since $\mathbf{V}$ and $\mathbf{I}$ are now phasor quantities, either $\mathbf{Z}$ or $\mathbf{Y}$ gives the relations between their amplitudes and phases. Thus

$$V_0/I_0 = |\mathbf{Z}| = (R^2 + X^2)^{1/2} \tag{9.31}$$

$$I_0/V_0 = |\mathbf{Y}| = (G^2 + B^2)^{1/2} \tag{9.32}$$

while the phase angle between **V** and **I** is either $\tan^{-1} X/R$ or $\tan^{-1} B/G$. Most of this material should already be familiar to the reader.

Because **V**(t) and **I**(t) may be regarded as excitation and response in a causal system, we should expect the theory of section 8.9 to apply. Thus the poles of the response function **Y** or the zeros of **Z** give ω's lying in the lower half of the complex plane if i is used instead of $-j$. Moreover, dispersion relations of the form of (8.60) and (8.61) relate the reactive part of **Y** or **Z** to the variation of the resistive part over all frequencies and vice versa. Finally, the real or resistive part of **Y** or **Z** is an even function of ω and the reactive part an odd function (see problem 9.2).

Resonance. Resonances are of various types. If the frequency at which the maximum amplitude of current response is wanted, for a constant voltage across the terminals, the minimum of $|\mathbf{Z}|$ or the maximum of $|\mathbf{Y}|$ must be found. Consequently, we seek values of ω for which $\partial|\mathbf{Z}|/\partial\omega$ or $\partial|\mathbf{Y}|/\partial\omega$ are zero. These will also yield frequencies giving minimum responses, which are also counted as resonances (in a parallel LCR network, for example). A more general criterion is to use the condition that resonance occurs when **V** and **I** are in phase and thus that X or B is zero (see problems 9.2 and 9.3).

Other uses of impedance or admittance functions. Impedance or admittance functions contain all the information needed to find the behaviour of any network under external excitations. A mention should be made here of a method enabling responses to pulses or steps in voltage or current to be obtained. The Laplace transform of a function of time $\mathrm{f}(t)$ is defined by

$$\mathscr{L}(\mathrm{f}) = \int_0^\infty \mathrm{e}^{-st}\mathrm{f}(t)\,\mathrm{d}t \tag{9.33}$$

and it is easily shown that

$$\mathscr{L}\left(\frac{\mathrm{d}y}{\mathrm{d}t}\right) = s\mathscr{L}(y) - y(0); \qquad \mathscr{L}\left(\int_0^\infty y\,\mathrm{d}t\right) = \frac{1}{s}\mathscr{L}(y). \tag{9.34}$$

If we apply the transformation to every term in the integro-differential equations for the network, such as that in equation (9.10), we end with

$$\mathscr{L}(V) = Z(s)\mathscr{L}(I) + \text{terms in } V(0) \text{ and } I(0). \tag{9.35}$$

It follows that, given the excitation V, the response I involves finding the function whose Laplace transform is $1/Z(s)$ of that of V (see problem 9.4). The power of the method lies in the ease with which it deals with pulses and step functions. Thus from Fig. 9.3, the Laplace

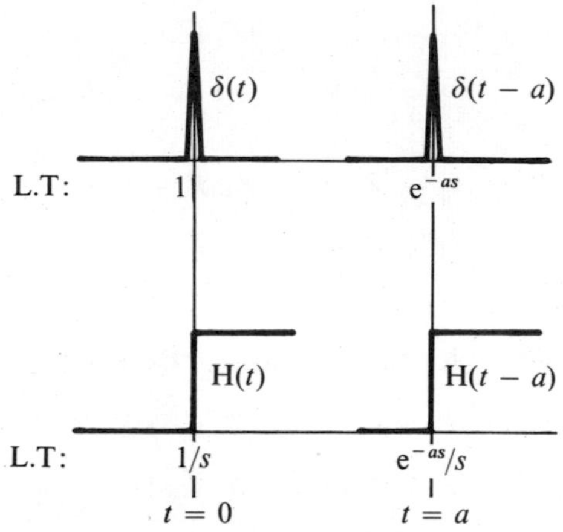

Fig. 9.3 Delta and step functions and their Laplace transforms. The pulses have unit area and the steps unit amplitude

transform of a rectangular pulse of unit amplitude and duration τ would be that of $\mathrm{H}(t) - \mathrm{H}(t - \tau)$, i.e., $(1 - \mathrm{e}^{-s\tau})/s$.

9.4 General network theorems (sinusoidal excitation)

A general network contains both active and passive elements. We choose to consider those with R, L, and C as passive elements and steady generators of e.m.f. $\mathscr{E}$ as active ones. We shall also confine the treatment to the steady sinusoidal state so that complex impedances and admittances $Z(j\omega)$ and $Y(j\omega)$ are appropriate. In this and succeeding sections, we drop the bold type, on the assumption that all Y's and Z's are complex.

Analysis of a network may proceed by loop or node methods. In the latter, each junction is allocated a potential V_1, V_2, etc., so that K2 is automatically satisfied and K1 is then applied at each junction. We shall find loop analysis more convenient. In this, each *mesh* is numbered and circulating currents I_1, I_2, etc., are inserted in each, thus automatically satisfying K1. The impedances are numbered according to the meshes they have in common, Z_{12} belonging to meshes 1 and 2 and being the same as Z_{21}. The e.m.f.s are similarly labelled and it will be found necessary to give the 'outside' region a mesh number as well. We use a special notation that Z_{11} is the sum of all impedances in mesh 1 and $\mathscr{E}_{11}$ the sum of all e.m.f.s in mesh 1, etc., with due regard to sign. Applying K2 to each mesh in turn yields linear equations of the form:

$$\text{mesh 1:} \quad (I_1 - I_2)Z_{12} + (I_1 - I_3)Z_{13} + \cdots = \mathscr{E}_{12} + \mathscr{E}_{13} + \cdots$$

or

$$\left.\begin{aligned} &\text{mesh 1:} \quad Z_{11}I_1 - Z_{12}I_2 - Z_{13}I_3 - \cdots = \mathscr{E}_{11} \\ &\text{mesh 2:} \quad -Z_{21}I_1 + Z_{22}I_2 - Z_{23}I_3 - \cdots = \mathscr{E}_{22} \\ &\qquad \cdots \end{aligned}\right\} \tag{9.36}$$

These can be solved for the currents and the equations are

$$\left.\begin{aligned} I_1 &= y_{11}\mathscr{E}_{11} + y_{12}\mathscr{E}_{22} + y_{13}\mathscr{E}_{33} + \cdots \\ I_2 &= y_{21}\mathscr{E}_{11} + y_{22}\mathscr{E}_{22} + y_{23}\mathscr{E}_{33} + \cdots \\ &\cdots \end{aligned}\right\} \tag{9.37}$$

in which y_{ij} = (co-factor of Z_{ij} in Δ)/Δ, where Δ is the determinant of Z's in (9.36). We have that $y_{ij} = y_{ji}$ since $Z_{ij} = Z_{ji}$.

Superposition theorem. The linearity of (9.36) and (9.37) means that superposition will apply. Thus, if the current in a branch is I_1 due to an e.m.f. $\mathscr{E}_1$ acting alone at its proper place in the network and if the current in the same branch is I_2 due to $\mathscr{E}_2$ acting alone, the current in the branch when both $\mathscr{E}_1$ and $\mathscr{E}_2$ act is $I_1 + I_2$. This is the superposition theorem and its detailed proof from (9.37) is left to the reader.

Reciprocity theorem. If an e.m.f. $\mathscr{E}_0$ acting alone in branch m produces a current I_0 in branch n, then $\mathscr{E}_0$ acting alone in branch n will produce a current I_0 in branch m. This is the reciprocity theorem and its proof from (9.37) is again left to the reader.

Thévenin's and Norton's theorems. Thévenin's theorem allows us to replace the whole of a network between two terminals by a single e.m.f. $\mathscr{E}_0$ in series with an impedance Z_0. The e.m.f. $\mathscr{E}_0$ is given by the open-circuit potential difference appearing across the terminals, and Z_0 is the impedance between the terminals looking into the network when all sources of e.m.f. are replaced by inert impedances equal to their internal impedances. The proof of this is the same as that for steady current networks and is given in *Electricity and*

Magnetism, section 6.4. An equivalent theorem is Norton's theorem, allowing any network to be replaced by a constant current generator $\mathscr{I}_0$ in parallel with an impedance Z_0. The value of $\mathscr{I}_0$ is the short-circuit current across the terminals and Z_0 is the same impedance as in the Thévenin case.

9.5 Passive 4-terminal networks

An important class of network is that depicted in Fig. 9.4a, with four

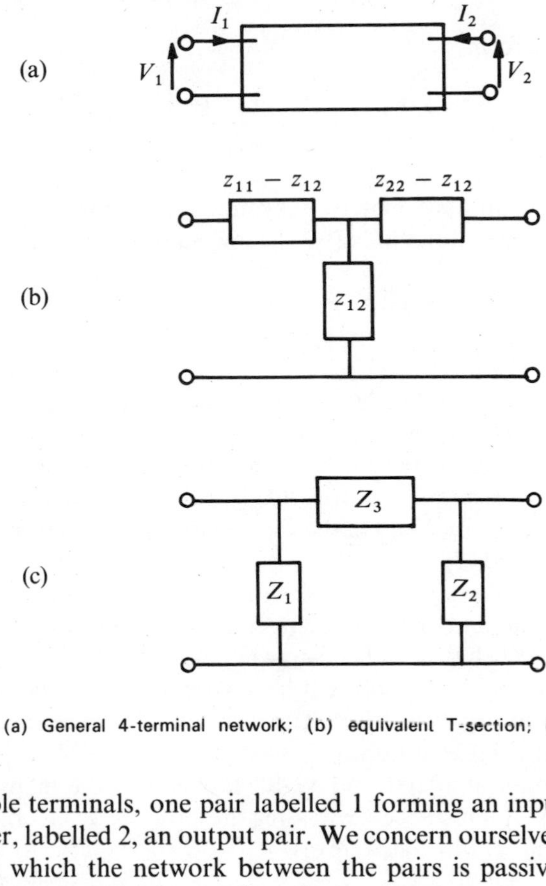

Fig. 9.4 (a) General 4-terminal network; (b) equivalent T-section; (c) equivalent π-section

accessible terminals, one pair labelled 1 forming an input pair and the other, labelled 2, an output pair. We concern ourselves here with cases in which the network between the pairs is passive although some of the analysis also applies when active elements are included. Particular examples include attenuators, filters, phase-shift networks, transformers, transmission lines, and bridges.

The currents and potential differences are conventionally given the directions shown. They may be produced by any form of external circuit including impedanceless e.m.f.s—we are only concerned that they represent corresponding values for the particular network. It follows that we may write down a set of equations similar to (9.37) in which only two effective e.m.f.s V_1 and V_2 remain. Since we are only interested in I_1 and I_2, we have

$$\left.\begin{aligned} I_1 &= y_{11}V_1 + y_{12}V_2 \\ I_2 &= y_{21}V_1 + y_{22}V_2 \end{aligned}\right\}\text{admittance form} \qquad (9.38)$$

or, in matrix form,

$$\begin{pmatrix} I_1 \\ I_2 \end{pmatrix} = \begin{pmatrix} y_{11} & y_{12} \\ y_{21} & y_{22} \end{pmatrix}\begin{pmatrix} V_1 \\ V_2 \end{pmatrix} \qquad (9.39)$$

where the admittance matrix is symmetric because $y_{12} = y_{21}$ if reciprocity holds. Equations (9.38) can also be written

$$\left.\begin{aligned} V_1 &= z_{11}I_1 + z_{12}I_2 \\ V_2 &= z_{21}I_1 + z_{22}I_2 \end{aligned}\right\}\text{impedance form} \qquad (9.40)$$

in which $z_{12} = z_{21}$. The y's and z's are admittance and impedance functions of the passive network only and are determined by the elements in the network and how they are connected. Each of the functions represents a quantity likely to be of interest in some problem: for instance, z_{11} is the input impedance when the output is open-circuited ($I_2 = 0$); $z_{12} = z_{21}$ is the transfer impedance on open-circuit.

It is evident that there are only three independent parameters describing the behaviour of the network, so that it would be always possible in principle to replace it by a T-section as in Fig. 9.4b or a π-section as in Fig. 9.4c. These equivalent networks are not always physically realizable, however.

Other forms of (9.38) and (9.40) are of interest in particular applications. For instance, expressing the input V_1, I_1 in terms of the output V_2, I_2, or vice versa, gives

$$\begin{aligned} V_1 &= AV_2 - BI_2 \\ I_1 &= CV_2 - DI_2 \end{aligned} \quad \text{or} \quad \left.\begin{aligned} V_2 &= DV_1 - BI_2 \\ I_2 &= CV_1 - AI_1 \end{aligned}\right\}ABCD\text{ form} \qquad (9.41)$$

in which $AD - BC = 1$, so that only three are independent again.

The advantage of this form becomes evident when written as a matrix equation

$$\begin{pmatrix} V_2 \\ I_2 \end{pmatrix} = \begin{pmatrix} D & B \\ C & A \end{pmatrix} \begin{pmatrix} V_1 \\ -I_1 \end{pmatrix}. \tag{9.42}$$

The *ABCD* matrix is known as the *transfer* matrix and if a number of 4-terminal networks are connected in cascade so that the output from one forms the input to the next, the transfer matrix for the set is simply the product of the individual matrices.

An important parameter in feedback circuits is the transfer function on open circuit (V_2/V_1 with $I_2 = 0$): in the various forms above, this is either $-y_{21}/y_{22}$, z_{21}/z_{11}, or $1/A$. There are also forms more suitable for cases in which the input current I_1 and the output voltage V_2 are best used as independent variables. These are the so-called *hybrid* forms $V_1 = h_{11}I_1 + h_{12}V_2$, etc. Examples in the use of some of these parameters are to be found in the problems at the end of the chapter.

Impedance matching is an important function of 4-terminal networks, since where the source and load impedances are fixed neither may present to the other the correct impedance for maximum power transfer. Since the problem involves three parameters—the two impedances to be matched and the desirable power transfer—it is often possible to design a 4-terminal network to perform the required function.

Many types of network are symmetrical, i.e., they look the same from either pair of terminals. In the above notations, this means that $y_{11} = y_{22}$, $z_{11} = z_{22}$, and $A = D$. Such networks are thus characterized by only two independent parameters and these are often chosen to be (a) the *characteristic impedance*, Z_k, defined as that impedance across the output which makes the input impedance also Z_k and (b) the *propagation constant*, γ defined as $\log_e (V_1/V_2)$ for a correctly terminated section.

9.6 Transmission lines

At high frequencies where the wave-length becomes comparable with the linear dimensions of the network, V and I become functions of position as well as of time and the network concepts can only be retained by assuming that resistance, inductance, and capacitance are distributed along conductors. The network theorems can then be applied to small enough lengths, but they lead to *partial* differential equations for V and I. These are wave equations and show that the quasi-steady assumptions are no longer tenable for the network as a whole.

Transmission lines form a link between the networks of the previous sections and the waveguides of the next chapter, and they can be considered as either. Here we briefly survey their properties, first as distributing leads and then as circuit elements, restricting ourselves to such high frequencies that losses due to conductance between and resistance along the lines can be neglected. A two-conductor line is often coaxial, but is better drawn as a twin line as in Fig. 9.4. Only the inductance per unit length, L, and the capacitance per unit length, C, of the pair need be taken account of for most purposes provided the line is not more than a few wave-lengths long.

For an element of the line of length dx, the increment in potential difference $-dV$ is equal to $L\,dx\,(dI/dt)$, and the increment in current $-dI$ is equal to $C\,dx\,(dV/dt)$. These give the equations

$$L\,\partial I/\partial t = -\partial V/\partial x; \qquad C\,\partial V/\partial t = -\partial I/\partial x \tag{9.43}$$

and from these can be obtained wave equations for I and V showing that variations are propagated with a phase velocity $1/(LC)^{1/2}$. For a single angular frequency ω propagated along an infinite line, we may assume variations of the form $V = V_0 \exp\{j(\omega t - kx)\}$, $I = I_0 \exp\{j(\omega t - kx)\}$ and substitution in (9.43) shows that V/I is always $\omega L/k$ or $(L/C)^{1/2}$ since ω/k is $1/(LC)^{1/2}$. This quantity plays the part of a characteristic impedance, Z_k.

Transmission lines as leads. Unless a finite line is terminated by an impedance Z_k, there is in general a reflected wave which sets up standing waves in the line. Not only does this mean that the load does not absorb all the energy fed in from the generator, but the standing waves are undesirable because of the high potential differences then occurring. The use of transmission lines as leads thus means matching the line to the load Z_L and one method of doing this is to insert a section of line with a different characteristic impedance. For if the length of the line is l, it can be shown that the input impedance (Fig. 9.5) is given by

$$Z_{in} = Z_k\left(\frac{Z_L + jZ_k \tan kl}{Z_k + jZ_L \tan kl}\right) \tag{9.44}$$

(see *Electricity and Magnetism*, section 10.10). For a $\lambda/4$ line this is

$$Z_{in} = Z_k^{\,2}/Z_L \tag{9.45}$$

It follows that if a line of characteristic impedance Z_1 has to be matched to Z_2, then a $\lambda/4$ line of $Z_k = (Z_1 Z_2)^{1/2}$ must be inserted between them.

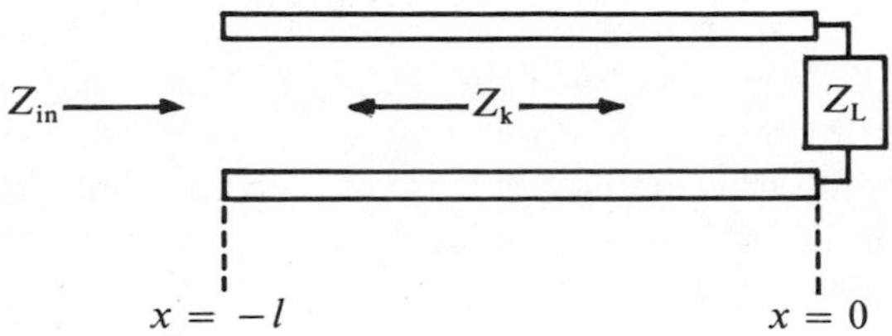

Fig. 9.5 A terminated transmission line

Transmission lines as circuit elements. If a fixed length of line is terminated in a resistance R, equation (9.44) with $Z_L = R$ shows that the input impedance passes through successive maxima and minima as the frequency increases and λ decreases. These are resonance effects similar to those exhibited by series and parallel LCR circuits. In fact, if $R < (L/C)^{1/2}$, then when $l = \lambda/4$, Z_{in} is a maximum at L/CR and when $l = \lambda/2$, Z_{in} is a minimum at R and in both cases V and I are in phase. The resonances are sharp when $R = 0$ or ∞ and $\lambda/4$ lengths of line are often used as tuned circuits in high frequency oscillators.

9.7 Active elements

We have defined an active element as one which injects energy from an external source into a network. Lumped elements of this type probably familiar to the reader include thermionic valves (vacuum tubes) and transistors: in both cases the energy needed is in the form of alternating current and the external energy comes from a direct current source. Details of networks involving these devices are outside the scope of this volume and we dwell on them only briefly as network elements.

Both the vacuum tube and the transistor are 3-terminal devices, but one terminal is usually common to both input and output so that they become essentially 4-terminal active elements to which the analysis of section 9.5 applies, except that reciprocity will not occur (i.e., $y_{12} \neq y_{21}$, etc.). We consider only the case of common-cathode and common-emitter connections although others are important (e.g., a cathode-follower is a common-anode or common-collector circuit).

Network analysis is best carried out using equivalent circuits and the two devices do not differ in that either can be represented as far as output is concerned by a constant voltage generator in series with an impedance (Thévenin case), or by a constant current generator in parallel with an impedance (Norton case). The apparent greater simplicity of thermionic valve circuits is often due to the negligible input (grid) current, so that the output is controlled by V_1. Figure 9.6a shows the equivalent output circuit using the Thévenin equivalent: μ is the amplification factor of the valve and corresponds to the parameter D of (9.41).

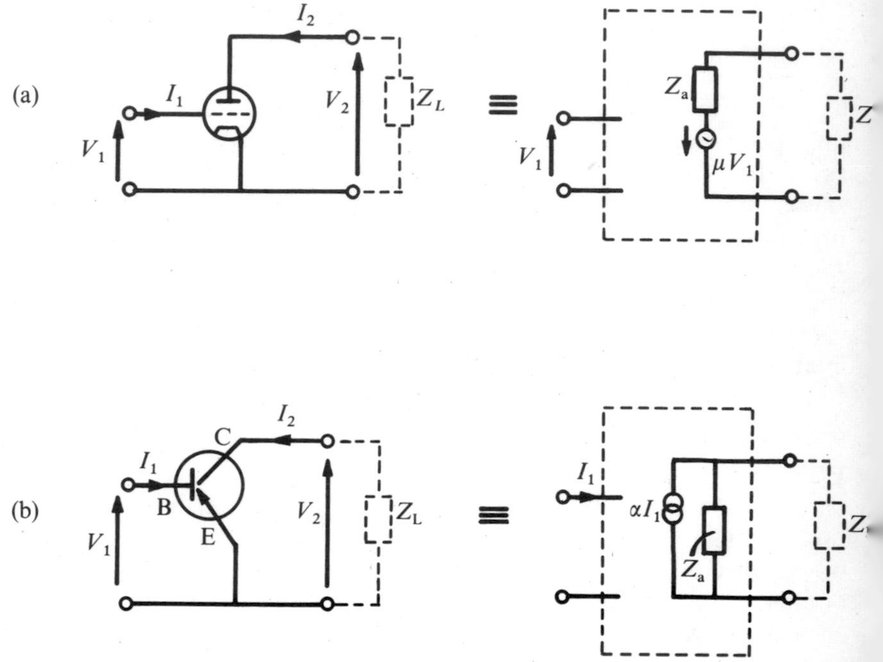

Fig. 9.6 Basic and equivalent output circuits for (a) a vacuum triode; (b) a transistor. The d.c. supplies are omitted

In the transistor circuit, no such simplification is possible as the base current is never negligible, although the input impedance is quite high with the configuration of Fig. 9.6b. The output in Norton form has a constant current generator αI_1 where α corresponds to the parameter h_{21} of section 9.5.

Feedback. The above are simple amplifiers whose voltage gain over a single stage is, say, A. We now look at the effect of feeding back a proportion β of the output to the input. Suppose the external input is V_1 and the final output is V_2 of which βV_2 is fed back to make the total input $V_1 + \beta V_2$. It follows that $V_2 = A(V_1 + \beta V_2)$ or the stage gain is now

$$\frac{V_2}{V_1} = \frac{A}{1 - A\beta}. \tag{9.46}$$

The sign of $A\beta$ depends on the phase shifts in the amplifier and feedback networks. If the feedback is positive, the gain increases as $A\beta$ increases from 0 to 1. At $A\beta = 1$, the gain becomes infinite and there is an output even with no input. This represents self-oscillation of the network, to be avoided in amplifiers but the underlying feature of oscillator circuits.

If $A\beta$ is negative and A is so large that $A\beta \gg 1$, then $V_2/V_1 \sim 1/\beta$, so that the behaviour of the system is controlled almost entirely by the feedback network. Naturally, the overall gain is much smaller but the stability is greatly increased and this is a more important feature in many cases, particularly in control systems. The negative feedback principle illustrated here is in use in many other fields than electronics.

References

Good elementary treatments of network theory are to be found in Earnshaw (1960) and, for Laplace transform methods, in Shaw (1962). More advanced texts are those by Paskusz and Bussell (1963), Tuttle (1965), and Faulkner (1966). Transistor circuits are dealt with in Dean (1964), non-linear devices in Hemenway, Henry, and Caulton (1962), while de Barr (1962) gives an introduction to control systems and feedback.

PROBLEMS

9.1 Two inductances L and two capacitances C are connected in series in a square. The corner between the capacitances is connected through a third capacitance C to the opposite corner between the inductances. Find the impedance function for the network between any two points and hence its natural and resonant frequencies. Neglect any resistance.

9.2 An inductance L with resistance R is connected in parallel with a capacitance C. Demonstrate the following facts about the 2-terminal network so formed:

(a) the resistive part of the impedance is an even function of ω, the reactive part an odd function;

(b) the poles and zeros of $Z(-i\omega)$ lie in the lower half of the complex plane with i as the imaginary operator. Show that it is the presence of R which ensures this;

(c) if resonance is defined as the frequency at which applied potential difference and current are in phase, the resonant frequency is given by $\omega_P{}^2 = \omega_0{}^2 - R^2/L^2$ where $\omega_0{}^2 = 1/LC$. Show that this is NOT the frequency of minimum response unless $R = 0$.

9.3 In a series LCR circuit, resonance could be defined as the condition for maximum voltage across L, R, or C. Show that three different angular frequencies ω_L, ω_R, and ω_C give such maxima and that $\omega_L\omega_C = \omega_R{}^2$.

9.4 The Laplace transform of $e^{-bt} \sin(at + \phi)$ is $[a \cos\phi + (s + b) \sin\phi]/[(s + b)^2 + a^2]$. From this, particular transforms can be obtained by giving b, a, and ϕ specific values. A step function of amplitude V_0, $V_0 H(t)$, is applied to an LR series combination. Find the current by the Laplace transform method.

9.5 Find the response to a unit voltage pulse at $t = 0$ of a series LR combination.

9.6 Find the current response of an RC series combination to a rectangular pulse of unit amplitude and duration τ, given that $\mathscr{L}[H(t - \tau) \exp\{-a(t - \tau)\}] = [\exp(-s\tau)]/(s + a)$. Sketch the variation of current with time.

9.7 Find the steady state current in a series LCR circuit subject to an external e.m.f. $\mathscr{E}_0 \sin \omega t$ using the Laplace transform given in problem 9.4 and confirm that it is the same as that given by the usual a.c. method.

9.8 A passive network has four accessible terminals W, X, Y, and Z. When W and X are short-circuited, a potential difference of 100 V connected across Y and Z supplies 250 mA to the network. When a potential difference is applied across WX, an open-circuit potential difference of 25 V appears across YZ. What current would pass through a 100 ohm resistance connected across YZ if 25 V were applied across WX?

9.9 A 4-terminal network consists of a single T-section with series impedances each Z_1 and a parallel impedance Z_2. Find the impedance matrix and the transfer matrix. Split the T-section into three 4-terminal networks in cascade (the first of Z_1 only, the second of Z_2 only, the third of Z_1 only). Find the separate transfer matrices for the three and show that their product yields the transfer matrix for the T-section.

9.10 Show that the characteristic impedance of the T-section of problem 9.9 is $(2Z_1Z_2 + Z_1{}^2)^{1/2}$.

9.11 Find the values of Z_1, Z_2, and Z_3 in the π-section of Fig. 9.4c in terms of z_{11}, z_{22}, and z_{12}.

9.12 An ideal transformer consists of a primary winding with self-inductance L_1, a secondary winding of self-inductance L_2, and a mutual inductance between windings of M. Find the impedance matrix for the transformer as a 4-terminal network and find an equivalent T-section. (Neglect all resistance.)

9.13 Show from equation (9.43) that waves of current or potential difference with phase velocity $1/(LC)^{1/2}$ may be propagated in either direction along a loss-less transmission line. Verify that the ratio of V to I for either wave is $(L/C)^{1/2}$. Since the line is symmetrical, the last paragraph of section 9.5 makes it clear that only two parameters are needed to characterize the line. Find the characteristic impedance Z_k and the propagation constant per unit length, γ, in terms of L, C, and ω.

9.14 A load Z_L is placed across the end $x = 0$ of a loss-less transmission line. The reflection coefficient ρ for a propagated wave of angular frequency ω is defined as the ratio of the reflected to the incident potential difference at $x = 0$. Show that $\rho = (Z_L - Z_k)/(Z_L + Z_k)$ where Z_k is the characteristic impedance. Show also that the current and voltage on the line can be expressed at any point by $I = I_0\,(e^{-j\beta x} - \rho\, e^{j\beta x})\, e^{j\omega t}$ and $V = Z_k I_0$ $(e^{-j\beta x} + \rho\, e^{j\beta x})\, e^{j\omega t}$ where I_0 is determined by the generator.

9.15 Using the result of problem 9.14, prove that (9.44) gives the input impedance of a terminated loss-less transmission line.

9.16 Suppose the transmission line of problem 9.13 is lossy, with resistance R and conductance G per unit length. Find the equation to replace (9.43) and hence show that the characteristic impedance becomes $\left[(R + j\omega L)/(G + j\omega C)\right]^{1/2}$ and the propagation constant $\left[(R + j\omega L)(G + j\omega C)\right]^{1/2}$

9.17 Show that the input impedance of a loaded lossy line is given by

$$Z_{in} = Z_k\left(\frac{Z_L + jZ_k \tanh \gamma l}{Z_k + jZ_L \tanh \gamma l}\right)$$

where γ is the propagation constant.

9.18 If Z_{oc} and Z_{sc} are the input impedances of a given length of transmission line terminated by an open-circuit and a short-circuit respectively, show that $Z_{oc}Z_{sc} = Z_k{}^2$.

9.19 Explain how the resistance, conductance, capacitance, and inductance per unit length of a line of known length could be obtained from measurements of Z_{oc} and Z_{sc} at a given frequency.

10

Waveguides, cavities, and aerials

At high frequencies above about 100 Mc/s ($\lambda = 3$ m), the network treatment becomes increasingly inapplicable. We have seen in the case of transmission lines that it is still possible to retain network concepts up to microwave frequencies if the lines are treated as sets of distributed elements. However, there exist more general devices for conveying electromagnetic energy known as *waveguides*, and in these the distributions of current and potential become so complicated that it is simpler in most cases to revert to the field theory based on Maxwell's equations, as we do in this chapter.

Waveguides, like transmission lines, have the dual function of conveying energy from one place to another (waveguides proper, sections 10.1–10.3) and of acting as network elements. The latter comprise short lengths of waveguide forming *electromagnetic cavities* (section 10.4). Sections 10.5 and 10.6 are respectively brief surveys of passive and active microwave devices and we end with a look at transmitting and receiving aerials over the whole range of radio frequencies.

10.1 Propagation of laterally-bounded waves

The problem to be investigated here is that of propagating an electromagnetic wave in a certain direction while bounding it laterally so that the fields and the energy do not spread. We shall assume that the cross-sections of any confining guide achieving this are constant, and that the guide walls are metallic conductors of effectively infinite conductivity. Since finite currents will flow in the waveguide materials, the relation $\mathbf{J} = \gamma\mathbf{E}$ means that $\mathbf{E}$ must be everywhere zero in the conducting walls. It follows that **curl E**, and therefore $\partial \mathbf{B}/\partial t$, are also zero and that there is no **B** field in the conducting walls other than a static one. The boundary conditions (4.10) thus yield the following conditions on any wave fields on the vacuum side of the guide walls:

$$E_{\mathrm{tan}} = 0; \qquad B_{\mathrm{normal}} = 0. \tag{10.1}$$

Let us now see what sort of wave can be propagated down a wave-guide whose cross-section may be irregular and multiply-connected as in Fig. 10.1, where the direction of propagation is again chosen as

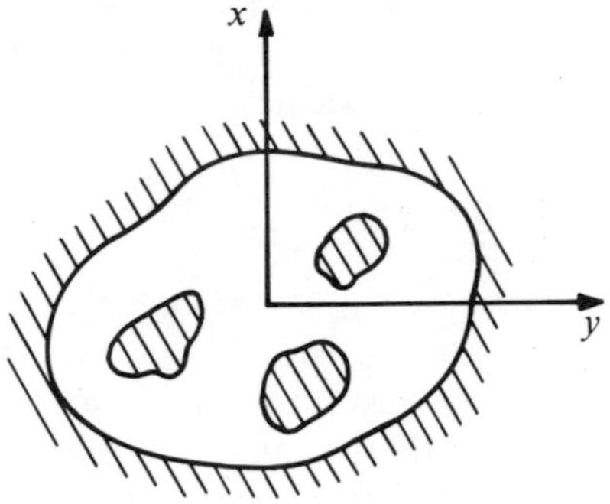

Fig. 10.1 Cross-section through a general waveguide. Shaded regions represent conductors

the z-direction. First, can plane waves be propagated with wave-fronts in the xy-plane and wave-normals in the z-direction? Such waves would have no variations in the fields with x or y within the boundaries and this leads, as in the general argument of section 4.4, to the conclusion that there would be no z-components of **E** or **B**—any waves would be wholly transverse or TEM waves. In addition, however, it is clear that round the boundaries, E_x and E_y must be zero at *some* points because the tangential component is always zero by (10.1) and the tangent must be in the x- and y-directions at some points on a closed curve in the xy-plane. Since there is no variation with x or y, both E_x and E_y must be zero everywhere. There is therefore no non-zero component of **E** or **B** and plane TEM waves cannot be propagated along the axis of a waveguide.

Two possibilities now suggest themselves. First, can waves which are TEM but *not* plane be propagated? Second, could plane waves be propagated in directions other than the z-direction, in which case there will be z-components of at least one field so that the waves are no longer TEM? We examine these possibilities in turn.

Guided TEM waves. The restriction to plane waves is now removed so that $\partial/\partial x$ and $\partial/\partial y$ are not necessarily zero. Instead, we ask whether waves with E_z and B_z both zero can be propagated in the z-direction and under what conditions. Maxwell's equations show at once that the z-components of **curl B** and **curl E** are zero or that

$$\frac{\partial E_y}{\partial x} - \frac{\partial E_x}{\partial y} = 0; \qquad \frac{\partial B_y}{\partial x} - \frac{\partial B_x}{\partial y} = 0. \tag{10.2}$$

These imply that in the two-dimensional region bounded by metallic conductors in Fig. 10.1, **E** and **B** can be regarded as each derivable from a potential function. If these are V and V_m respectively, then $E_y = -\partial V/\partial y$, etc., and so, because div $\mathbf{E} = 0$,

$$\frac{\partial^2 V}{\partial x^2} + \frac{\partial^2 V}{\partial y^2} = 0 \tag{10.3}$$

with a similar equation for V_m. Both V and V_m thus satisfy Laplace's equation in two dimensions. In addition, the boundary condition $E_t = 0$ means that V is constant round each conducting boundary and V thus satisfies exactly the same conditions as the electrostatic potential. *Thus the electric field in this cross-section must have the form of an electrostatic field of charged conductors whose boundaries coincide with those of the guide.*

It follows that TEM waves cannot exist inside a hollow waveguide with no inner conductor at all because no electric field can exist inside a hollow charged conductor. On the other hand, when more than one conducting surface exists as in the coaxial or twin transmission lines, TEM waves can be propagated and the electric field has exactly the configuration it would have if the line were simply a cylindrical condenser.

The lines of **B** in the xy-plane are always perpendicular to those of **E** as in a plane wave (problem 10.1) so that they would follow the direction of the equipotentials in a cylindrical condenser: alternatively, they are the same as those produced by steady currents flowing along the conductors in the z-direction.

These results are expected on other grounds because closed curves in the xy-plane cannot link any flux of **E** or **B** in a TEM wave, except for that due to any B_z *within a conductor*. The line integral of **E** round a closed path is therefore zero, the condition for a single-valued potential to exist. The line integral of **B** round a closed path is zero if the path links no conductors: if it does, then the line integral is exactly equal to the current linked, as in the case of steady current fields. All the steady field solutions in two dimensions are thus solutions for TEM waves.

Notice that in the above it is shown that each conductor has a V which is constant over its cross-section, and that this characteristic enables the network concept of potential difference between two cross-sections to be used just as it is with a connecting wire at low frequencies. This justifies the extension of the parallel twin transmission line treatment of section 9.6 to twin lines with any cross-section.

Propagation of non-axial plane waves. We now see what happens if we try to propagate plane waves along a tube at an angle to the axis (Fig. 10.2). Although these have **E** and **B** transverse to the direction

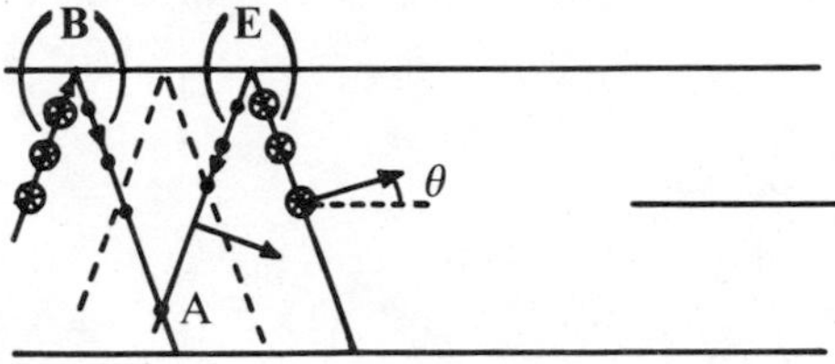

Fig. 10.2 A plane wave propagated non-axially along a waveguide. The diagram shows the case in which $E_z = 0$ in both incident and reflected waves. The resultant fields have the correct values at the boundaries and there is in general a z-component of **B**

of propagation, there will in general be z-components of both fields so that propagation in the z-direction cannot be described by TEM waves. Moreover, successive reflections will take place at the sides of the guide as we saw in chapter 7 and the resultant fields will be obtained by superposition. The example illustrated in Fig. 10.2 could represent propagation in a rectangular guide, and if **E** and **B** were oriented as shown, the resultant would still have only transverse components of **E** but would possess longitudinal components of **B**. It would thus be designated as a TE (transverse electric) wave. Moreover, the superposition of incident and reflected travelling waves leads to stationary waves, so that we should expect stationary wave patterns in the x- and y-directions. The solution in the z-direction, however, should be that appropriate to a progressive wave.

This is consistent with the general observation that solutions of a wave equation may be expressed either as a combination of progressive or of stationary waves. When boundary conditions are imposed, stationary solutions are usually more appropriate because it is possible for a single mode to be excited independently of any other, while a travelling type of solution will always involve several components. Without boundary conditions it is possible for a progressive wave with a single frequency to be excited on its own, whereas stationary solutions must be superposed.

It is possible to continue the treatment of non-TEM waves as combinations of reflected plane waves and such a treatment is physically very revealing. For instance, the phase velocity of the wave in the z-direction would be that of a typical point in the wave-pattern such as A in Fig. 10.2 and this can be shown to be $c/\cos\theta$ (problem 10.2), i.e., greater than c. On the other hand, the energy propagates with a velocity $c\cos\theta$. We shall continue the analysis, however, in terms of the resultant fields found from Maxwell's equations which gives the quantitative information needed more concisely.

10.2 Hollow waveguides

We now consider hollow guides with perfectly conducting walls, for which it is no longer possible to assume plane wave solutions. Instead, we simplify the analysis by considering monochromatic waves of a single angular frequency ω propagated in the z-direction as progressive waves with a guide wave-length λ_g and wave number $k_g = 2\pi/\lambda_g$. Thus **E** and **B** are given by

$$\mathbf{E} = \mathbf{E}_0\, \mathrm{e}^{i(k_g z - \omega t)}; \qquad \mathbf{B} = \mathbf{B}_0\, \mathrm{e}^{i(k_g z - \omega t)} \tag{10.4}$$

in which, unlike plane waves, $\mathbf{E}_0$ and $\mathbf{B}_0$ are functions of x and y. We have to find how the components of these fields vary with x and y by applying Maxwell's equations and the boundary conditions. We shall work in cartesian co-ordinates for which $\partial/\partial z$ is equivalent to ik_g and $\partial/\partial t$ to $-i\omega$. We shall drop the zero subscripts on the x, y, z components of $\mathbf{E}_0$ and $\mathbf{B}_0$ on the understanding that our relations are for the amplitudes and that variations with z and t can be restored by multiplying by $\exp\{i(k_g z - \omega t)\}$. We also use the free space wave number k_0 and wave-length λ_0 appropriate to the frequency ω and given by

$$k_0 = 2\pi/\lambda_0 = \omega/c. \tag{10.5}$$

It is possible to express the x and y components of $\mathbf{E}_0$ and $\mathbf{B}_0$ entirely in terms of the z-components as follows. The x-component of **curl E** $= -\partial\mathbf{B}/\partial t$ becomes

$$\partial E_z/\partial y - ik_g E_y = i\omega B_x = ik_0 c B_x \tag{10.6}$$

while the y-component of **curl B** $= \partial\mathbf{E}/c^2\,\partial t$ becomes

$$ik_g B_x - \partial B_z/\partial x = -i\omega E_y/c^2 = -ik_0 E_y/c. \tag{10.7}$$

E_y and B_x can be eliminated in turn from (10.6) and (10.7) to give the following:

$$B_x = \frac{i}{(k_0{}^2 - k_g{}^2)}\left[-\frac{k_0}{c}\frac{\partial E_z}{\partial y} + k_g\frac{\partial B_z}{\partial x}\right] \tag{10.8}$$

$$E_y = \frac{i}{(k_0{}^2 - k_g{}^2)}\left[k_g\frac{\partial E_z}{\partial y} - k_0 c\frac{\partial B_z}{\partial x}\right] \tag{10.9}$$

and similarly,

$$E_x = \frac{i}{(k_0{}^2 - k_g{}^2)}\left[k_g\frac{\partial E_z}{\partial x} + k_0 c\frac{\partial B_z}{\partial y}\right] \tag{10.10}$$

$$B_y = \frac{i}{(k_0{}^2 - k_g{}^2)}\left[\frac{k_0}{c}\frac{\partial E_z}{\partial x} + k_g\frac{\partial B_z}{\partial y}\right]. \tag{10.11}$$

Thus it is possible to express the transverse fields in terms of a linear superposition of two independent solutions, one for which $E_z = 0$ (TE) and one for which $B_z = 0$ (TM or transverse magnetic waves). Transverse magnetic waves are sometimes known as E waves and transverse electric as H waves.

For TM waves, $B_z = 0$ and (10.8)–(10.11) reduce to

$$E_x = \frac{ik_g}{(k_0{}^2 - k_g{}^2)}\,\partial E_z/\partial x; \qquad E_y = \frac{ik_g}{(k_0{}^2 - k_g{}^2)}\,\partial E_z/\partial y \tag{10.12}$$

$$B_x = -\frac{ik_0/c}{(k_0{}^2 - k_g{}^2)}\,\partial E_z/\partial y; \qquad B_y = \frac{ik_0/c}{(k_0{}^2 - k_g{}^2)}\,\partial E_z/\partial x \tag{10.13}$$

and to find E_z in particular instances we remember that it satisfies the wave equation $\Box^2 E_z = 0$ in common with all other components so that using $E_z = E_{z0}\exp\{i(k_g z - \omega t)\}$, the amplitude satisfies

$$\frac{\partial^2 E_z}{\partial x^2} + \frac{\partial^2 E_z}{\partial y^2} = (k_g{}^2 - k_0{}^2)E_z \tag{10.14}$$

again dropping the zero subscripts. Equation (10.14) also follows from (10.12) using Maxwell's equations. At any boundaries the tangential component of **E** is zero so that the solution of (10.14) is a boundary-value problem of the type met in chapter 6. Having found E_z, the other components can be obtained from (10.12) and (10.13). The transverse components have the general property from (10.12) and (10.13) that

$$E_x/E_y = -B_y/B_x \tag{10.15}$$

so that in the xy-plane, **E** and **B** are in phase and are perpendicular in direction.

Similar considerations apply to TE waves for which $E_z = 0$, except that the boundary conditions on B_z needed to solve

$$\partial^2 B_z/\partial x^2 + \partial^2 B_z/\partial y^2 = (k_g{}^2 - k_0{}^2)B_z \tag{10.16}$$

are imposed by the zero tangential component of **E** through (10.8)–(10.11). For instance, if $E_x = 0$ at a boundary, then (10.10) for a TE wave gives $\partial B_z/\partial y = 0$ at the same boundary.

Further properties are best exhibited by choosing a particular example.

10.3 Rectangular waveguides

The solutions for rectangular guides involve only elementary functions and the shape is one often used in practice. We use the geometry of Fig. 10.3a.

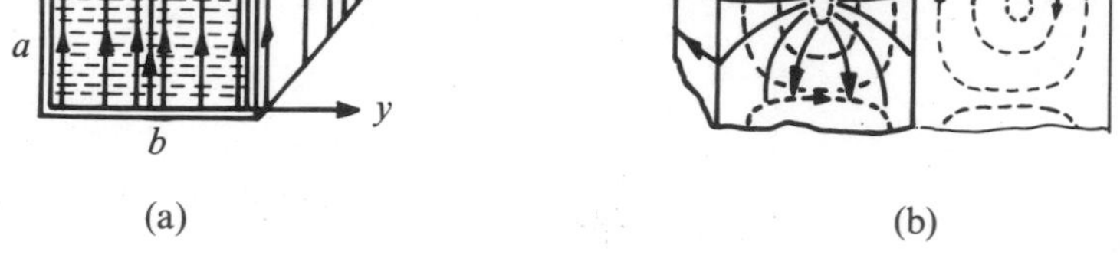

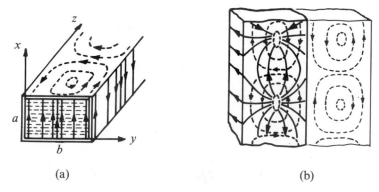

Fig. 10.3 (a) the TE_{01} mode in a rectangular waveguide. Lines of **E** are full, lines of **B** are broken; (b) lines of current flow in the walls of the waveguide for the TE_{01} mode—lines of **B** are shown dashed. The pattern of **B** lines for a TE_{02} mode is shown by the double width waveguide in (b)

TM modes. E_z satisfies (10.14) and if we seek a solution by assuming that

$$E_z = X(x)Y(y)$$

in the manner of section 6.4, we find that X takes the form sin px or cos px and Y the form sin qy or cos qy, where p and q are separation constants satisfying

$$p^2 + q^2 = k_0{}^2 - k_g{}^2. \tag{10.17}$$

Since E_z must be zero at $x = 0$ and $y = 0$, only the sine forms are possible, and since E_z must also be zero at $x = a$, $y = b$, we must also have that $pa = l\pi$ and $qb = m\pi$ where l and m are integers. Hence

$$E_z = E_0 \sin\frac{l\pi x}{a} \sin\frac{m\pi y}{b} \, \mathrm{e}^{i(k_g z - \omega t)} \tag{10.18}$$

in which E_0 is now a constant representing the amplitude throughout the guide, varying only with the input from a generator, and in which from (10.17):

$$l^2/a^2 + m^2/b^2 = (k_0{}^2 - k_g{}^2)/\pi^2. \tag{10.19}$$

The transverse components are obtained using (10.12) and (10.13). The numbers l and m specify the particular mode being propagated and also give the number of anti-nodes in the field variations across the x- and y-directions of the cross-section.

The mode is specified by the notation TM_{lm} or E_{lm}. It will be clear that TM_{00}, TM_{01}, and TM_{10} modes do not exist. The guide wavelength for a given mode is given from (10.19) by

$$\frac{1}{\lambda_g{}^2} = \frac{1}{\lambda_0{}^2} - \frac{1}{4}\left(\frac{l^2}{a^2} + \frac{m^2}{b^2}\right) \tag{10.20}$$

$$= \frac{\nu^2}{c^2} - \frac{1}{4}\left(\frac{l^2}{a^2} + \frac{m^2}{b^2}\right) \tag{10.21}$$

where ν is the frequency being propagated. For a given guide and mode there is a frequency below which λ_g does not exist. Equation (10.21) shows that as the frequency falls λ_g increases and becomes infinite at a critical frequency, the cut-off frequency, given by

$$\nu_c{}^2 = \frac{c^2}{4}\left(\frac{l^2}{a^2} + \frac{m^2}{b^2}\right). \tag{10.22}$$

Below this frequency only an evanescent wave exists in the guide, similar to that occurring in total internal reflection (section 7.3)—no propagation occurs and the attenuation is very great.

To gain some idea of orders of magnitude, the cut-off frequency for the TM_{11} mode in a guide 3 cm × 4 cm is $6{\cdot}25 \times 10^{10}$ c/s which corresponds to a free space wave-length of nearly 5 cm. If the free-space wave-length corresponding to ν_c is λ_c, then from (10.22)

$$1/\lambda_c^2 = (l/2a)^2 + (m/2b)^2 \tag{10.23}$$

and the guide wave-length is given by

$$1/\lambda_g^2 = 1/\lambda_0^2 - 1/\lambda_c^2. \tag{10.24}$$

TE modes. Here $E_z = 0$ and the boundary conditions on B_z are that $\partial B_z/\partial x = 0$ at $x = 0$ and a, $\partial B_z/\partial y = 0$ at $y = 0$ and b. As above, this leads to

$$B_z = B_0 \cos\frac{l\pi x}{a} \cos\frac{m\pi y}{b}\, e^{i(k_g z - \omega t)} \tag{10.25}$$

where l and m satisfy (10.19). All the other formulae (10.20)–(10.24) hold for TE modes as well as TM modes: this time, however, only the TE_{00} mode is non-existent.

For a given guide, (10.23) gives the cut-off wave-lengths for the various modes. For $a = 3$ cm, $b = 4$ cm these would be

TE_{01}, 8 cm; TE_{10}, 6 cm; TE_{11}, TM_{11}, 4·8 cm; TE_{02}, 4 cm, etc.

and the TE_{01} mode is called the dominant mode here. At free-space wave-lengths of 7 cm, say, this would be the only mode which could be propagated. It is generally desirable to use a guide which will only propagate in its dominant mode, and for this reason most rectangular guides use the TE_{01} or TE_{10} mode whose field patterns are shown in Fig. 10.3.

Phase and group velocities. The phase velocity in the guide, v_p, is given by $\nu\lambda_g$ or $c\lambda_g/\lambda_0$. Using (10.24) this can be written

$$v_p = c/(1 - \lambda_0^2/\lambda_c^2)^{1/2} \tag{10.26}$$

which can be greater than c. However, the group velocity v_g obtained from $d\omega/dk_g$ is, again using (10.24) in the form $k_g^2 = \omega^2/c^2 +$ constant, given by

$$v_p v_g = c^2. \tag{10.27}$$

Thus the group velocity is less than c.

10.4 Electromagnetic cavities

If a short length of waveguide were blocked at both ends with plane conducting walls perpendicular to the axis, then a cavity is formed in which the further boundary conditions produce stationary wave patterns in all three directions. Although practical cavities are most often circular in section, the principles are exposed just as well by consideration of a rectangular section as before. If a length of waveguide, *d*, in the *z*-direction is used as a cavity, then the solution for a typical TE_{lmn} mode would be

$$B_z = B_0 \cos\frac{l\pi x}{a}\cos\frac{m\pi y}{b}\sin\frac{n\pi z}{d}\,\mathrm{e}^{-i\omega t} \tag{10.28}$$

where

$$\nu^2 = \frac{c^2}{4}\left[\frac{l^2}{a^2}+\frac{m^2}{b^2}+\frac{n^2}{d^2}\right] \tag{10.29}$$

is the relation giving the frequencies at which solutions exist. The cavity thus resonates at certain specific frequencies and can be used as a network element at micro-wavelengths just as *LC* networks are at longer wave-lengths.

The numbers l, m, n are akin to quantum numbers specifying the particular states which can be excited in the system. If two of the dimensions are equal, then degeneracy occurs as in an atom with two states corresponding to the same energy level. Thus, if $a = b$, the TE_{123} and TE_{213} modes for instance would be degenerate and have the same resonant frequency. A small perturbation, such as a probe or a distortion in the walls, could remove the degeneracy much as a magnetic field can in an atom.

10.5 Passive microwave elements

Waveguides. Ordinary waveguides may be regarded as the straightforward equivalent of connecting wires in a network. In most cases, they consist of metal tubes rectangular in section, although dielectric rods have special uses. (In these, the wave is propagated within the dielectric and total internal reflection occurs at the dielectric–air interface.) In practice, reflection is never perfect in any form of guide and there are losses causing attenuation of the wave due either to wall currents in metal guides or to leakage of radiation in dielectric guides. However, losses are small if the runs are kept short.

Coaxial lines are a particular form of waveguide frequently used at microwave frequencies and they have the advantages of being flexible, easily fitted together through plugs and sockets and not restricted to particular wave-lengths. Hollow guides are often preferred, however, because the absence of an inner conductor means that no supports are necessary and the guide is thus less lossy. In addition, radiation loss is negligible, the larger distance apart of surfaces at different potentials enables higher voltages to be handled and the larger surface area gives smaller ohmic losses.

We can only touch on a few of the devices used in waveguide practice and refer the reader to the references for more detail.

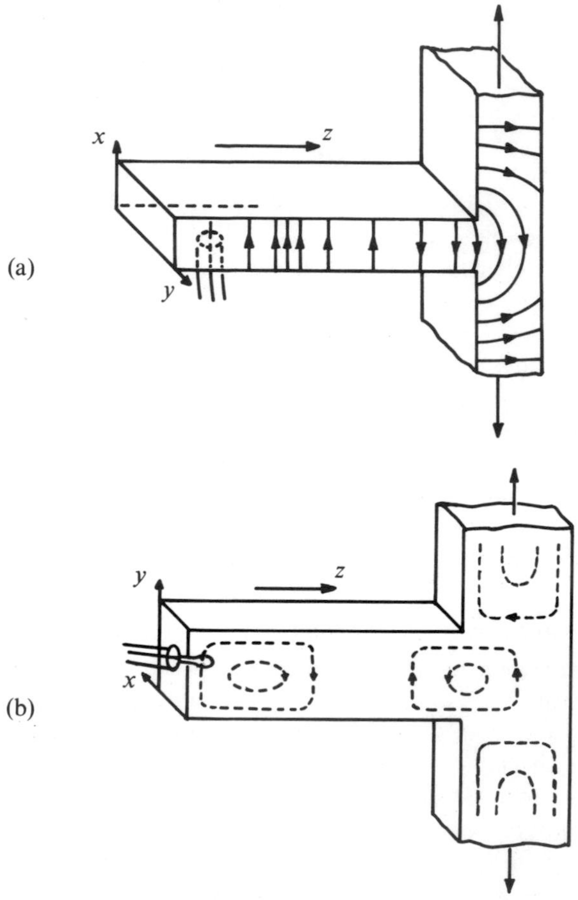

Fig. 10.4 Waveguide junctions or tees using (a) electric field (b) magnetic field. The method of injecting or abstracting power by a vertical probe in (a) or by a horizontal loop in (b) is also shown

Figure 10.4 illustrates the methods used to inject power into a guide from a generator by means of probes or loops properly related to the electric or magnetic fields. The same methods can be used to extract the power. The absence of flexibility in hollow guides means that corners and junctions must be carefully designed to avoid mismatching. Figure 10.4 shows two methods of feeding two guides from a single one at a junction.

More complex junctions, with non-reciprocal properties, are often needed. For instance, where an aerial is used for both transmission and reception, the output from the transmitter must reach the aerial but not the receiver (which it would damage), while the incoming signal must be fed to the receiver and none dissipated in the transmitter (Fig. 10.5b). Figure 10.5a illustrates diagrammatically a

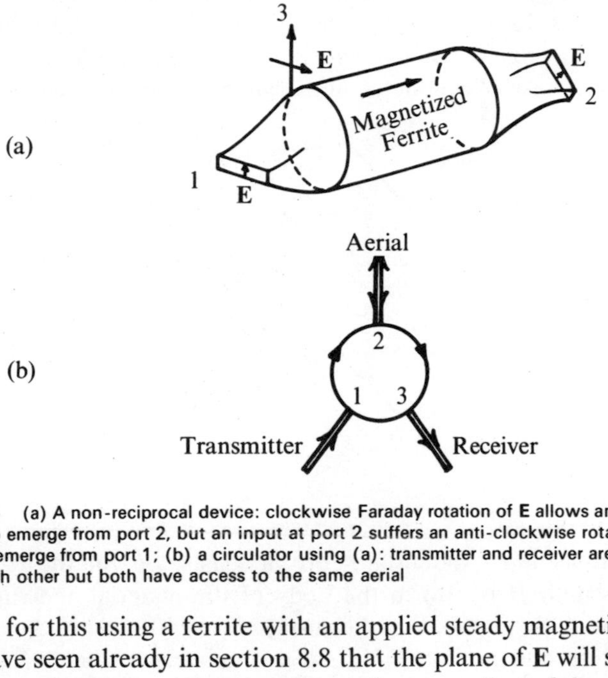

Fig. 10.5 (a) A non-reciprocal device: clockwise Faraday rotation of **E** allows an input at port 1 to emerge from port 2, but an input at port 2 suffers an anti-clockwise rotation and will not emerge from port 1; (b) a circulator using (a): transmitter and receiver are isolated from each other but both have access to the same aerial

device for this using a ferrite with an applied steady magnetic field. We have seen already in section 8.8 that the plane of **E** will suffer a Faraday rotation in a direction depending upon that of the applied field. The input from port 1 is therefore arranged to have the requisite rotation for an output at port 2. But an input at port 2 would have the **E** vector further rotated in the same sense and if each rotation were 45° the **E** vector at port 1 would be horizontal and would not emerge. A third port at 3, however, could be so arranged that it would accept a wave with a horizontal **E** vector and it would therefore accept the input from 2 but not from 1. This device, known as a *circulator*, would thus satisfy the requirements of Fig. 10.5b.

Electromagnetic cavities. These find their principal use as resonant network elements of very high Q factor, for instance, in frequency-measuring devices and in microwave generators (next section). Some estimate of the Q factor can be obtained by using

$$Q = 2\pi \times \frac{\text{energy stored}}{\text{energy loss in 1 period}}. \tag{10.30}$$

The fields in the cavity are *in vacuo* and the energy is equally shared between the electric and magnetic field. Hence the energy stored in a cavity can be obtained by integrating $\mu_0 H^2$ over the volume or simply by finding $\mu_0 \overline{H^2}\tau$ where τ is the volume of the cavity. The energy loss is due to ohmic loss in the walls of the cavity, in which the currents flow to a depth α given by (7.73). The rate of dissipation of energy in a sheet of conducting material (Fig. 10.6) is given by RI^2 as

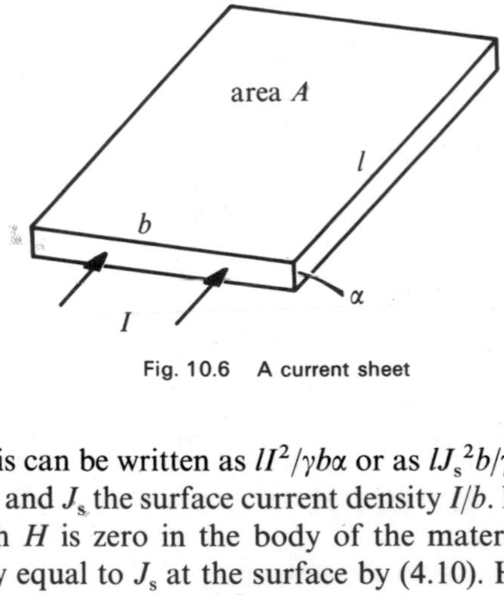

Fig. 10.6 A current sheet

usual and this can be written as $lI^2/\gamma b\alpha$ or as $lJ_s{}^2 b/\gamma\alpha$, where γ is the conductivity and J_s the surface current density I/b. But the magnetic field strength H is zero in the body of the material and suffers a discontinuity equal to J_s at the surface by (4.10). Hence the energy loss per second is simply $H_w{}^2/\gamma\alpha$ per unit area, where H_w is the magnetic field strength at the walls. Hence

$$Q = \omega \times \mu_0 \overline{H^2}\tau\gamma\alpha / \overline{H_w{}^2} A$$

where A is the total wall area. The magnetic fields are greater near the walls but $\overline{H_w{}^2}$ is still likely to be the same order of magnitude as

$\overline{H^2}$ and using (7.73) for α we have that

$$Q \approx 2\tau/\alpha A. \quad (10.31)$$

For cavities of a few cm linear dimensions with α about 10^{-4} cm, the Q value is thus of the order of 10,000.

10.6 Active microwave elements

Low frequency active elements, such as vacuum pentodes and transistors, depend for their operation upon the density modulation of a stream of charges by a varying potential applied between cathode and grid or between emitter and base. The density variations interact with a second circuit which extracts energy from the system for amplification or, through positive feedback to the input, for oscillation. The transit time of charges is of the order of 10^{-9} s in these devices so that at microwave frequencies there arise difficulties due to the different phases in the modulated charge beams. There are, as well, the same problems as in passive elements concerning radiation losses from open electrodes. There are two general types of active element designed specifically for microwave frequencies. One is based on velocity modulation of the charge stream and the other on parametric amplification.

Velocity modulation. If a steady stream of electrons *in vacuo* is subjected to an alternating field across a very small distance, some will be retarded and some accelerated depending on the phase of the field at the time of transit. No resultant transfer of energy will take place between the applied field and the charges, but the stream becomes bunched as shown in Fig. 10.7a. If these bunches are fed at the correct phases across another small region containing an alternating field, retardation may take place just as the bunches are in transit and this would now result in a transfer of energy from the charges to the field (because fewer are accelerated than are retarded). Figure 10.7b illustrates the arrangement in the *klystron* where the alternating fields are those in resonant cavities known as the buncher and catcher. Klystrons are usually used as low power oscillators and the same cavity is then used as both buncher and catcher, the electron beam being reflected at the end of the tube by a high negative potential. This is the *reflex klystron*.

Similar bunching occurs in the *travelling-wave tube*, but here the bunches are produced over a longer distance. A helix of wire coaxial with the electron beam carries a high-frequency wave whose component of velocity down the axis is just less than that of the electrons. Energy is thus fed into the beam at the same time as bunching occurs. The bunches then proceed further down the tube and the original wave is removed by an attenuator. A second helix has induced in it by the bunches a wave whose field extracts energy

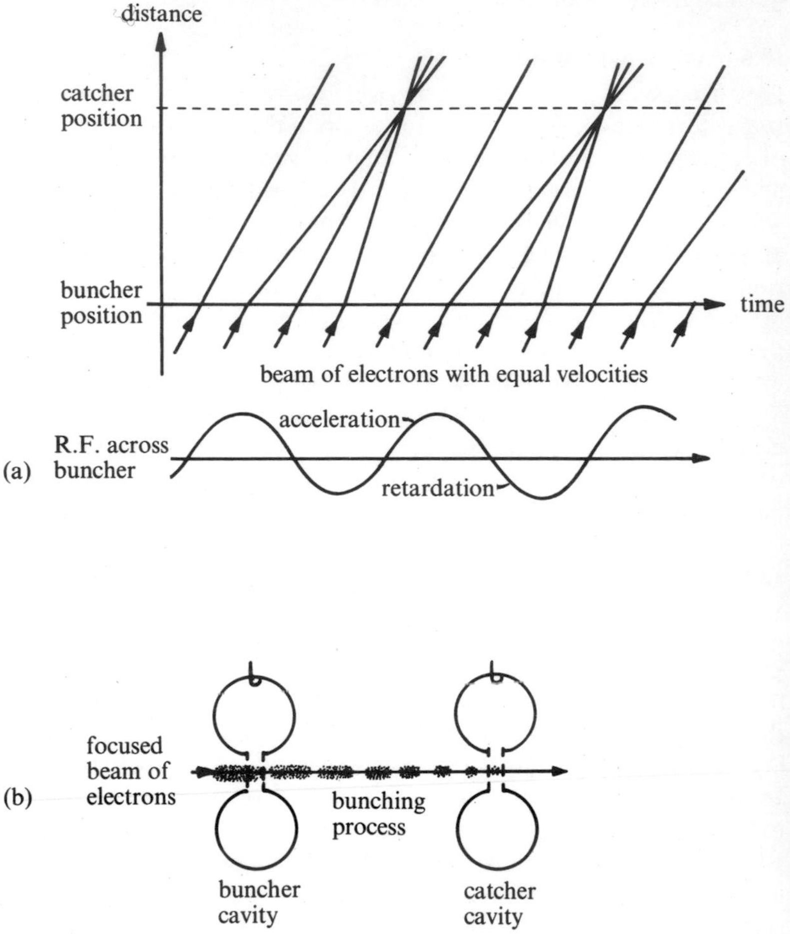

Fig. 10.7 (a) Velocity modulation of an electron beam; (b) the klystron: most practical klystrons reflect the electron beam after bunching so that the same resonant cavity is used for catching (reflex klystron)

from the electron beam by slight retardation. The travelling-wave tube is not limited in frequency range as is the klystron.

For high power oscillations needed for transmission over large distances, the klystron is too feeble and a pulsed multi-cavity *magnetron* is used. For details of these, see the references at the end of the chapter.

Parametric amplifiers. These are so called because they operate by alteration of a parameter during an oscillation cycle. The *maser* comes into this category and is worthy of mention if only as providing an extremely stable frequency standard. Its operation depends on the stimulated emission of energy from molecules in an upper energy level E_3 to a lower one E_2. The emission frequency $(E_3 - E_2)/h$ is also that of a resonant cavity around the molecules and interaction between the cavity field and the molecules produces the stimulated emission. The upper energy level E_3 must have a population greater than its equilibrium value, and one way of achieving this is to raise molecules from an even lower level E_1 using a field of frequency $(\mathrm{E}_3 - E_1)/h$. The Harvard hydrogen maser has a stability better than 1 second in 30 million years.

10.7 Aerials

Over large terrestrial and astronomic distances, transmission of high frequency electromagnetic energy by waveguides or lines is often undesirable (where all-round broadcasting is required) and usually impracticable. Instead, the energy is fed from the transmitter to a radiating system known as an *aerial* or *antenna* from which it is propagated through space to a similar element feeding a receiver. The properties of an aerial which are of interest are its efficiency as a radiator, its directional properties and its effect on the transmitter or receiver to which it is attached. We look at these in turn and illustrate them with reference to the Hertzian dipole of section 4.7.

Radiation resistance. The power radiated from an aerial is usually expressed in terms of the r.m.s. current at the point at which it is fed, in the form

$$\bar{P} = R_{\text{rad}} I_{\text{rms}}^2. \tag{10.32}$$

The coefficient R_{rad} has the dimensions of a resistance and is known as the *radiation resistance* of the aerial as a transmitter. In the Hertzian dipole, in which the current is the same at all points, equation (4.81) shows that

$$R_{\text{rad}} = \frac{2\pi}{3\varepsilon_0 c}\left(\frac{\mathrm{d}l}{\lambda}\right)^2 \sim 800\left(\frac{\mathrm{d}l}{\lambda}\right)^2 \text{ ohms.} \tag{10.33}$$

The efficiency of an aerial thus depends upon its radiation resistance compared with its loss resistance, which mainly arises from ohmic heat losses in the conducting material. For a Hertzian dipole with $dl = \lambda/100$, the radiation resistance is about 0·08 ohms and this may be considerably smaller than the ohmic resistance particularly at low frequencies, so that it is relatively inefficient.

Directivity and gain. The directional properties of an aerial are usually expressed by means of polar diagrams as in Fig. 10.8b, c.

(a)

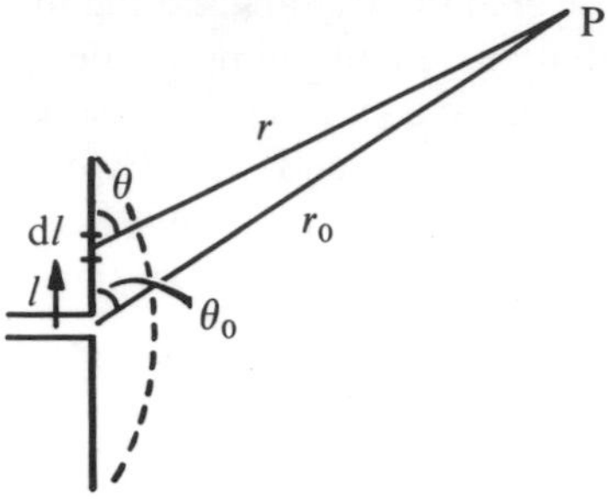

(b)

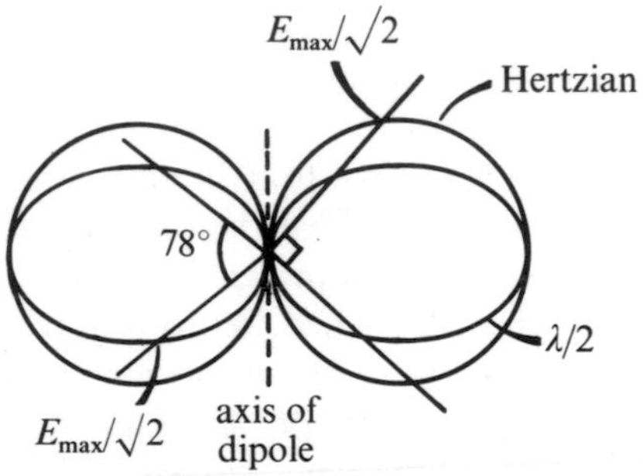

(c)

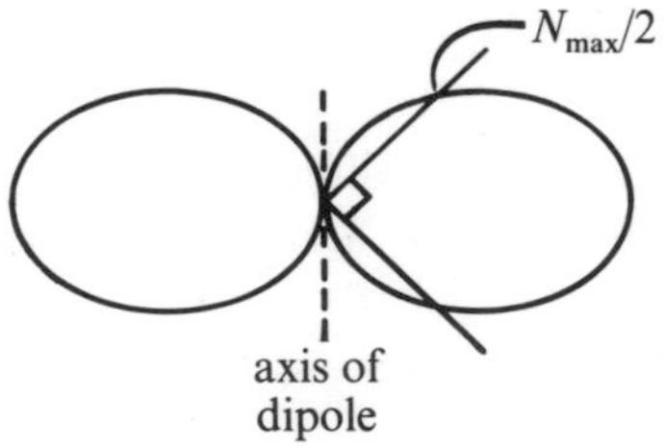

Fig. 10.8 (a) Geometry for a $\lambda/2$ dipole. The broken line shows the distribution of current; (b) polar diagrams of **E** for Hertzian and $\lambda/2$ dipoles; (c) polar diagram of **N** for Hertzian dipole

These give either the electric field strength or the power at a given distance as a function of angle θ. The electric field strength from a Hertzian dipole expressed in terms of current $I = I_0\, e^{j\omega t}$ is, using (4.77) with $\dot{p} = I\, dl$,

$$\mathbf{E} = j\frac{\omega I_0 \sin\theta}{4\pi\varepsilon_0 c^2 r}\, e^{j\omega(t - r/c)}\, dl\, \hat{\boldsymbol{\theta}} \qquad (10.34)$$

while the Poynting vector is, from (4.78),

$$\bar{N} = \frac{I_{rms}^2}{4\varepsilon_0 r^2 c}\left(\frac{dl}{\lambda}\right)^2 \sin^2\theta. \qquad (10.35)$$

Thus the polar diagrams of Fig. 10.8b, c are those showing the variations of $\sin\theta$ or $\sin^2\theta$ with θ. In the azimuthal plane at right angles to the dipole axis, the radiation is the same in all directions and the polar diagrams are circles.

More briefly, the directivity of an aerial can be expressed as the angle over which the power radiated is at least half the maximum (90° for the Hertzian dipole). A further quantity frequently quoted is the *gain* of an aerial. This is defined in terms of a standard aerial with the same input as the given one, the standard usually being an isotropic oscillator. The gain is then the ratio of the Poynting vector in the direction of maximum radiation to the Poynting vector of the standard aerial. Thus for a Hertzian dipole, the maximum is given by (10.35) with $\sin\theta = 1$, while the Poynting vector of an isotropic oscillator is the total power input given by (4.81) divided by $4\pi r^2$ and is thus

$$\frac{I_{rms}^2}{6\varepsilon_0 c r^2}\left(\frac{dl}{\lambda}\right)^2.$$

The gain of a Hertzian dipole is thus 1·5.

Impedance. The final property of importance is the impedance of the aerial presented to the transmitter. The resistive part of this is given by the sum of radiation and loss resistances, but there is also a reactive part which is extremely difficult to calculate. For a Hertzian dipole, this reactance is large and negative and must be matched by an inductive output impedance in the transmitter if good power transfer is to be effected.

The half-wave dipole. We now look at the possibility of using aerials other than the Hertzian dipole with a view to obtaining possibly desirable variations in efficiency, gain, and input impedance.

Once the dipole is lengthened beyond a fraction of the wave-length, the current in it no longer has the same amplitude at all points, and we must also take into account the differences in phase of the radiated waves arriving at the receiving point P (Fig. 10.8a) from the various elements of the aerial with different retarded times.

We consider the important special case of a centre-fed dipole consisting of a thin wire a half-wavelength long. Each element dl radiates as a Hertzian dipole, but the current distribution is such that if $I = I_0 \exp(j\omega t)$ is the current at the centre, that for the typical element is $I_0 \cos(2\pi l/\lambda) \exp(j\omega t)$. The electric field at P due to this element is, from (10.34)

$$dE_\theta = j\frac{\omega I_0 \cos(2\pi l/\lambda)\, e^{j\omega(t-r/c)} \sin\theta}{4\pi\varepsilon_0 c^2 r}\, dl.$$

Now if $r \gg \lambda$, as it should be in the wave zone, $(\sin\theta)/r$ can be regarded as constant over the length of the aerial and equal to $(\sin\theta_0)/r_0$. Each dE_θ has a slightly different direction, but again we may neglect the components along r_0 which will cancel to a first approximation if $r \gg \lambda$. The phases vary along the aerial due to the variation of r in the exponential, but we may not neglect this although we may put $r = r_0 - l\cos\theta_0$ to a first approximation. The total electric field at P is then

$$E_\theta = j\frac{\omega I_0\, e^{j\omega(t-r_0/c)} \sin\theta_0}{4\pi\varepsilon_0 c^2 r_0}\int_{-\lambda/4}^{+\lambda/4} \cos\left(\frac{2\pi l}{\lambda}\right) e^{j\omega l\cos\theta_0/c}\, dl$$

$$= j\frac{I_0\, e^{j\omega(t-r_0/c)} \sin\theta_0}{4\pi\varepsilon_0 c r_0}\int_{-\pi/2}^{\pi/2} \cos x\, e^{jx\cos\theta_0}\, dx$$

where $x = 2\pi l/\lambda$. Repeated integration by parts yields

$$E_\theta = j\frac{2I_0\, e^{j\omega(t-r_0/c)}}{4\pi\varepsilon_0 c r_0}\frac{\cos\left(\frac{\pi}{2}\cos\theta_0\right)}{\sin\theta_0} \tag{10.36}$$

giving the polar diagram of Fig. 10.8c and a directivity of 78° which is little better than the Hertzian dipole. The radiation resistance, however, is

$$R_{rad} = 73{\cdot}1 \text{ ohms}$$

a value obtained by integration of the square of (10.36) over a sphere (not expressible in terms of simple functions). Not only does this value mean normally a greater efficiency of radiation, but the aerial is also easily matched to coaxial line whose characteristic impedance is usually resistive and of the order of 75 ohms. An exact $\lambda/2$ dipole can be shown to present a slightly inductive load to the feeding line, but the reactance can be made zero by using a length slightly shorter than $\lambda/2$, and this is invariably done.

The half-wave dipole is a common element in many aerial systems. It lacks directivity and so is suitable for all-round broadcasting. Vertical $\lambda/4$ elements are often used just above ground level so that reflection from the earth produces an effective image and creates the effect of a $\lambda/2$ dipole.

Aerial arrays. The only property not possessed by a $\lambda/2$ dipole which is sometimes desirable is a good degree of directivity: this can only be achieved by using arrays of aerials fed in a certain phase relationship so that reinforcement occurs in some directions and cancellation in others. Accurate calculation is often difficult because the aerials may be close enough to each other to interact through their induction fields and, in practice, many arrangements are finally adjusted empirically.

A common feature accompanying a $\lambda/2$ dipole is a second parallel dipole, undriven and spaced about $\lambda/4$ in front of or behind the driven one. This *parasitic aerial* contains currents induced in it by the driven aerial and it re-radiates in a phase relationship causing increased radiation in one direction and decreased in the opposite. If the radiation is increased in a direction opposite to that of the parasitic aerial it is called a *reflector*, while if it is increased in the same direction it is a *director*. A system may incorporate both a director and a reflector (or several of either) to achieve greater gain.

Linear or rectangular arrays of $\lambda/2$ dipoles can be fed to produce extreme directivity. The problem of calculating the polar diagram in these cases is very similar to that involved in calculating Fraunhofer diffraction patterns produced by one- and two-dimensional gratings. For instance, a linear array of parallel dipoles fed in phase behaves like a linear diffraction grating and produces an intense zero-order beam at right angles to the plane of the array and a succession of much less intense beams at angles corresponding to the first, second, etc., orders. These other orders are usually unwanted and can be eliminated by spacing the dipoles a distance apart less than λ.

In general, a very narrow beam of great directivity requires an aerial array large compared with λ (cf. the resolving power of a grating in a given order is proportional to the number of lines). At microwave frequencies great directivity may be achieved with quite small aerials because of the shorter wave-lengths. A common form of microwave aerial is illustrated in Fig. 10.9. The driven dipole is at the focus of a metallic paraboloidal dish which produces a narrow beam by reflection at its surface.

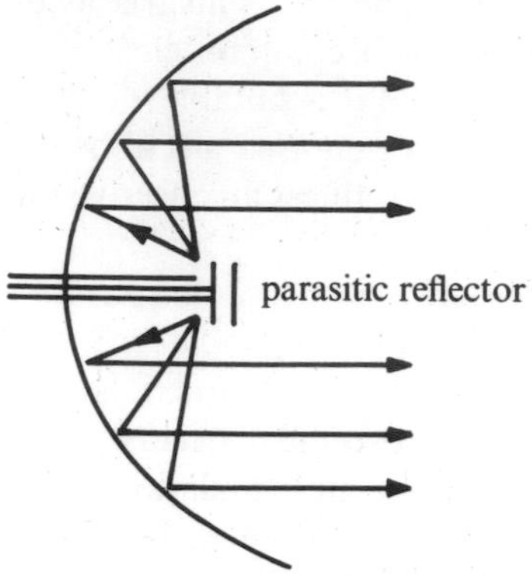

Fig. 10.9 A typical microwave aerial

Receiving aerials. Although all the above has concerned aerials principally as transmitting devices, most of it is relevant to receiving aerials. The reciprocity theorem of network theory can be shown to apply to radiating systems, so that if a current I in aerial A produces a potential V in an aerial B at an angle θ, the same I in B produces a potential V in A. Thus at various angles θ, the aerial A acting as a transmitter produces the same variations in electric field $\mathbf{E}$ as those induced in it as a receiving aerial. Thus the polar diagram, the gain, and the directivity are the same.

References

Details of microwave devices and practice are to be found in Mariner (1961) or, more comprehensively, in Ginzton (1957). A good semi-quantitative account of waveguides, aerials, and wave propagation is to be found in Glazier (1958).

PROBLEMS

10.1 Show that $\mathbf{E}$ and $\mathbf{B}$ in a bounded TEM wave propagated in the z-direction along any transmission line are orthogonal.

10.2 Sketch the lines of $\mathbf{E}$ and $\mathbf{B}$ for a TEM wave propagated in the z-direction along a coaxial line with conductors of circular cross-section. If ω

and k are the angular frequency and wave number respectively, write down expressions for **E** and **B** in cylindrical co-ordinates.

10.3 Pursue analytically the propagation of bounded waves as reflected plane waves (Fig. 10.2). Let the incident plane wave be given by

$$\mathbf{E}_i = \hat{\mathbf{x}} E_0 \, e^{i(-k_0 y \sin\theta + k_0 z \cos\theta - \omega t)}$$

i.e., the y-direction is vertically upwards in the figure. Find the reflected wave $\mathbf{E}_r$, taking due account of the phase change, and hence the resultant. Apply the boundary condition at $y = 0$ and $y = a$, the vertical width of the guide. Show (a) the phase velocity along z is $c/\cos\theta$; (b) the boundary condition limits transmission to discrete modes for which $k_0 a \sin\theta = n\pi$; (c) as a consequence of (b), the guide wave-length λ_g for a parallel-plate guide is related to the vacuum wave-length λ_0 by $1/\lambda_g{}^2 = 1/\lambda_0{}^2 - n^2/4a^2$; (d) there is a cut-off frequency $\nu_c = nc/2a$, n in all cases being an integer. At what velocity will energy be propagated?

10.4 Show that (10.15) implies the orthogonality of **E** and **B** in the xy-plane.

10.5 Find the transverse **E** and **B** fields in a rectangular waveguide transmitting a TE_{01} mode in the z-direction as in Fig. 10.3.

10.6 Using the fields of problem 10.5 together with (4.48) show that energy is propagated in the z-direction. What is the total transmitted power?

10.7 N vertical half-wave dipoles are fixed in a horizontal line so that they are coplanar and spaced equally a distance a apart. If they are fed in phase with a signal of frequency ω, find an expression for the intensity of radiation in the horizontal plane of the array in terms of the polar angle θ made with the normal to the plane of the dipoles. Show that the polar diagram of intensity shows maxima at θ's given by $\theta = 0$ and $\cos\theta = (2n + 1)\pi c/\omega a N$, where n is an integer ranging from 1 to $N - 1$. (Assume N is large.)

Part 5

Field Theory

Electromagnetism was one of the great classical theories of the nineteenth century. At first sight, therefore, it seems surprising that it should survive almost intact as a vital part of physical theory, in spite of the ravages caused by special relativity in the domain of the very rapid and by quantum mechanics in the domain of the very small. In this part, we examine the relationship between electromagnetism and these two modern theories to see how the survival has occurred.

11

Electromagnetism and special relativity

The development of special relativity in the first decade of this century was very closely connected with electromagnetism. Indeed, the transformations of Lorentz, which are the fundamental relations of the theory, were derived by him from purely electromagnetic considerations before the Einstein postulates of 1905. To consider special relativity in relation to present-day concepts, however, it is essential that we look first at general questions concerning the invariance of physical laws under various transformations, together with associated problems of symmetry and conservation.

The reader is expected to have some acquaintance with the Lorentz transformations and their kinematic and dynamic consequences (important equations are summarized in section 11.5): in addition, the Lagrangian and Hamiltonian forms of the laws of motion should be familiar, at any rate for conservative systems (see the references at the end of this chapter).

11.1 Invariance under displacement

Physical laws are framed in terms of quantities which are specified for various points in space and instants in time. For the moment we deal only with locations in space, specified for any point P with respect to a co-ordinate system S, origin O, by three numbers (the co-ordinates) fixing P in a three-dimensional space or 3-space. Of all the possible choices, only orthogonal cartesian co-ordinates are used in this chapter.

Let P be a point whose location in S is (x, y, z), P being typical of a set of points similarly specified, at which physical quantities will have various values. What is the effect of describing any physical laws not with respect to S but with respect to S' in which the location of P is (x', y', z'), both x, y, z and x', y', z' being obtained by sets of rigid measuring rods? In general (Fig. 11.1a), we find that the

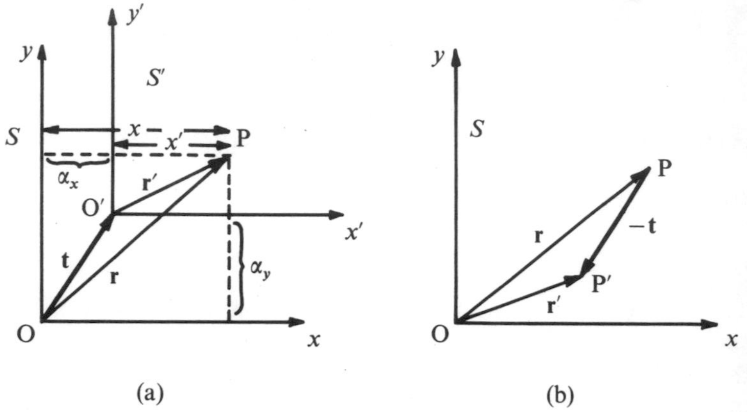

Fig. 11.1 (a) Displacement of origin: the location of P is described by the radius vector **r** in S, **r**′ in S', where $\mathbf{r}' = \mathbf{r} - \mathbf{t}$; (b) displacement of P to P′ by $-\mathbf{t}$: the relation of P′ to S is the same as that of P to S' in (a)

relation when S' differs from S by a simple displacement of origin by $(\alpha_x, \alpha_y, \alpha_z)$ is

$$x' = x - \alpha_x; \qquad y' = y - \alpha_y; \qquad z' = z - \alpha_z \tag{11.1}$$

or

$$\mathbf{r}' = \mathbf{r} - \mathbf{t} \tag{11.2}$$

where **r**, **r′** are the position vectors of P in S and S' and $(\alpha_x, \alpha_y, \alpha_z)$ are the co-ordinates of O′ in S expressed as a vector **t**.

Experience shows that physical laws are unchanged in form when we merely displace the origin of the reference co-ordinate system. For instance, the laws of motion in mechanics are dependent on accelerations and because $\ddot{x}' = \ddot{x}$, etc., the form of the laws will be the same whether they are in Newtonian, Lagrangian, or Hamiltonian notation. Similarly, the electromagnetic laws involve the *relative* positions of source and field points which are clearly unchanged by a displacement of the origin. Thus we state the general principle that *laws of physics are invariant under a transformation representing a displacement of the origin*, like (11.1) or (11.2). We assert that there is no preferred origin in the universe.

Operators. The displacement of the origin by $\mathbf{t}$ is equivalent to keeping the origin fixed and displacing the system by $-\mathbf{t}$ (Fig. 11.1b). In this case, P moves to P′ (x', y', z') and (11.1) and (11.2) still apply. Whichever view is adopted, we may think of the displacement as a translating operation, either on the co-ordinate axes or on the physical system, which has the effect of causing the transformation (11.2) in any function $\mathrm{f}(\mathbf{r})$ of the co-ordinates. Symbolically, we can denote the transformation by an *operator* T so that

$$\mathsf{T}\{\mathrm{f}(\mathbf{r})\} = \mathrm{f}(\mathbf{r}'). \tag{11.3}$$

In particular,

$$\mathbf{r}' = \mathsf{T}\{\mathbf{r}\} \tag{11.4}$$

means the same as (11.2). Scalar quantities are invariant under T.

Conservation laws and symmetry. It is important not to confuse invariance with conservation. A conserved quantity is one whose value for a system remains constant in time, yet there is a connection with the considerations above, as we now see.

A mechanical system can be described by Lagrange's equations (Kibble, 1966)

$$\frac{\mathrm{d}}{\mathrm{d}t}\left(\frac{\partial L}{\partial \dot{q}_i}\right) - \frac{\partial L}{\partial q_i} = 0 \tag{11.5}$$

where L is the Lagrangian (given in suitable cases by $K - U$, the difference between the kinetic and potential energies) and a function of generalized co-ordinates q_i and velocities $\dot{q}_i$. If there is sufficient symmetry in the system that L does not depend on a particular co-ordinate q_j, then (11.5) shows that $\partial L/\partial \dot{q}_j$ is constant in time. This quantity, however, defines p_j, the momentum conjugate to q_j and p_j is thus a constant of the motion.

Similar considerations apply to the Hamiltonian $H(p_i, q_i)$ obeying the equations

$$\frac{\partial H}{\partial q_i} = -\frac{\mathrm{d}p_i}{\mathrm{d}t}; \qquad \frac{\partial H}{\partial p_i} = \frac{\mathrm{d}q_i}{\mathrm{d}t}. \tag{11.6}$$

For if H does not depend on q_j, then p_j is constant.

These ideas are particularly valuable for systems of particles moving in external fields, but let us consider an isolated system which by definition is one moving only under the action of internal forces with no external fields at all. In this case, the Lagrangian or Hamiltonian may be expressed as the sum of terms involving the co-ordinates of the particles *relative to* the centre of mass and others involving the co-ordinates *of* the centre of mass itself. These latter terms, expressed in cartesian co-ordinates, cannot include dependence on x, y, or z (they are not in K, and $U = 0$). In other words, L and H are invariant under $\mathbf{T}$. But this means that p_x, p_y, and p_z are constants of the motion and *the linear momentum of the whole system is conserved.* There is a quantum mechanical equivalent to this: if the operator representing a physical quantity commutes with the Hamiltonian operator, it is a quantum integral of motion. The operator corresponding to a translation in the x-direction is that of p_x: $(h/2\pi i)\ \partial/\partial x$.

11.2 Invariance under angular displacement

Exactly similar considerations arise if S' is a system of co-ordinates with the same origin as S but with axes displaced through a certain angle. Here we find that

$$\left.\begin{aligned} x' &= a_{11}x + a_{12}y + a_{13}z \\ y' &= a_{21}x + a_{22}y + a_{23}z \\ z' &= a_{31}x + a_{32}y + a_{33}z \end{aligned}\right\} \tag{11.7}$$

where the a's are functions of the angles between x and x', y and y', and z and z'. This is a linear transformation which may be written

$$\mathbf{r}' = \mathbf{A} \,.\, \mathbf{r} \tag{11.8}$$

where $\mathbf{A}$ is the matrix

$$\mathbf{A} = \begin{pmatrix} a_{11} & a_{12} & a_{13} \\ a_{21} & a_{22} & a_{23} \\ a_{31} & a_{32} & a_{33} \end{pmatrix} \tag{11.9}$$

and $\mathbf{r}'$, $\mathbf{r}$ are column vectors (see appendix B). The coefficient $\mathbf{A}$ is an operator like $\mathbf{T}$ above and may equally be regarded as rotating the system instead of the co-ordinate axes.

As a particular example of importance, consider the rotation of axes through an angle θ about the z-axis (Fig. 11.2a). It is shown by elementary geometry that

$$\left.\begin{aligned} x' &= x\cos\theta + y\sin\theta \\ y' &= -x\sin\theta + y\cos\theta \\ z' &= z \end{aligned}\right\} \tag{1.1.10}$$

so that the operator representing this rotation would be

$$\mathbf{R} = \begin{pmatrix} \cos\theta & \sin\theta & 0 \\ -\sin\theta & \cos\theta & 0 \\ 0 & 0 & 1 \end{pmatrix} \tag{11.11}$$

and it is easily shown that $\mathbf{R}(\theta)\mathbf{R}(\theta) = \mathbf{R}(2\theta)$ by matrix multiplication.

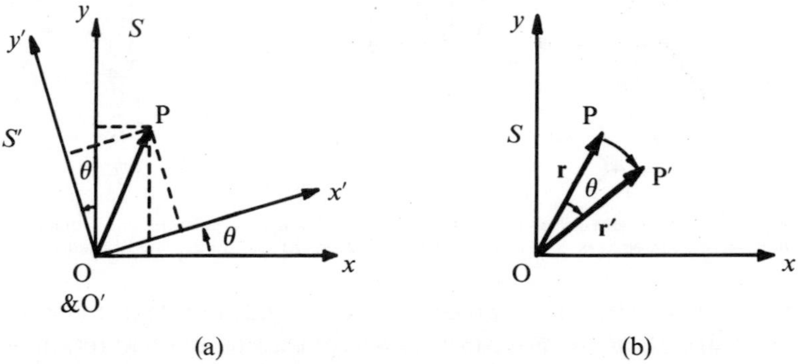

Fig. 11.2 (a) Rotation of axes through θ about Oz: location of P is described by the radius vector $\mathbf{r}$ in S, $\mathbf{r}'$ in S' whose components transform according to (11.10); (b) displacement of P to P′ under the operator $\mathbf{R}(\theta)$: the relation of P′ to S is the same as that of P to S' in (a)

Once again we find that *laws of physics are invariant under a transformation representing a rotational displacement of the axes*: there is no preferred direction in space. In particular, the laws of mechanics and electromagnetism do not change form under (11.10) for the same reasons as in the last section. Invariant *quantities* under a rotation $\mathbf{R}$ are all *scalars*, while *vectors* have components which transform like (11.10) and this can indeed be used to categorize quantities (see appendix B). In particular, the length of a position vector is an invariant for it can be shown from (11.10) that

$$x'^2 + y'^2 + z'^2 = x^2 + y^2 + z^2. \tag{11.12}$$

As in section 11.1, if the transformation (11.10) applied to the

Lagrangian or Hamiltonian in a particular instance leave it invariant, then the angle θ is an ignorable co-ordinate and the corresponding momentum, p_θ (angular momentum about z) is a constant of the motion. Absence of external torques about the z-axis would ensure this.

11.3 Invariance under reflection or inversion

So far we have assumed that any co-ordinate system is right-handed, as in Fig. 11.3a. Reversing the sign of one axis (Fig. 11.3b) or of all

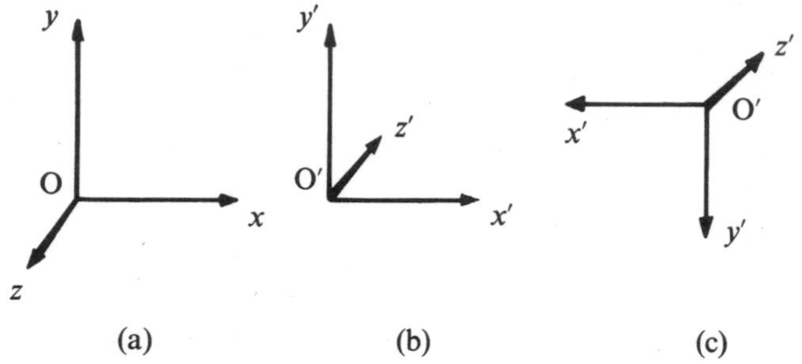

Fig. 11.3 (a) A right-handed system; (b) reversal of z-axis = reflection in xy-plane; (c) reversal of all three axes = inversion through O. Both (b) and (c) are left-handed systems

three axes (Fig. 11.3c) produces a left-handed system and these transformations are not combinations of translations and rotations. It is clear that the co-ordinate transformation is equivalent in Fig. 11.3b to a reflection of the physical system in the xy-plane and in Fig. 11.3c to an inversion through the origin.

The operator corresponding to inversion would yield the transformation

$$x' = -x; \qquad y' = -y; \qquad z' = -z \tag{11.13}$$

or

$$\mathbf{r}' = \mathbf{M} . \mathbf{r} \tag{11.14}$$

where

$$\mathbf{M} = \begin{pmatrix} -1 & 0 & 0 \\ 0 & -1 & 0 \\ 0 & 0 & -1 \end{pmatrix} \tag{11.15}$$

In the previous section, we saw that scalars and vectors were distinguished by their behaviour under the transformation representing a rotation of the axes. At first sight a similar distinction occurs under **M**: a scalar quantity like charge density ρ or mass m is invariant, while a vector quantity like velocity $\mathbf{v}$ or electric field strength $\mathbf{E}$ will change sign under **M**—such quantities are called *polar vectors*. The name is to distinguish them from a class of vectors of the form $\mathbf{A} \times \mathbf{B}$ where $\mathbf{A}$ and $\mathbf{B}$ are both polar vectors. Since both $\mathbf{A}$ and $\mathbf{B}$ change sign under inversion, the vector product will not and it is known as an axial vector or *pseudo-vector*. Examples are angular momentum $\mathbf{L} = \mathbf{r} \times \mathbf{p}$, and magnetic flux density $\mathbf{B} = \mu_0 I \,\mathrm{d}\mathbf{l} \times \mathbf{r}/4\pi r^3$: neither of these change direction under reflection or inversion. Moreover, if $\mathbf{A}$ is a polar vector and $\mathbf{P}$ a pseudo-vector, $\mathbf{A} \cdot \mathbf{P}$ is a scalar which *does* change sign under **M** and is known as a *pseudo-scalar*.

Maxwell's equations (see problem 11.5) and the laws of mechanics are invariant under inversion and until recently it was thought that this applied to all laws of physics. The symmetry leading to the invariance gives rise to a quantum mechanical conservation law, that of *parity*, and it is now known that in weak interactions occurring in nuclear processes (of which an example is β-decay), the parity is not a conserved quantity and the laws take different forms in left- and right-handed systems. The breakdown is basically due to the equating of a pseudo-scalar to a scalar in the laws describing some weak nuclear interactions. We see that in Maxwell's equations scalars are equated to scalars, pseudo-scalars to pseudo-scalars, etc.

11.4 Classical or Galilean relativity

To describe an *event*, we need both a co-ordinate system and a time scale to give a *frame of reference*. Typically, (x, y, z, t) are the four co-ordinates of an event. So far we have considered only frames which are stationary relative to each other and in these we could easily set up a system of stationary clocks giving t at every point. We now wish to look at frames in relative *uniform* motion. Without loss of generality (as should be clear from previous sections), the cartesian co-ordinates can be so arranged that all x-axes lie along each other and in the same direction as the relative uniform velocity v between any two frames S and S'. In addition, the zeros of all time scales are so chosen that $t = t' = 0$ when the origins O and O′ of any two frames are coincident. This will be called the *standard configuration*.

We are now concerned to find a transformation between the co-ordinates (x, y, z, t) of an event in S and those of the same event, (x', y', z', t') in S' which will satisfy us in producing any invariances in physical laws and quantities which are in fact observed.

Classical mechanics. It is a well-known property of the laws of Newtonian or classical mechanics that if they are valid in one frame (called an *inertial frame*), they are valid in all frames in relative uniform motion. Thus, as far as mechanical experiments are concerned, there is no preferred velocity in the universe. In addition, it was *assumed* that there can be set up a universal time scale common to all frames so that in the standard configuration $t = t'$ always.

These ideas, coupled with the necessity for linearity in the transformation laws, lead to the following relations between events in S and S':

$$x' = x - vt; \qquad y' = y; \qquad z' = z; \qquad t' = t \tag{11.16}$$

where v is the velocity of S' with respect to S (and hence $-v$ the velocity of S with respect to S'). This is the *Galilean transformation* which certainly carries with it the correct consequence of the invariance of the laws of mechanics (because $\ddot{x}' = \ddot{x}$, etc., as in section 11.1) for frames in relative uniform motion. This invariance is said to embody the principle of Newtonian or classical relativity.

The Galilean transformation can be written

$$\mathbf{x}' = \mathbf{G} . \mathbf{x} \tag{11.17}$$

where

$$\mathbf{G} = \begin{pmatrix} 1 & 0 & 0 & -v \\ 0 & 1 & 0 & 0 \\ 0 & 0 & 1 & 0 \\ 0 & 0 & 0 & 1 \end{pmatrix} \tag{11.18}$$

and where we use $\mathbf{x}'$ for the column vector with components (x', y', z', t') and similarly for $\mathbf{x}$. It has the property of reciprocity in that $x = x' + vt'$, etc., $(\mathbf{x} = \mathbf{G}^{-1} . \mathbf{x}')$ as would be expected in transforming from S to S' if neither are preferred systems.

One important deduction from (11.16) is that the sum of two velocities in the same direction, u_1 and u_2, is given by

$$u = u_1 + u_2 \tag{11.19}$$

which can be verified at low velocities with such accuracy as to convince us that it is valid. (Note that (11.19) is not self-evident because u_1 and u_2, to have meaning in an actual situation, must be velocities with respect to *two* frames S and S'. Thus either an experiment or the Galilean transformation are involved.)

Electromagnetism. What of the laws of electromagnetism derived in chapters 1 to 4, and of optics, regarded as a branch of electromagnetism? First let us look at the situation as it appeared in the nineteenth century. Experiment certainly indicated that electromagnetic laws were relativistic in a limited sense: for instance, the laws of motional e.m.f.s involve only the relative motion of the source of **B** and the conductor and not an 'absolute' velocity of either. Nevertheless, the Galilean transformation does yield (11.19) and the velocity of light *in vacuo* should therefore show some variation with the velocity of the observer, where it is assumed that both velocities are measured with respect to the same reference frame.

Furthermore, the Galilean transformation could be used to find the form taken by Maxwell's equations in S' assuming that they held in their normal form in S. It turns out that they cannot be invariant under **G** no matter what transformations for **E** and **B** are assumed. Thus $\mathbf{curl\,E} = -\partial\mathbf{B}/\partial t$ in S does not imply $\mathbf{curl\,E'} = -\partial\mathbf{B'}/\partial t'$ in S' although any differences are quite small for $v \ll c$. It would appear that electromagnetic or optical experiments should yield a preferred frame, that of the so-called *luminiferous aether*, although all indications were that any positive effects would be very small.

It was the search for this frame that first showed the incorrectness of the above arguments: the Michelson–Morley and other experiments do not yield any preferred velocity. From our present point of view, all these electromagnetic and optical experiments confirm us in the view that *all physical laws are invariant under a transformation representing uniform relative velocity*. It is clear that the Galilean transformation is not one that gives this result and that it is at best an approximation.

11.5 Special relativity

The demand that *all* physical laws shall be invariant under the transformation representing uniform motion is the principle of *special relativity* and we now seek a set of relations linking the event described as (x, y, z, t) in S and as (x', y', z', t') in S' to take the place of **G** above.

The constancy and isotropy of the velocity of light *in vacuo* links mechanics with electromagnetism and is a basic consequence of special relativity as we have seen. Two inertial observers whose origins coincide at $t = t' = 0$ describe the wavefront of a flash of light emitted from the origins at this time as spheres. After times t and t', these spheres have equations

$$x^2 + y^2 + z^2 - c^2t^2 = 0 \tag{11.20}$$

$$x'^2 + y'^2 + z'^2 - c^2t'^2 = 0. \tag{11.21}$$

The correct transformation must ensure that (11.21) transforms to (11.20) and it is a matter of simple algebra to see that the Galilean transformation does not do this. It is also relatively simple to find a linear transformation which does (and which also correctly describes the motion of the origin O in S' and of O′ in S). This is the *Lorentz transformation*

$$x' = \gamma(x - vt); \qquad y' = y; \qquad z' = z; \qquad t' = \gamma(t - \beta x/c) \tag{11.22}$$

where $\beta = v/c$ and $\gamma = 1/(1 - \beta^2)^{1/2}$. The quantity

$$s^2 = x^2 + y^2 + z^2 - c^2t^2 \tag{11.23}$$

is clearly then an invariant.

A geometrical way of looking at the transformation is to use as a fourth co-ordinate $\tau = ict$ instead of t $(i^2 = -1)$. Then (11.22) becomes

$$x' = \gamma(x + i\beta\tau); \qquad y' = y; \qquad z' = z; \qquad \tau' = \gamma(\tau - i\beta x) \tag{11.24}$$

or

$$\mathbf{s'} = \mathbf{L} \,.\, \mathbf{s} \tag{11.25}$$

where $\mathbf{L}$ is the matrix

$$\mathbf{L} = \begin{pmatrix} \gamma & 0 & 0 & i\beta\gamma \\ 0 & 1 & 0 & 0 \\ 0 & 0 & 1 & 0 \\ -i\beta\gamma & 0 & 0 & \gamma \end{pmatrix} \tag{11.26}$$

and $\mathbf{s}$ and $\mathbf{s'}$ are column vectors with four components (x, y, z, τ) and

(x', y', z', τ'). If we let $\gamma = \cos\theta$, then $\sin\theta = (1 - \gamma^2)^{1/2} = i\beta\gamma$ and

$$\mathbf{L} = \begin{pmatrix} \cos\theta & 0 & 0 & \sin\theta \\ 0 & 1 & 0 & 0 \\ 0 & 0 & 1 & 0 \\ -\sin\theta & 0 & 0 & \cos\theta \end{pmatrix} \tag{11.27}$$

Thus $\mathbf{L}$ is an extension to four dimensions or 4-space of the rotation operator $\mathbf{R}$ (equation (11.11)) as could be seen more clearly by rewriting $\mathbf{L}$ in the order (x', τ', y', z'). We can thus think of **s** as a position vector in 4-space or a *4-vector*, only two axes of which are shown in Fig. 11.4. The transformation $\mathbf{L}$ is equivalent to a rotation

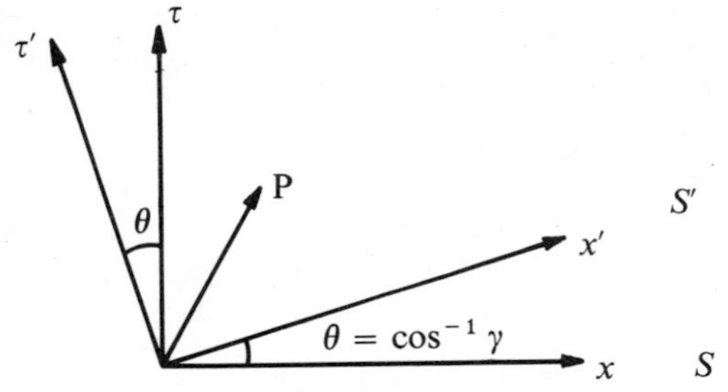

Fig. 11.4 The x- and τ-axes of 4-space

of the x- and τ-axes through an angle $\theta = \tan^{-1} i\beta$, and we can define a 4-vector, in general, as any quantity with four components transforming in the same way as those of **s** as in (11.22) (compare the definition of a 3-vector in section 11.2).

Four-vectors in 4-space have similar properties to 3-vectors in 3-space. For instance, if $\mathbf{a} = (a_1, a_2, a_3, a_4)$ and $\mathbf{b} = (b_1, b_2, b_3, b_4)$ are both 4-vectors, their scalar product is defined as $(a_1b_1 + a_2b_2 + a_3b_3 + a_4b_4)$ as with 3-vectors. Since $a_1' = \gamma(a_1 + i\beta a_4)$, etc., it is easily shown that the scalar product is invariant under $\mathbf{L}$: in particular, the magnitude of a 4-vector is the scalar product of the vector with itself and like s^2 is invariant.

Relativistic mechanics. For full derivations of the equations of relativistic mechanics the reader is referred to other texts: here we summarize some of the more important results.

The Lorentz transformation leads directly to the law of combination of velocities in the same direction

$$u = \frac{u_1 + u_2}{1 + u_1 u_2/c^2} \tag{11.28}$$

which replaces (11.19), to which it reduces when velocities are small compared with c.

When a body is at rest in a frame, values associated with its properties such as length, mass, etc., are known as *proper* or *rest* values. It is easily shown that if l_0 is the proper length of a body, its relative length when moving with a velocity v in the direction of l_0 is

$$l = l_0(1 - \beta^2)^{1/2} \tag{11.29}$$

and this can be derived from Fig. 11.4 (see problem 11.12). Equations like (11.29) should not be confused with transformation equations connecting relative values in two frames S and S' in both of which a body may be moving. If a body is moving with u in S and u' in S' both velocities being lengthwise, then the relative lengths are related by

$$l(1 - u^2/c^2)^{-1/2} = l'(1 - u'^2/c^2)^{-1/2} \tag{11.30}$$

since both are equal to l_0. If v is the velocity of S' with respect to S, then (11.30) can be shown to be the same as

$$l' = l(1 - \beta^2)^{1/2}/(1 - u_x v/c^2) \tag{11.31}$$

where u_x is the component of u along the common x-axis, which is also the direction of v.

Similarly, the transformation for mass is

$$m' = \gamma m(1 - u_x v/c^2) \tag{11.32}$$

while in terms of rest mass, inertial mass is given by

$$m = m_0(1 - u^2/c^2)^{-1/2}.$$

If total energy E and momentum $\mathbf{p}$ are defined by

$$E = mc^2; \qquad \mathbf{p} = m\mathbf{v} \tag{11.33}$$

then the components of the 3-vector $\mathbf{p}$ together with iE/c transform like (x, y, z, τ). Thus $(p_x, p_y, p_z, iE/c)$ is a 4-vector† and its magnitude

† The conventional notation for a 4-vector is the 3-vector symbol with a subscript μ. Thus $\mathbf{p}_\mu$ is the 4-momentum, $\mathbf{A}_\mu$ the 4-potential, etc. To avoid subscripts, we shall instead use the lower case letter where no ambiguity arises. Thus $\mathbf{a}$ will be used for $\mathbf{A}_\mu$, $\mathbf{j}$ for $\mathbf{J}_\mu$, etc.

$p^2 - E^2/c^2$ is an invariant under **L**, equal in fact to $-m_0{}^2c^2$ so that for any particle

$$E^2 - c^2p^2 = m_0{}^2c^4. \tag{11.34}$$

Finally, it is possible to obtain transformations for the components of force, but we shall content ourselves with the useful special case of a particle *at rest in S* subject to force components F_x, F_y, F_z. For S' in standard configuration, the force is

$$F_x' = F_x; \qquad F_y' = (1 - \beta^2)^{1/2}F_y; \qquad F_z' = (1 - \beta^2)^{1/2}F_z. \tag{11.35}$$

11.6 Electromagnetic transformations

We now seek transformations for the quantities occurring in the various electromagnetic laws which will make these laws invariant under **L**.

Electric charge and current. The conservation of charge is one of the results which can be deduced from Maxwell's equations (section 4.1), so that if these equations are to be invariant the charge Q possessed by a given body or set of bodies must be the same to all observers.

The same is not true of charge density ρ and current density $\mathbf{J}$, the quantities occurring in Maxwell's equations. Suppose an observer in S sees n charges per unit volume each of magnitude Q moving with a velocity $\mathbf{u}$. Then, using (1.21),

$$\rho = nQ; \qquad J_x = nQu_x; \qquad J_y = nQu_y; \qquad J_z = nQu_z. \tag{11.36}$$

In S', assuming standard configuration, the number of charges per unit volume changes to n' because every length in the x-direction transforms according to (11.31). Thus

$$n' = \gamma n(1 - u_xv/c^2) \tag{11.37}$$

and therefore

$$\rho' = n'Q = \gamma(nQ - nQu_xv/c^2) = \gamma(\rho - \beta J_x/c). \tag{11.38}$$

Moreover, using the transformations for 3-velocity:

$$u_x' = (u_x - v)/(1 - u_xv/c^2); \qquad u_y' = u_y/\gamma(1 - u_xv/c^2), \text{ etc.} \tag{11.39}$$

we find easily that

$$J_x' = \gamma(J_x - v\rho); \qquad J_y' = J_y; \qquad J_z' = J_z. \tag{11.40}$$

Equations (11.38) and (11.40) together show that $(J_x, J_y, J_z, ic\rho)$ is a 4-vector which we shall denote by **j**.

Electromagnetic potentials. The 4-vector operator corresponding to ∇ in 3-space should be one with components $(\partial/\partial x, \partial/\partial y, \partial/\partial z, \partial/\partial \tau)$ denoted by $\Box$. To see that this *is* a 4-vector, examine the transformation of the components by direct differentiation:

$$\frac{\partial}{\partial x'} = \frac{\partial}{\partial x}\frac{\partial x}{\partial x'} + \frac{\partial}{\partial t}\frac{\partial t}{\partial x'} = \gamma\left(\frac{\partial}{\partial x} + \frac{v}{c^2}\frac{\partial}{\partial t}\right) = \gamma\left(\frac{\partial}{\partial x} + i\beta\frac{\partial}{\partial \tau}\right)$$

$$\frac{\partial}{\partial \tau'} = \frac{1}{ic}\frac{\partial}{\partial x}\frac{\partial x}{\partial t'} + \frac{1}{ic}\frac{\partial}{\partial t}\frac{\partial t}{\partial t'} = \frac{\gamma}{ic}\left(\frac{\partial}{\partial t} + v\frac{\partial}{\partial x}\right) = \gamma\left(-i\beta\frac{\partial}{\partial x} + \frac{\partial}{\partial \tau}\right)$$

and $\partial/\partial y' = \partial/\partial y$, $\partial/\partial z' = \partial/\partial z$. The components of $\Box$ thus transform like those of (x, y, z, τ). The scalar product of $\Box$ with itself, $\Box^2$, is therefore a scalar operator invariant under **L** and is seen to be the D'Alembertian operator defined in equation (4.24). Similarly, the operators $\Box$, $\Box\cdot$, and $\Box\times$ will be the 4-vector equivalents of **grad**, div, and **curl** respectively in 3-space.

Now, using the Lorentz gauge (4.58) we saw that the vector and scalar potentials satisfied (4.59) and (4.60), namely (for a frame S)

$$\Box^2 A_x = -\mu_0 J_x; \qquad \Box^2 A_y = -\mu_0 J_y; \qquad \Box^2 A_z = -\mu_0 J_z;$$

$$\Box^2 V = -\rho/\varepsilon_0 \tag{11.41}$$

in vacuo. We know in transforming to a new frame S', $\Box^2$ is invariant and $(J_x, J_y, J_z, ic\rho)$ is a 4-vector, so that for equations (11.41) to be invariant it is only necessary for $(A_x, A_y, A_z, i\varepsilon_0\mu_0 cV)$ to be a 4-vector as well. If we put this equal to **a**:

$$\mathbf{a} = (A_x, A_y, A_z, iV/c) \tag{11.42}$$

then (11.41) can be written

$$\Box^2\mathbf{a} = -\mu_0\mathbf{j} \tag{11.43}$$

while the transformations for the potentials must, because of (11.42), be

$$A_x' = \gamma(A_x - vV/c^2); \qquad A_y' = A_y; \qquad A_z' = A_z;$$

$$V' = \gamma(V - vA_x). \tag{11.44}$$

That these make (11.41) invariant can be checked by direct substitution. The Lorentz condition (4.58) can be written as

$$\Box \,.\, \mathbf{a} = 0 \tag{11.45}$$

and this is seen to be the 4-vector equivalent of the Coulomb gauge.

Transformations for **E** *and* **B**. The fields **E** and **B** are obtained from the potentials using (4.52) and (4.53): $\mathbf{B} = \mathbf{curl}\,\mathbf{A}$ and $\mathbf{E} = -\mathbf{grad}\,V - \partial\mathbf{A}/\partial t$. The same equations will hold in S' with primes throughout, so that from (11.44) we can obtain the following:

$$\left.\begin{aligned} E_x' &= E_x & B_x' &= B_x \\ E_y' &= \gamma(E_y - vB_z) & B_y' &= \gamma(B_y + vE_z/c^2) \\ E_z' &= \gamma(E_z + vB_y) & B_z' &= \gamma(B_z - vE_y/c^2). \end{aligned}\right\} \tag{11.46}$$

In the derivation of these it should be remembered that $\partial/\partial x' = \gamma(\partial/\partial x + (v/c^2)\,\partial/\partial t)$ and $\partial/\partial t' = \gamma(\partial/\partial t + v\,\partial/\partial x)$. The lack of preference between S and S' is shown by the fact that when (11.46) is solved for the unprimed field components, the same equations are obtained except for the interchange of primed and unprimed quantities and the substitution of $-v$ for v.

It is easily seen that (11.46) can be written in a form independent of the co-ordinate system by resolution into components parallel to and perpendicular to the relative velocity of the two frames:

$$\left.\begin{aligned} \mathbf{E}_{\parallel}' &= \mathbf{E}_{\parallel} & \mathbf{B}_{\parallel}' &= \mathbf{B}_{\parallel} \\ \mathbf{E}_{\perp}' &= \gamma(\mathbf{E} + \mathbf{v} \times \mathbf{B})_{\perp} & \mathbf{B}_{\perp}' &= \gamma(\mathbf{B} - (\mathbf{v} \times \mathbf{E})/c^2)_{\perp}. \end{aligned}\right\} \tag{11.47}$$

It is clear that **E** and **B** do not transform like 4-vectors: in fact, their six components together transform like the six independent elements of an anti-symmetric 4-tensor, but we shall not pursue this representation.

It is easily checked that Maxwell's equations are invariant under a Lorentz transformation together with (11.46), so that our original question is answered: classical electromagnetism survives because it is already relativistically invariant and unlike classical mechanics, which is only an approximation for small velocities, needs no modification. It might seem, therefore, that special relativity would add nothing to our knowledge of electromagnetism and over the limited range of fields *in vacuo* this is to some extent true. However, looking at standard results from the relativistic angle gives us new insight and, in some cases, simpler methods of calculation. In addition, problems concerning fields in moving bodies (conductors, dielectrics, magnets) are only correctly solved in relativistic terms. We look at a few typical problems in the next section and refer the reader to the references for a fuller discussion.

11.7 Applications

Field of a moving charge. If Q is at rest at (x, y, z) in S, then the potentials at the origin are $\mathbf{A} = 0$, $V = Q/4\pi\varepsilon_0 r$, where $r^2 = x^2 + y^2 + z^2$. In S', the charge is at (x', y', z') and the potentials at the origin are, by (11.44):

$$A_x' = -\gamma Q v/4\pi\varepsilon_0 rc^2; \qquad A_y' = 0; \qquad A_z' = 0;$$
$$V' = \gamma Q/4\pi\varepsilon_0 r.$$

To obtain these in primed quantities only, r must be expressed in terms of r'. This transformation takes its simplest form if we agree to express the potentials in terms of retarded quantities. Thus, if t' and t are the times r'/c and r/c respectively (taken for light to travel from the charge to the origin in the two frames), then

$$r = ct = \gamma c(t' + vx'/c^2) = \gamma r'(1 + vx'/r'c) = \gamma r'(1 + v_r'/c)$$

where v_r' is the radial component of the velocity *away* from O′ in S'. Hence,

$$A_x' = -\frac{Q[v]}{4\pi\varepsilon_0 c^2[r'(1 + v_r'/c)]}; \qquad V = \frac{Q}{4\pi\varepsilon_0[r'(1 + v_r'/c)]} \tag{11.48}$$

and these together with $A_y' = 0$, $A_z' = 0$ can be identified with the Liénard–Wiechert potentials of (4.84) and (4.85) for a charge moving in the x-direction with a velocity $-v$. Thus, (4.86) and (4.87), giving $\mathbf{E}$ and $\mathbf{B}$ due to a moving charge, will not be changed by any relativistic corrections.

Field of a steady current. Consider an infinite line charge of linear density λ stationary in S and lying along the x-axis. The electric field in the xy-plane a distance y from the charge is $E_y = \lambda/2\pi\varepsilon_0 y$, $E_x = 0$, $E_z = 0$, and $\mathbf{B} = 0$. In S', in standard configuration, the charge moves with velocity $-v$ along the x'-axis and the density λ' thus appears greater ($\lambda' = \gamma\lambda$) while there now also appears to be a current $-\lambda' v$. The electric field $E_y' = \gamma(E_y - vB_z) = \gamma\lambda/2\pi\varepsilon_0 y = \lambda'/2\pi\varepsilon_0 y'$ and is unchanged in form. We have, however, that $B_z' =$

$-\gamma v E_y/c^2 = -\gamma v \lambda / 2\pi\varepsilon_0 y c^2 = \mu_0 I'/2\pi y'$ as given by the current element formula (2.5).

Two points arise from this simple example. First, as we can see from the transformations (11.46) already, the particular combination of electric and magnetic fields observed depends not only on the sources but also on the frame of reference of the observer. This leads to any forces $\mathbf{F}'$ in S' being not necessarily equal to $\mathbf{F}$ in S, a completely non-classical result and one which again shows that electromagnetism is essentially relativistic (see problem 11.9). Second, the magnetic field can be considered to arise as a result of the electrostatic Coulomb's law combined with the principle of special relativity and the conservation of charge. The accuracy with which Coulomb's law is established can thus be extended to the laws governing magnetic interactions.

Charge moving in electric and magnetic fields. Suppose a charge Q is moving with a velocity $\mathbf{v}$ in any direction in a frame S in which there is an electric field $\mathbf{E}$ and a magnetic field of flux density $\mathbf{B}$. Take S' now to be a frame moving with a velocity $\mathbf{v}$ with respect to S (non-standard configuration) so that Q is at rest in S' and can only therefore experience a force

$$\mathbf{F}' = Q\mathbf{E}'. \tag{11.49}$$

Now, according to (11.35), the force in S is given by

$$\mathbf{F}_{\parallel} = \mathbf{F}_{\parallel}'; \qquad \mathbf{F}_{\perp} = \mathbf{F}_{\perp}'/\gamma$$

so that in S, using (11.49) and (11.47),

$$\mathbf{F}_{\parallel} = Q\mathbf{E}_{\parallel}' = Q\mathbf{E}_{\parallel} \quad \text{and} \quad \mathbf{F}_{\perp} = Q\mathbf{E}_{\perp}'/\gamma = Q(\mathbf{E} + \mathbf{v} \times \mathbf{B})_{\perp}$$

and these two together give, in general, that

$$\mathbf{F} = Q(\mathbf{E} + \mathbf{v} \times \mathbf{B}). \tag{11.50}$$

This is the Lorentz force formula, introduced as a postulate in (2.63) and now deduced from the principles of special relativity.

Plane waves. It only remains to point out that the transformation applied to plane waves shows as it should that the velocity *in vacuo* is always c. Moreover, it can be shown that the quantities $\mathbf{E} . \mathbf{B}$ and $E^2 - c^2B^2$ are, in general, invariant (problem 11.8), so that the orthogonality of $\mathbf{E}$ and $\mathbf{B}$ ($\mathbf{E} . \mathbf{B} = 0$) and the relation $E = cB$ ($E^2 - c^2B^2 = 0$) are invariant properties of plane electromagnetic waves. Nevertheless, the frequency and direction of the waves will vary with the frame of reference and this leads to the phenomena of the Doppler effect and aberration.

References

For an elementary account of Lagrangian and Hamiltonian mechanics see Kibble (1966); for a more advanced treatment see Goldstein (1950). Special relativity, including electromagnetism, is treated comprehensively in Rosser (1964), while an excellent account is also included in Panofsky and Phillips (1962): Pauli (1958), however, is the classic. Cullwick (1959) is interesting on the electrodynamics of moving systems, and Arzeliès (1966) contains lucid discussions of kinematic problems.

PROBLEMS

11.1 Confirm that repeated application of $\mathbf{R}(\theta)$ as defined in equation (11.11) yields a rotation of 2θ.

11.2 Show that the inverse of the matrix representing $\mathbf{R}$ in (11.11) can be obtained by replacing θ by $-\theta$. Hence show that the matrix is orthogonal (see appendix B).

11.3 Show that under inversion the helicity of an axial vector changes sign.

11.4 Classify electromagnetic quantities, such as **H**, **p**, **curl H**, *V*, charge density ρ, as scalars, pseudo-scalars, vectors, or pseudo-vectors.

11.5 Show that Maxwell's equations are invariant under a transformation representing inversion.

11.6 Show that both the Galilean and Lorentz transformations are reciprocal by proving that $\mathbf{G}(-v) = \mathbf{G}^{-1}$ and $\mathbf{L}(-v) = \mathbf{L}^{-1}$, where $\mathbf{G}$ and $\mathbf{L}$ are given respectively by (11.18) and (11.26).

11.7 Confirm that equation (11.46) follows from (11.44).

11.8 Show from (11.46) that the quantities $\mathbf{E} \cdot \mathbf{B}$ and $\mathbf{E}^2 - c^2\mathbf{B}^2$ are invariant under the relativistic transformations. By considering cases in which these quantities are zero, what conclusions about the magnitudes and directions of **E** and **B** can be drawn? Is it always possible to find a frame of reference in which (a) **E** is zero, (b) **B** is zero?

11.9 Consider the force between two point charges with the same x and z co-ordinates, but separated along y by a distance r. The charges are stationary in S. Find the force in S' (standard configuration), using first the apparently non-relativistic formulae of chapter 4 and second the formulae of chapter 11. Discuss the results.

11.10 A plane wave has an electric vector $\mathbf{E} = \mathbf{E}_0 \, e^{i(\mathbf{k}\cdot\mathbf{r} - \omega t)}$. Show that $(\mathbf{k}, i\omega/c)$ is a 4-vector and hence derive expressions giving the relativistic Doppler effect and aberration.

11.11 Use the Lorentz transformation to obtain formulae relating the components of velocity and acceleration in S' to those in S (standard configuration). Show that, if a particle has zero velocity in S, the acceleration $\mathbf{a}$ in S is given in terms of $\mathbf{a}'$ by

$$a^2 = \frac{a'^2 - \beta^2(a_y'^2 + a_z'^2)}{(1 - \beta^2)^3}.$$

Hence, using (4.91), find the total power radiated from a fast moving charge. Compare the instantaneous radiation of power in actual accelerators (a) from linear and circular orbits, (b) from electrons and protons.

11.12 Using Fig. 11.4, show that the distance between two points l_0 in S measured at the same t would be given by l in S' measured at the same t', where $l = l_0(1 - \beta^2)^{1/2}$.

12

Electromagnetism and quantum theory

In this chapter, we touch on matters which have concerned physicists from the time of Planck's foundations of the quantum theory in the early twentieth century to the present day, when quantum electrodynamics presents many unresolved problems. Throughout this book, discussions have been confined almost entirely to non-quantum aspects of electromagnetic fields and charged particles, and it would be unrealistic to conclude without examining the way electromagnetism fits the contemporary view of the physical world, a view which is essentially quantum mechanical.

It is not possible here to deal very deeply with these matters, and we shall content ourselves with obtaining some idea of the way quantum theory deals with electromagnetic fields *in vacuo* and with the interaction between charged particles and fields. We shall want to ask in each case under what circumstances the classical approach we have previously adopted is valid, and, as in the quantum mechanics of particles, the correspondence principle is expected to hold (i.e., that in cases where quantum numbers become very large, the quantum laws yield classical ones as a limiting case). To approach the quantum theory at all we need the various laws governing the phenomena to be put into Lagrangian or Hamiltonian form, so that in each case this is a primary task (see Goldstein (1950) for Lagrangian and Hamiltonian methods).

12.1 Electromagnetic fields *in vacuo*

When we examined the propagation of electromagnetic radiation in chapter 4, we saw that it was essential to attribute energy and momentum to the electromagnetic field if we were to retain the conservation principles. This came about because of the finite time of propagation of effects and is reinforced by the relativistic considerations of the last chapter. The *quantization* of electromagnetic energy was first suggested by Planck as a means of achieving agreement between experimental results and theoretical predictions of the energy distribution in the radiation from a black body, while the quantization of the momentum was first demanded by the Compton effect. The present-day view is that we *expect* quantization of these quantities, and our problem is to find the appropriate representation of the system enabling standard quantum mechanical procedures to be used.

These procedures, in the quantum mechanics of particles, involve first writing the equations governing the system in Lagrangian or Hamiltonian form with the aid of generalized co-ordinates q_i, generalized velocities $\dot{q}_i$, and generalized momenta $p_i = \partial L/\partial \dot{q}_i$ (L being the Lagrangian). Once the Hamiltonian is obtained and equated to the total energy, each classical quantity is replaced by its appropriate quantum mechanical operator and if the resultant equations operate on a state function ψ the correct quantum mechanical equation for the system is obtained. From this, eigenvalues and eigenfunctions may be found.

With the electromagnetic field *in vacuo* we have to proceed in a heuristic manner. In other words, we are not in a position to lay down a set of postulates and deduce the appropriate laws from them but look for promising ways of proceeding by analogy with similar and familiar situations. The space co-ordinates in a field vary continuously and are not appropriate for using as Hamiltonian or Lagrangian co-ordinates. However, if we look at the case of electromagnetic fields confined to a conducting cavity as in section 10.4, we see that the possible fields can be expressed as a set of independent modes completely analogous to the vibrations of an elastic solid.

There is a well-established technique for dealing with such problems by using *normal co-ordinates*. These are linear functions q_i of the actual co-ordinates having the property that the equations of motion of the system are separable into a number of independent equations of the form

$$\ddot{q}_i + \omega_i^2 q_i = 0 \tag{12.1}$$

each ω_i being the characteristic frequency of the ith mode. Moreover, the Lagrangian and Hamiltonian (the latter giving the total energy) are each expressible in separable form

$$L = \tfrac{1}{2}\sum_i (\dot{q}_i^{\,2} - \omega_i^{\,2} q_i^{\,2}); \qquad H = \tfrac{1}{2}\sum_i (p_i^{\,2} + \omega_i^{\,2} q_i^{\,2}) \quad (12.2)$$

with the generalized momentum $p_i = \dot{q}_i$.

These considerations suggest that we try using the *potentials* as normal co-ordinates because they satisfy the same type of equations as (12.1). For instance **A** satisfies, in the absence of sources,

$$\ddot{\mathbf{A}} - c^2\nabla^2\mathbf{A} = 0. \quad (12.3)$$

from (4.59).

Radiation in an enclosure. We shall now restrict our treatment to the case mentioned above: the radiation is confined to a rectangular cavity with perfectly conducting walls as in section 10.4, the dimensions being a, b, and d. We choose a Lorentz gauge (see section 4.6), but because there are no sources in the cavity itself we may choose the potentials so that $V = 0$ and thus

$$\mathbf{E} = -\partial\mathbf{A}/\partial t; \qquad \mathbf{B} = \mathbf{curl}\,\mathbf{A}; \qquad \operatorname{div}\mathbf{A} = 0 \quad (12.4)$$

and these together with (12.3) are enough to ensure that Maxwell's equations are satisfied. There will be boundary conditions on **A**: the normal component at the walls is zero because div **A** = 0 and **A** in the material of the walls is zero; the tangential component at the walls is also zero because $E_{\tan}$ is zero. Thus **A** is zero at the boundaries and must therefore vary spatially like **B** in (10.28) except that all factors must be sine:

$$\sin\frac{l\pi x}{a}\sin\frac{m\pi y}{b}\sin\frac{n\pi z}{d}. \quad (12.5)$$

Each mode is characterized by an angular frequency ω_λ and frequency ν_λ given by

$$\nu_\lambda = \frac{c}{2}\left(\frac{l^2}{a^2} + \frac{m^2}{b^2} + \frac{n^2}{d^2}\right)^{1/2} \quad (12.6)$$

from (10.29) and a corresponding wave-length λ. Thus when a number of modes coexist the total vector potential can be expressed as the sum

$$\mathbf{A} = \sum q_\lambda \mathbf{A}_\lambda \quad (12.7)$$

where q_λ is a co-ordinate expressing the time variation and $\mathbf{A}_\lambda$ gives the space variations in the form of (12.5). The space parts have the property (which we shall not prove) of being orthogonal over the volume of the cavity τ, i.e.,

$$\int_\tau \mathbf{A}_\lambda \cdot \mathbf{A}_\mu \, \mathrm{d}\tau = 0 \qquad \lambda \neq \mu \tag{12.8}$$

while we shall normalize the $\mathbf{A}_\lambda$ by choosing q_λ in such a way that

$$\varepsilon_0 \int_\tau \mathbf{A}_\lambda \cdot \mathbf{A}_\lambda \, \mathrm{d}\tau = 1. \tag{12.9}$$

To find the Hamiltonian for the field, we try to put the total energy in the form of (12.2). From (4.14) we have *in vacuo* that

$$U_{\mathrm{EM}} = \int_\tau (\tfrac{1}{2}\varepsilon_0 E^2 + \tfrac{1}{2}B^2/\mu_0) \, \mathrm{d}\tau = \tfrac{1}{2}\varepsilon_0 \int_\tau (E^2 + c^2 B^2) \, \mathrm{d}\tau. \tag{12.10}$$

Now $\mathbf{E} = -\dot{\mathbf{A}} = -\sum \dot{q}_\lambda \mathbf{A}_\lambda$ so that

$$\varepsilon_0 \int_\tau E^2 \, \mathrm{d}\tau = \varepsilon_0 \int_\tau (\sum \dot{q}_\lambda \mathbf{A}_\lambda)^2 \, \mathrm{d}\tau = \sum \dot{q}_\lambda{}^2 \tag{12.11}$$

using (12.8) and (12.9). To transform the term in B^2 we need the following identity from (A.26) with $\mathbf{B} = \mathbf{curl\ A}$:

$$\begin{aligned} \operatorname{div} (\mathbf{A} \times \mathbf{curl\ A}) &= (\mathbf{curl\ A}) \cdot (\mathbf{curl\ A}) - \mathbf{A} \cdot \mathbf{curl\ curl\ A} \\ &= (\mathbf{curl\ A}) \cdot (\mathbf{curl\ A}) - \mathbf{A} \cdot \nabla^2 \mathbf{A} \end{aligned} \tag{12.12}$$

using (A.34) and $\operatorname{div} \mathbf{A} = 0$. Now $\mathbf{B} = \mathbf{curl\ A} = \sum q_\lambda \, \mathbf{curl\ A}_\lambda$ so that B^2 contains terms of the form $(\mathbf{curl\ A}_\lambda) \cdot (\mathbf{curl\ A}_\mu)$ each of which by (12.12) can be put into the form

$$\operatorname{div} (\mathbf{A}_\lambda \times \mathbf{curl\ A}_\mu) + \mathbf{A}_\lambda \cdot \nabla^2 \mathbf{A}_\mu .$$

When integrated over the volume τ, the first of these terms can be converted to a surface integral of $\mathbf{A}_\lambda \times \mathbf{curl\ A}_\mu$ over the boundary using Gauss's divergence theorem and this term is zero because $\mathbf{A}$ itself is zero over the same boundary. In the second term, we have that $\nabla^2 \mathbf{A}_\mu = \omega_\mu{}^2 \mathbf{A}_\mu / c^2$ (from (12.5) and (12.6)) and when integrated over the volume τ every term is zero except that for which $\mu = \lambda$ by (12.8) and (12.9). Thus, finally

$$\varepsilon_0 \int_\tau B^2 \, \mathrm{d}\tau = \omega_\lambda{}^2 q_\lambda{}^2 / c^2. \tag{12.13}$$

Thus from (12.11) and (12.13) the energy in (12.10) may be written

$$U_{\text{EM}} = \tfrac{1}{2}\sum (\dot{q}_\lambda^{\,2} + \omega_\lambda^{\,2} q_\lambda^{\,2}). \tag{12.14}$$

The Hamiltonian must be in terms of momenta and not velocities so that if we put

$$p_\lambda = \dot{q}_\lambda \tag{12.15}$$

we may write for the Hamiltonian

$$H = \sum H_\lambda = \tfrac{1}{2}\sum (p_\lambda^{\,2} + \omega_\lambda^{\,2} q_\lambda^{\,2}) \tag{12.16}$$

which is of the form (12.2). Application of Hamilton's equations yields (12.15) together with

$$\ddot{q}_\lambda + \omega_\lambda^{\,2} q_\lambda \tag{12.17}$$

for each λ.

We have thus expressed the system's behaviour in terms of normal co-ordinates q_λ, and see that it behaves as a set of linear harmonic oscillators each with a characteristic frequency $\nu_\lambda = \omega_\lambda/2\pi$. It is possible to show that the Lagrangian for the system must be of the form

$$L = \tfrac{1}{2}\sum (\dot{q}_\lambda^{\,2} - \omega_\lambda^{\,2} q_\lambda^{\,2}) = \tfrac{1}{2}\varepsilon_0 \int_\tau (E^2 - c^2 B^2)\,d\tau \tag{12.18}$$

and we have already seen that in the latter form it will be relativistically invariant.

Number of modes of oscillation. The frequencies of the possible modes are given by (12.6) and this enables us to count the number to be found in a given frequency range. For this purpose, we use an (l, m, n)-space as shown in Fig. 12.1 where each point represents one mode and a point occurs in the space for every integral value of l, m, or n. We shall be interested in regions where the wave-lengths are much shorter than the linear dimensions of the cavity and the frequencies of the modes form almost a continuous spectrum. The points in (l, m, n)-space are then very dense.

All modes of the same frequency lie on the surface of the ellipsoid given by (12.6), namely

$$\frac{l^2}{(4a^2\nu_\lambda^{\,2}/c^2)} + \frac{m^2}{(4b^2\nu_\lambda^{\,2}/c^2)} + \frac{n^2}{(4d^2\nu_\lambda^{\,2}/c^2)} = 1. \tag{12.19}$$

Since only positive values of l, m, n occur, the number of modes with frequencies up to a given frequency ν will be those contained in the positive octant of the ellipsoid. Since there is clearly one mode per unit volume of the space, we need to find the volume of the octant if we wish to obtain the number of modes in the frequency range 0 to ν.

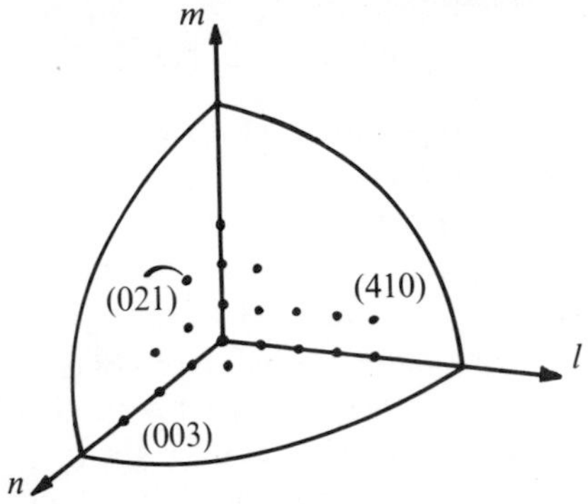

Fig. 12.1 Modes of oscillation in a cavity represented in (l, m, n)-space. Each point represents one mode with indices as shown. The ellipsoidal surface passes through points representing modes with the same frequency

The volume of an ellipsoid is $4\pi/3$ times the product of the lengths of its three principal axes, which are (from (12.19)) $2a\nu/c$, $2b\nu/c$, and $2d\nu/c$. Thus the number of modes with frequencies up to ν is $4\pi abd(2\nu/c)^3/24$ or $4\pi\nu^3\tau/3c^3$ where τ is the volume of the cavity. Finally, we must not forget that the field is a vector so that there can be two quite independent modes for each set (l, m, n) with polarization in perpendicular directions. Thus

$$\text{Number of modes with frequencies up to } \nu = 8\pi\nu^3\tau/3c^3 \qquad (12.20)$$

and thus the number with frequencies in the range ν to $\nu + \mathrm{d}\nu$ is

$$g(\nu)\,\mathrm{d}\nu = \frac{8\pi\nu^2}{c^3}\,\tau\,\mathrm{d}\nu. \qquad (12.21)$$

12.2 Photons

The expression (12.21) allows a calculation of the distribution of energy over the various frequencies provided the mean energy per oscillating mode is known, and for this we return to (12.16) and (12.17). If the enclosure is at a temperature T, classical equipartition demands that the mean energy per mode is just kT, and the product of this with (12.21) yields the Rayleigh–Jeans law which does not accord with the experimentally determined distribution.

Quantum mechanically, the Hamiltonian H_λ of (12.16) is put into operator form by the substitution $p_\lambda \to (h/2\pi i)\,\partial/\partial q_\lambda$ and the Schrödinger equation $H_\lambda \psi = E_\lambda \psi$, being that for a harmonic oscillator, has eigenvalues

$$E_\lambda = (n_\lambda + \tfrac{1}{2})\hbar\omega_\lambda \qquad (12.22)$$

where n_λ is a quantum number which may take any integral value from 0 to infinity.

We may now proceed in one of two equivalent ways. The first is similar to that adopted by Planck. The modes of oscillation are regarded as forming a statistical assembly of independent and identical but *distinguishable* elements of energies $h\nu$, $2h\nu$, $3h\nu$, etc., the so-called zero-point energy of $\frac{1}{2}h\nu$ per mode being omitted. The elements are distinguishable because of their localization spatially within the enclosure. The Maxwell–Boltzmann distribution law is then applicable and this leads to the following expression for the number of elements with energies in the range $h\nu$ to $h(\nu + \mathrm{d}\nu)$:

$$\mathrm{d}n = \frac{g(\nu)\,\mathrm{d}\nu}{\mathrm{e}^{h\nu/kT} - 1} \qquad (12.23)$$

where $g(\nu)$ is given by (12.21). Multiplication by $h\nu$ gives the energy in the range and yields the Planck formula for the distribution of energy which does agree with experiment.

Being aware of such phenomena as the photo-electric effect, we may prefer a second interpretation of (12.22) as describing a collection of particles such that there are n_λ occupying the state λ each with energy $\hbar\omega$ or $h\nu$. We then ascribe to free space in the absence of fields a zero-point energy $\sum \frac{1}{2}h\nu$ which we ignore in our treatment but which does cause difficulties in the theory (see for example, Power (1964) section 3.4). These particles we identify with *photons*, as postulated by Einstein to explain the photo-electric effect.

What properties would such particles have? With an energy $h\nu$, (11.33) shows that they should have a mass $h\nu/c^2$ and because their velocity is c, a momentum $h\nu/c$ or h/λ, and a rest mass zero. These are precisely the properties needed to explain such phenomena as the Compton effect.

An assembly of photons in a constant temperature enclosure we would expect to behave as a collection of identical and *indistinguishable* particles, and the fact that more than one can exist in the same energy level indicates that they are probably *bosons*. If so, Bose–Einstein statistics can be applied and the expression (12.23) is obtained directly from this since the distribution law has the form

$$dn = \frac{g(E)\,dE}{e^{\alpha + E/kT} - 1}$$

where E is the energy of one particle and α is a constant normally determined by the condition that the total number of particles is fixed. Photons may be created or destroyed however so that this condition is not applicable: this leads to $\alpha = 0$ and thus to (12.23).

Although we have restricted ourselves to radiation in an enclosure, it is possible to regard electromagnetic waves in unbounded space in a similar way as collections of photons, although the quantization of the field appears more artificial in that some form of boundary condition is still imposed, usually making **A** periodic throughout space. In practical cases, the flux of photons is often extremely large and any fluctuations correspondingly small. For example, a microwave photon has an energy of about 10^{-5} eV or 10^{-24} joule, so that with a milliwatt source at 1 metre giving an energy flux of 10^{-6} joule/sec. cm^2 there are about 10^{18} photons/sec over each cm^2 and even at 10^6 metres the flux is still 10^6 per sec per cm^2. Specifically quantum effects become more prominent as the individual photon energy increases, i.e., at higher frequencies. Thus at radio frequencies the photon energies are so low that scattering is classical and the number of photons very large (i.e., quantum numbers are high); the wave aspect is here most suitable as a description of the interaction of radiation and matter. At the other extreme, the extremely large photon energies of γ-rays produce completely non-classical effects, such as the photo-electric effect, the Compton effect, and pair production, when interacting with matter, and the particle aspect is most prominent.

12.3 Interaction of charged particle and electromagnetic field

We now consider the interaction between a charged particle and an electromagnetic field. In the first two sections, we dealt entirely with the quantization of the electromagnetic field *in vacuo* with no charges present, and this forms one aspect of quantum field theory. A complete system, however, consists of both the fields and the charges which interact with them. In order once again to use quantum theory, we must put the appropriate equations in the form of Lagrange's or Hamilton's equations.

For this, we must consider a slightly more general form of Lagrange's equations than (11.5):

$$\frac{\mathrm{d}}{\mathrm{d}t}\left(\frac{\partial K}{\partial \dot{q}_i}\right) - \frac{\partial K}{\partial q_i} = Q_i \tag{12.24}$$

in which K is the kinetic energy and Q_i the generalized force such that $Q_i\,\mathrm{d}q_i$ has the dimensions of work or energy. Normally, we can express Q_i for a conservative force as the negative gradient of a potential energy $U(q_i)$ so that $Q_i = -\partial U/\partial q_i$ and defining $L = K - U$ gives (11.5). Suppose, however, that Q_i is not so expressible. Then it may still be possible to find a function U' so that

$$Q_i = -\frac{\partial U'}{\partial q_i} + \frac{\mathrm{d}}{\mathrm{d}t}\left(\frac{\partial U'}{\partial \dot{q}_i}\right) \tag{12.25}$$

the second term arising from a velocity potential. If we now define the Lagrangian by $L = K - U'$, the normal form of Lagrange's equation (11.5) is again obtained.

The electromagnetic force on a charged particle in an electromagnetic field is precisely of this type, for we have that for an electron

$$\begin{aligned}\mathbf{F} &= e(\mathbf{E} + \mathbf{v} \times \mathbf{B}) \\ &= e(-\mathbf{grad}\ V - \partial \mathbf{A}/\partial t + \mathbf{v} \times \mathbf{curl}\ \mathbf{A})\end{aligned} \tag{12.26}$$

where $\mathbf{v}$ is the velocity and e the electronic charge. Because $\mathbf{v}$ is not a function of the field co-ordinates, the identity (A.27) applies as if $\mathbf{v}$ were constant to give

$$\mathbf{v} \times \mathbf{curl}\ \mathbf{A} = \mathbf{grad}\ (\mathbf{v} \cdot \mathbf{A}) - (\mathbf{v} \cdot \mathbf{grad})\ \mathbf{A}.$$

Substituting this in (12.26) gives

$$\begin{aligned}\mathbf{F} &= e\left[-\mathbf{grad}\ (V - \mathbf{v} \cdot \mathbf{A}) - \partial \mathbf{A}/\partial t - (\mathbf{v} \cdot \mathbf{grad})\ \mathbf{A}\right] \\ &= e\left[-\mathbf{grad}\ (V - \mathbf{v} \cdot \mathbf{A}) - \frac{\mathrm{d}\mathbf{A}}{\mathrm{d}t}\right].\end{aligned} \tag{12.27}$$

If we put

$$U' = e(V - \mathbf{v} \cdot \mathbf{A})$$

then

$$F_x = -\frac{\partial U'}{\partial x} + \frac{\mathrm{d}}{\mathrm{d}t}\left(\frac{\partial U'}{\partial \dot{x}}\right)$$

with similar expressions for F_y and F_z, so that U' satisfies (12.25) and we may take as the Lagrangian for the electron

$$L = K - eV + e\mathbf{v} \cdot \mathbf{A} \tag{12.28}$$

in which $e\mathbf{v}$ may be replaced by the volume integral of $\mathbf{J}\,d\tau$ and e by the volume integral of $\rho\,d\tau$ for extended distributions if necessary.

The momenta are given by $\partial L/\partial \dot{x}$, etc., and thus

$$p_x = m\dot{x} + eA_x, \text{ etc.}$$

if we use the non-relativistic $K = mv^2/2$. Thus

$$\mathbf{p} = m\mathbf{v} + e\mathbf{A} \quad \text{(non-relativistic).} \tag{12.29}$$

The Hamiltonian is defined in general by $\sum p_i\dot{q}_i - L$ and the non-relativistic expression for it is easily shown to be

$$H = \frac{(\mathbf{p} - e\mathbf{A})^2}{2m} + eV \quad \text{(non-relativistic)} \tag{12.30}$$

where $\mathbf{p}$ is given by (12.29). This is clearly the same as $\frac{1}{2}mv^2 + eV$.

Relativistically, the kinetic energy K is replaced in (12.28) by $-m_0c^2(1 - v^2/c^2)^{1/2}$, and (12.29) then becomes

$$\mathbf{p} = \frac{m_0\mathbf{v}}{(1 - v^2/c^2)^{1/2}} + e\mathbf{A} \tag{12.31}$$

and the Hamiltonian becomes

$$H = c[(\mathbf{p} - e\mathbf{A})^2 + m_0c^2]^{1/2} + eV. \tag{12.32}$$

There is nothing specifically quantum mechanical in the above treatment, and indeed the Lagrangian and Hamiltonian can be used to solve purely classical problems in electrodynamics such as the motion of a free charged particle in electric and magnetic fields (provided that radiation from the particle when accelerated is ignored or approximated to). However, by substituting appropriate operators in the Hamiltonian it is possible to obtain quantum mechanical solutions to problems, even if only approximately. For instance, (12.30) can be used to find the effect of an external magnetic field on atomic energy levels (Zeeman effect), or to calculate the absorption by, and stimulated emission of radiation from, atoms under the influence of an external periodic field (see Dicke and Wittke (1960)). This latter calculation yields dispersion formulae very similar to those of the classical theory of chapter 8. In addition, the Dirac theory of the electron stems from (12.32).

In spite of this, the method of this section can only be an approximation at best. This is because the problems are treated purely as those involving a particle subject to an external field which is (a) not itself treated quantum mechanically, (b) assumed to be unaffected by the motion of the particle. As far as (a) is concerned, it means that we are neglecting entirely the quantization of periodic fields developed in sections 12.1 and 12.2. Assumption (b) means that we are neglecting the radiation of energy and momentum from the accelerated charge. This last effect produces an extra force on the particle due to its own fields, a force which can often be approximated to by a damping term in the equation of motion and leading to *radiation damping* (see next section).

The two approximations (a) and (b) are connected in that a completely quantum mechanical treatment of the interaction between radiation and matter must regard the two together as a single system. The Hamiltonian is then the sum of (1) a term due to the radiation given by (12.10) or (12.16), (2) a term due to the particle given non-relativistically by $p^2/2m$, and (3) interaction terms involving $\mathbf{p} \cdot \mathbf{A}$ and A^2 from (12.30) or (12.32). The interaction is pictured as a process of continual emission and absorption of photons by the particle and the development of this treatment applied to electrons is the problem of *quantum electrodynamics*. This has had some success in predicting the Lamb shift and the anomalous magnetic moment of the electron, but there are still great difficulties in the theory. To discuss these would be outside the scope of this book, and we must leave the reader to consult the references for further details: articles by Weisskopf (1949) and Peierls (1955) are particularly recommended.

The methods of quantum electrodynamics are not needed in most cases because the radiation from the particle is usually small compared with its gain in energy due to motion. Moreover, if the flux of photons is large enough for a wave description to be meaningful, the quantization of the external field can be ignored.

12.4 The electron

Of all the particles responsible for electromagnetism, the electron (and its heavier relation, the muon) offers the greatest challenge because there is as yet no indication of any internal structure, i.e., it behaves, unlike the proton and others, as if it were strictly a point charge. We end by discussing various models of the electron and link this with an approximate treatment of radiation damping.

If an electron is regarded as a sphere of radius a with its total charge e distributed with spherical symmetry over the volume, the total electromagnetic energy and momentum can be obtained on the assumption that the formulae derived in chapter 4 are still valid:

$$U_{EM} = \int (\tfrac{1}{2}\varepsilon_0 E^2 + B^2/2\mu_0)\,d\tau; \qquad \mathbf{G} = \int (\mathbf{E} \times \mathbf{H}/c^2)\,d\tau. \tag{12.33}$$

For an electron at rest, and with e distributed uniformly over the surface:

$$U_{EM} = e^2/8\pi\varepsilon_0 a; \qquad \mathbf{G} = 0. \tag{12.34}$$

For an electron moving with a velocity $v \ll c$, $\mathbf{E} = e\mathbf{r}/4\pi\varepsilon_0 r^3$ and $\mathbf{B} = \mathbf{v} \times \mathbf{E}/c^2$ as shown in problem 4.15. Because $U_M \ll U_E$, we have

$$U_{EM} = e^2/8\pi\varepsilon_0 a; \qquad \mathbf{G} = e^2\mathbf{v}/6\pi\varepsilon_0 ac^2 = 4U_{EM}\mathbf{v}/3c^2 \tag{12.35}$$

as can be checked by integration from the surface of the electron to infinity (remembering that $\mathbf{G}$ is a vector whose direction at any point is that of $\mathbf{E} \times \mathbf{H}$). It can be shown that the relation between U_{EM} and $\mathbf{G}$ in (12.35) is independent of the detailed charge distribution, provided it is spherically symmetric, though U_{EM} and $\mathbf{G}$ themselves are not.

The momentum $\mathbf{G}$ is carried along with the electron and would give an electromagnetic contribution to the mass (assuming $\mathbf{G} = m_{EM}\mathbf{v}$) of

$$m_{EM} = 4U_{EM}/3c^2 \tag{12.36}$$

in contradiction to the relativistic relation between mass and energy. Although the 4/3 factor has given rise to an apparent difficulty, Rohrlich (1965) and others have pointed out that (12.33) are not relativistically invariant expressions and that, in any case, the expression for $\mathbf{G}$ is that for radiation in free space and not for the velocity fields of an electron. Invariant expressions for U_{EM} and $\mathbf{G}$ can be derived and they bring in additional terms which, in the limit $v \ll c$, are negligible in their effect on U_{EM} but add a term $-U_{EM}\mathbf{v}/3c^2$

to **G**. Thus we should have, instead of (12.35):

$$U_{\text{EM}} = e^2/8\pi\varepsilon_0 a; \qquad \mathbf{G} = e^2\mathbf{v}/8\pi\varepsilon_0 ac^2 = U_{\text{EM}}\mathbf{v}/c^2; \quad (12.37)$$

and

$$m_{\text{EM}} = U_{\text{EM}}/c^2. \quad (12.38)$$

From this point models have taken one of two courses: letting a remain finite; or letting $a \to 0$, the point-particle model. Both lead to difficulties.

Suppose we let a remain finite. If the only forces acting are electromagnetic, then m_{EM} should give the observed mass, in which case $a \approx e^2/4\pi\varepsilon_0 mc^2 \approx 2{\cdot}8 \times 10^{-13}$ cm, the classical electron radius, for which there is no experimental evidence. In any case, such a model would be unstable and other forces, of a non-electromagnetic nature, would be needed to ensure stability. These would then add a further contribution to the mass and would decrease the necessary a, which seems more satisfactory. Unfortunately, any model of finite size involves forces on one part due to the fields of another part, leading to a total self-force equivalent to the radiation damping term mentioned above. By arbitrarily neglecting terms involving the radius a explicitly, the form of this force can be made the same as that in (12.41) below but is subject to the same difficulty of runaway solutions unless the effect is very small.

If, on the other hand, we adopt the point-particle model, both U_{EM} and m_{EM} tend to infinity since, whatever the detailed charge distribution, they are both proportional to $1/a$. One can overcome this by subtracting a contribution from a non-electromagnetic mass, also infinite, so as to leave only a finite mass equal to the observed mass in the equations of motion. This process, known in quantum electrodynamics as *renormalization*, still gives trouble and it is arguable whether it has yet been overcome (see Peierls (1955)).

Radiation damping. We conclude by showing how radiation damping can be taken care of if small enough. First, let us take an oscillating electron with angular frequency ω_0 and amplitude x_0 and find the condition for the radiated energy to be small compared with the energy of oscillation, which elementary mechanics shows is $mx_0{}^2\omega_0{}^2$. In one period, of duration $2\pi/\omega_0$, the charge radiates at a rate given by (4.91) with $\dot{v} \approx \omega_0{}^2 x_0$. Hence the radiated energy in one period is approximately $e^2\omega_0{}^3 x_0{}^2/3\varepsilon_0 c^3$ and the required condition is that

$\omega_0 \ll 3\varepsilon_0 mc^3/e^2$ or $\sim 10^{24}$ s^{-1}, a condition fulfilled in the cases considered in this book.

Even if the radiation is not small, we expect the reaction force $\mathbf{F}_r$ to be obtained by equating the work done by it over a period of time to the gain of energy over that time, or

$$\int_0^t \mathbf{F}_r \cdot \mathbf{v}\, dt = \frac{e^2}{6\pi\varepsilon_0 c^3}\int_0^t - \dot{v}^2\, dt \tag{12.39}$$

$$= \frac{e^2}{6\pi\varepsilon_0 c^3}\left\{[\mathbf{v} \cdot \dot{\mathbf{v}}]_0^t - \int_0^t \mathbf{v} \cdot \ddot{\mathbf{v}}\, dt\right\}.$$

There are several situations in which the $\mathbf{v} \cdot \dot{\mathbf{v}}$ term is zero or can be neglected (periodic motion; change in $\mathbf{v}$ or $\dot{\mathbf{v}}$ small over time t; $\mathbf{v}$ perpendicular to $\dot{\mathbf{v}}$) and if we assume that this is so, then a solution of (12.39) is clearly

$$\mathbf{F}_r = \frac{e^2\ddot{\mathbf{v}}}{6\pi\varepsilon_0 c^3} = \frac{e^2\dddot{\mathbf{r}}}{6\pi\varepsilon_0 c^3}. \tag{12.40}$$

The equation of motion under an external force $\mathbf{F}$ becomes

$$\mathbf{F} = m\dot{\mathbf{v}} - B\ddot{\mathbf{v}} \tag{12.41}$$

where $B = e^2/6\pi\varepsilon_0 c^3$. If there is no external force, the solutions of this equation are the trivial $\dot{\mathbf{v}} = 0$, and $\dot{\mathbf{v}} = \mathbf{a}_0\, e^{tm/B}$, which increases indefinitely with time. This is a physically inadmissible solution and we may only employ (12.40) in the limit of small radiation corrections. Thus, suppose we wish to calculate the motion of a charge under the action of an elastic force giving it an undamped natural frequency of oscillation ω_0. To a first approximation we neglect the radiation damping term (12.40) so that the motion is given by

$$\mathbf{r} = \mathbf{r}_0\, e^{-i\omega_0 t}.$$

The force (12.40) can now be added to the equation of motion as a small correction, and since

$$\dddot{\mathbf{r}} = -\omega_0^{\,2}\dot{\mathbf{r}}$$

the correction can have the normal form for such a correction, namely $b\dot{\mathbf{r}}$, where $b = e^2\omega_0^{\,2}/6\pi\varepsilon_0 c^3$. This was the form assumed in section 8.2, although the value for b derived here does not agree well with absorption measurements and a full quantum mechanical treatment is necessary.

References

For the quantum theory of dispersion see Ditchburn (1962) or, for a more general and more advanced text on the quantum theory of radiation, see Heitler (1954). Power (1964) on quantum electrodynamics would supplement the articles mentioned in the chapter.

Appendix A

Relations in vector and scalar fields

The relations gathered in this appendix include all those used in the text or needed for problems. All are identities: **A**, **B**, **C**, may be *any* vectors, U, V, any scalars, τ any volume, S any surface and C any path. Vectors with circumflexes are always unit vectors.

The spherical polar co-ordinates (r, θ, ϕ) are specified in relation to right-handed cartesians as in Fig. A.1 and the orthogonal unit

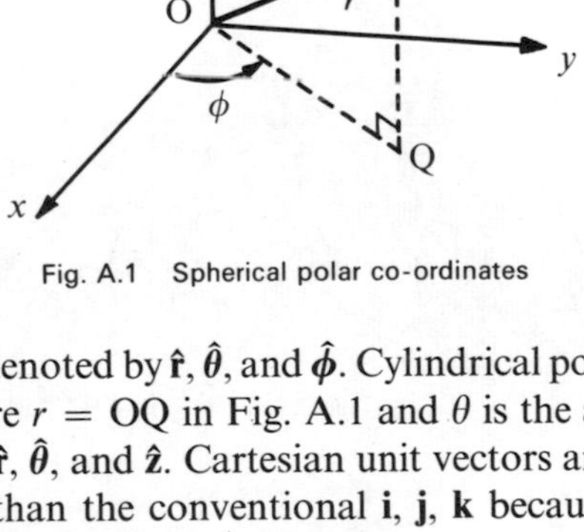

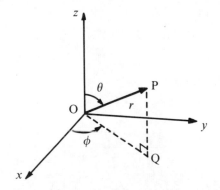

Fig. A.1 Spherical polar co-ordinates

vectors at P are denoted by $\hat{\mathbf{r}}$, $\hat{\boldsymbol{\theta}}$, and $\hat{\boldsymbol{\phi}}$. Cylindrical polar co-ordinates are (r, θ, z) where r = OQ in Fig. A.1 and θ is the angle xOQ. The unit vectors are $\hat{\mathbf{r}}$, $\hat{\boldsymbol{\theta}}$, and $\hat{\mathbf{z}}$. Cartesian unit vectors are denoted by $\hat{\mathbf{x}}$, $\hat{\mathbf{y}}$, and $\hat{\mathbf{z}}$ rather than the conventional **i**, **j**, **k** because the latter are needed in other connections.

Multiple products

$$\mathbf{A}\,.\,(\mathbf{B}\times\mathbf{C}) = \mathbf{B}\,.\,(\mathbf{C}\times\mathbf{A}) = \mathbf{C}\,.\,(\mathbf{A}\times\mathbf{B}) = -\mathbf{A}\,.\,(\mathbf{C}\times\mathbf{B}), \text{ etc.} \tag{A.1}$$

$$\mathbf{A}\times(\mathbf{B}\times\mathbf{C}) = \mathbf{B}(\mathbf{A}\,.\,\mathbf{C}) - \mathbf{C}(\mathbf{A}\,.\,\mathbf{B}). \tag{A.2}$$

Cartesian forms

$$\mathbf{A}\,.\,\mathbf{B} = A_xB_x + A_yB_y + A_zB_z \tag{A.3}$$

$$\mathbf{A}\times\mathbf{B} = \hat{\mathbf{x}}(A_yB_z - A_zB_y) + \hat{\mathbf{y}}(A_zB_x - A_xB_z) + \hat{\mathbf{z}}(A_xB_y - A_yB_x) \tag{A.4}$$

$$\textbf{grad}\ V = \nabla V = \hat{\mathbf{x}}\frac{\partial V}{\partial x} + \hat{\mathbf{y}}\frac{\partial V}{\partial y} + \hat{\mathbf{z}}\frac{\partial V}{\partial z} \tag{A.5}$$

$$\text{div}\ \mathbf{A} = \nabla\,.\,\mathbf{A} = \frac{\partial A_x}{\partial x} + \frac{\partial A_y}{\partial y} + \frac{\partial A_z}{\partial z} \tag{A.6}$$

$$\textbf{curl A} = \nabla\times\mathbf{A} = \hat{\mathbf{x}}\left(\frac{\partial A_z}{\partial y} - \frac{\partial A_y}{\partial z}\right) + \hat{\mathbf{y}}\left(\frac{\partial A_x}{\partial z} - \frac{\partial A_z}{\partial x}\right) + \hat{\mathbf{z}}\left(\frac{\partial A_y}{\partial x} - \frac{\partial A_x}{\partial y}\right). \tag{A.7}$$

$$\nabla^2 V = \frac{\partial^2 V}{\partial x^2} + \frac{\partial^2 V}{\partial y^2} + \frac{\partial^2 V}{\partial z^2} \tag{A.8}$$

$$\nabla^2\mathbf{A} = \hat{\mathbf{x}}\nabla^2 A_x + \hat{\mathbf{y}}\nabla^2 A_y + \hat{\mathbf{z}}\nabla^2 A_z. \tag{A.9}$$

Cylindrical polar forms

$$\textbf{grad}\ V = \hat{\mathbf{r}}\frac{\partial V}{\partial r} + \hat{\boldsymbol{\theta}}\frac{1}{r}\frac{\partial V}{\partial \theta} + \hat{\mathbf{z}}\frac{\partial V}{\partial z} \tag{A.10}$$

$$\text{div}\ \mathbf{A} = \frac{1}{r}\frac{\partial}{\partial r}(rA_r) + \frac{1}{r}\frac{\partial A_\theta}{\partial \theta} + \frac{\partial A_z}{\partial z} \tag{A.11}$$

$$\textbf{curl A} = \hat{\mathbf{r}}\left(\frac{1}{r}\frac{\partial A_z}{\partial \theta} - \frac{\partial A_\theta}{\partial z}\right) + \hat{\boldsymbol{\theta}}\left(\frac{\partial A_r}{\partial z} - \frac{\partial A_z}{\partial r}\right) + \hat{\mathbf{z}}\frac{1}{r}\left(\frac{\partial}{\partial r}(rA_\theta) - \frac{\partial A_r}{\partial \theta}\right) \tag{A.12}$$

$$\nabla^2 V = \frac{1}{r}\frac{\partial}{\partial r}\left(r\frac{\partial V}{\partial r}\right) + \frac{1}{r^2}\frac{\partial^2 V}{\partial \theta^2} + \frac{\partial^2 V}{\partial z^2}. \tag{A.13}$$

Spherical polar forms

$$\mathbf{grad}\ V = \hat{\mathbf{r}}\frac{\partial V}{\partial r} + \hat{\boldsymbol{\theta}}\frac{1}{r}\frac{\partial V}{\partial \theta} + \hat{\boldsymbol{\phi}}\frac{1}{r\sin\theta}\frac{\partial V}{\partial \phi} \tag{A.14}$$

$$\text{div}\ \mathbf{A} = \frac{1}{r^2}\frac{\partial}{\partial r}(r^2 A_r) + \frac{1}{r\sin\theta}\frac{\partial}{\partial\theta}(A_\theta \sin\theta) + \frac{1}{r\sin\theta}\frac{\partial A_\phi}{\partial\phi} \tag{A.15}$$

$$\mathbf{curl}\ \mathbf{A} = \hat{\mathbf{r}}\frac{1}{r\sin\theta}\left(\frac{\partial}{\partial\theta}(A_\phi\sin\theta) - \frac{\partial A_\theta}{\partial\phi}\right) + \hat{\boldsymbol{\theta}}\frac{1}{r}\left(\frac{1}{\sin\theta}\frac{\partial A_r}{\partial\phi} - \frac{\partial}{\partial r}(rA_\phi)\right) + \hat{\boldsymbol{\phi}}\frac{1}{r}\left(\frac{\partial}{\partial r}(rA_\theta) - \frac{\partial A_r}{\partial\theta}\right) \tag{A.16}$$

$$\nabla^2 V = \frac{1}{r^2}\frac{\partial}{\partial r}\left(r^2\frac{\partial V}{\partial r}\right) + \frac{1}{r^2\sin\theta}\frac{\partial}{\partial\theta}\left(\sin\theta\frac{\partial V}{\partial\theta}\right) + \frac{1}{r^2\sin^2\theta}\frac{\partial^2 V}{\partial\phi^2}. \tag{A.17}$$

Various uses of scalar product notation

Component of **A** in direction $\hat{\mathbf{s}}$: $A_s = \mathbf{A}\,.\,\hat{\mathbf{s}}$ (A.18)
Increment of V along ds: $\mathrm{d}V = \mathbf{ds}\,.\,\mathbf{grad}\ V$ (A.19)
Solid angle subtended by d**S** at O: $\mathrm{d}\Omega = \mathbf{r}\,.\,\mathrm{d}\mathbf{S}/r^3$ (A.20)

$$(\mathbf{A}\,.\,\mathbf{grad})\mathbf{B} = (\mathbf{A}\,.\,\nabla)\mathbf{B} = \hat{\mathbf{x}}\left(A_x\frac{\partial B_x}{\partial x} + A_y\frac{\partial B_x}{\partial y} + A_z\frac{\partial B_x}{\partial z}\right) + \hat{\mathbf{y}}\left(A_x\frac{\partial B_y}{\partial x} + A_y\frac{\partial B_y}{\partial y} + A_z\frac{\partial B_y}{\partial z}\right) + \hat{\mathbf{z}}\left(A_x\frac{\partial B_z}{\partial x} + A_y\frac{\partial B_z}{\partial y} + A_z\frac{\partial B_z}{\partial z}\right) \tag{A.21}$$

$$(\mathbf{A}\,.\,\mathbf{grad})V = \mathbf{A}\,.\,\mathbf{grad}\ V. \tag{A.22}$$

Relations between differential operators

Grad, div, and **curl** of products:

$\mathbf{grad}\ UV = U\,\mathbf{grad}\ V + V\,\mathbf{grad}\ U$ (A.23)
$\text{div}\ V\mathbf{A} = V\,\text{div}\ \mathbf{A} + \mathbf{A}\,.\,\mathbf{grad}\ V$ (A.24)
$\mathbf{curl}\ V\mathbf{A} = V\,\mathbf{curl}\ \mathbf{A} - \mathbf{A}\times\mathbf{grad}\ V$ (A.25)
$\text{div}\,(\mathbf{A}\times\mathbf{B}) = \mathbf{B}\,.\,\mathbf{curl}\ \mathbf{A} - \mathbf{A}\,.\,\mathbf{curl}\ \mathbf{B}$ (A.26)

$$\textbf{grad}\,(\mathbf{A}\,.\,\mathbf{B}) = \mathbf{A} \times \textbf{curl}\,\mathbf{B} + (\mathbf{A}\,.\,\textbf{grad})\,\mathbf{B} + \mathbf{B} \times \textbf{curl}\,\mathbf{A} + (\mathbf{B}\,.\,\textbf{grad})\,\mathbf{A} \qquad \text{(A.27)}$$

$$\textbf{curl}\,(\mathbf{A} \times \mathbf{B}) = \mathbf{A}\,\text{div}\,\mathbf{B} - (\mathbf{A}\,.\,\textbf{grad})\,\mathbf{B} - \mathbf{B}\,\text{div}\,\mathbf{A} + (\mathbf{B}\,.\,\textbf{grad})\,\mathbf{A}. \qquad \text{(A.28)}$$

If **A** is not a function of the co-ordinates, note that these last two reduce to

$$\textbf{grad}\,(\mathbf{A}\,.\,\mathbf{B}) = \mathbf{A} \times \textbf{curl}\,\mathbf{B} + (\mathbf{A}\,.\,\textbf{grad})\,\mathbf{B} \quad \mathbf{A}\text{ constant} \qquad \text{(A.29)}$$

$$\textbf{curl}\,(\mathbf{A} \times \mathbf{B}) = \mathbf{A}\,\text{div}\,\mathbf{B} - (\mathbf{A}\,.\,\textbf{grad})\,\mathbf{B} \quad \mathbf{A}\text{ constant.} \qquad \text{(A.30)}$$

Combinations of **grad**, div, and **curl**. Possible ones are **grad** div, div **grad**, div **curl**, **curl grad**, **curl curl**:

$$\textbf{curl grad}\,V = 0 \qquad \text{(A.31)}$$

$$\text{div}\,\textbf{curl}\,\mathbf{A} = 0 \qquad \text{(A.32)}$$

$$\text{div}\,\textbf{grad}\,V \equiv \nabla^2 V \qquad \text{(A.33)}$$

$$\textbf{curl curl}\,\mathbf{A} = \textbf{grad}\,\text{div}\,\mathbf{A} - \nabla^2\mathbf{A}. \qquad \text{(A.34)}$$

Identity (A.34) is only useful in cartesian co-ordinates: in other systems of co-ordinates it merely defines $\nabla^2\mathbf{A}$.

Integral relations

Gauss's divergence theorem: if a closed surface S bounds a volume τ, then

$$\int_\tau \text{div}\,\mathbf{A}\,d\tau = \oint_S \mathbf{A}\,.\,d\mathbf{S}. \qquad \text{(A.35)}$$

Corollary: apply the divergence theorem to the vector $(\mathbf{A} \times \mathbf{B})$, where **B** is any constant vector. Then, using (A.26) and (A.1):

$$\int_\tau \textbf{curl}\,\mathbf{A}\,d\tau = \oint_S -\mathbf{A} \times d\mathbf{S}. \qquad \text{(A.36)}$$

Stokes's theorem: if a closed path C bounds a surface S, then

$$\int_S (\textbf{curl}\,\mathbf{A})\,.\,d\mathbf{S} = \oint_C \mathbf{A}\,.\,d\mathbf{l}. \qquad \text{(A.37)}$$

Corollary: apply Stokes's theorem to the vector $V\mathbf{A}$, where **A** is any constant vector. Then, using (A.25) and (A.1):

$$\int_S (-\textbf{grad}\,V) \times d\mathbf{S} = \oint_C V\,d\mathbf{l}. \qquad \text{(A.38)}$$

Note on source- and field-point co-ordinates

Many formulae in electromagnetism give the value of a field quantity at a *field point* P arising from charges, currents, etc., situated at *source points* O. Where the source is small enough it can be situated at the origin and the field-point co-ordinate $\mathbf{r}$ (= OP) is the only co-ordinate in the formula. For more complicated sources, however, such as systems of charge or large circuits, it is no longer possible to use only one co-ordinate. Thus a simple formula like

$$V_{\mathrm{P}} = \frac{Q}{4\pi\varepsilon_0 r} \tag{A.39}$$

for a single point charge, must become

$$V_{\mathrm{P}} = \frac{Q_i}{4\pi\varepsilon_0 \left|(\mathbf{r} - \mathbf{r}_i)\right|} \tag{A.40}$$

for one of a system of charges, where $\mathbf{r}_i$ is the position of Q_i and $\mathbf{r}$ is the co-ordinate of the field point P (see Fig. 5.1).

For the complete system of sources, the notation of (A.40) should strictly be used, with appropriate summation signs or integrals. In practice, for brevity, the form (A.39) is often used and the sum or integral written as in equation (1.15). This does not usually lead to confusion in working out specific problems but it may give rise to an incorrect sign when differentiation or integration is performed. It is implicitly assumed in the operations **grad**, div, and **curl** that the derivatives are taken with respect to a displacement of the field point whose position is $\mathbf{r}$ in (A.40). If, however, the derivatives are taken with respect to displacement of a source point at $\mathbf{r}_i$, then the operations must change sign. For example, if we use subscripts f and s to denote derivatives with respect to field and source points, then

$$\mathbf{grad}\, V = \mathbf{grad}_{\mathrm{f}}\, V = -\mathbf{grad}_{\mathrm{s}}\, V \tag{A.41}$$

as is easily verified by writing

$$|\mathbf{r} - \mathbf{r}_i| = \left[(x - x_i)^2 + (y - y_i)^2 + (z - z_i)^2\right]^{1/2}$$

and realizing that $\mathbf{grad}_{\mathrm{f}}$ means differentiation with respect to x, y, and z while $\mathbf{grad}_{\mathrm{s}}$ means differentiation with respect to x_i, y_i, z_i. Similarly, integration over a source as in section 1.5 can lead to a change of sign.

(While we shall refer generally to entities such as charge and current as 'sources' of fields, we shall also use the special term 'vortex' to mean a source giving rise to a curl in the vector field: thus electric currents form vortices of **B**.)

Note on boundary conditions

The use of Gauss's divergence theorem and Stokes's theorem enables differential laws like div $\mathbf{D} = \rho$ to be converted into integral forms like $\oint \mathbf{D} \cdot \mathrm{d}\mathbf{S} = \sum Q$ and vice versa. Conditions which must apply at a boundary between two media are easily derived from the integral forms and the standard method of obtaining these is needed frequently in chapters 1–4. It is as follows.

Where the divergence of a vector **X** is known, say div $\mathbf{X} = \rho$, the corresponding integral form is a flux theorem akin to Gauss's electrostatic theorem and this can be applied to a Gaussian surface in the form of a pill-box as in Fig. A.2a. The outward flux of **X** over

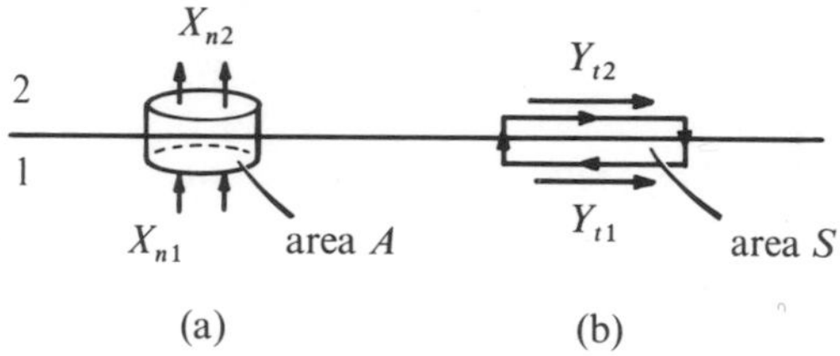

Fig. A.2 Derivation of boundary conditions (a) where div **X** is known, (b) where **curl Y** is known. The boundary possesses in general a surface source density σ and a surface vortex density J_s

the surface is $(X_{n2} - X_{n1})A$ where the X_n are the normal components of **X**. Any flux over the curved surface can be made as small as we like by taking a shallow enough pill-box. The sources of **X** within the box are distributed over the boundary with a surface density σ and the flux theorem thus tells us that $(X_{n2} - X_{n1})A = \sigma A$, the total source strength enclosed. Hence the normal component of **X** is discontinuous by σ. Thus the following statements can be made

$$\left.\begin{aligned} \text{div } \mathbf{X} &= \text{volume density of sources, } \rho \\ &\text{or} \\ \oint_S \mathbf{X} \cdot \mathrm{d}\mathbf{S} &= \text{total source strength within } S \end{aligned}\right\} \quad \text{(A.42)}$$

imply

$$X_n \text{ is discontinuous by surface source density, } \sigma. \quad \text{(A.43)}$$

Similarly, where the **curl** of a vector **Y** is known, say **curl** $\mathbf{Y} = \mathbf{J}$, the corresponding integral form is a circuital theorem which can be applied to the path in Fig. A.2b. The reader should follow the argument through and show that the following applies

$$\left.\begin{aligned} \mathbf{curl\ Y} &= \text{density of vortices, } \mathbf{J} \\ &\qquad\qquad \text{or} \\ \oint_C \mathbf{Y} \cdot \mathbf{ds} &= \text{total flux of } \mathbf{J} \text{ across } S \text{ bounded by path } C \end{aligned}\right\} \quad \text{(A.44)}$$

imply, where Y_t is the tangential component of $\mathbf{Y}$,

$$Y_t \text{ is discontinuous by surface vortex density, } J_s. \quad \text{(A.45)}$$

The physical significance of $\mathbf{J}$, J_s, and the flux of $\mathbf{J}$ is most easily appreciated if it is applied to current density as in chapter 2.

Reference

Davis (1967) is recommended.

Appendix B

Elementary properties of matrices

A matrix is merely a rectangular array of numbers which combines with other such arrays according to certain rules summarized below. Because the applications needed in this book concern only square matrices and single column or single row matrices, illustrative examples will be restricted to these types although the rules apply generally.

The array of numbers forming a matrix is generally enclosed in parentheses and the whole matrix may be denoted for brevity by a single symbol, usually in some form of bold type. Thus **a** may stand for a matrix whose general element is a_{ij}:

$$\mathbf{a} = \begin{pmatrix} a_{11} & a_{12} & a_{13} & \cdots \\ a_{21} & a_{22} & a_{23} & \cdots \\ a_{31} & a_{32} & a_{33} & \cdots \\ . & . & . & . \end{pmatrix}$$

Addition of matrices. Two matrices can be added only if they have the same number of rows and columns. The sum is obtained by adding corresponding elements, so that

$$\mathbf{a} + \mathbf{b} = \mathbf{c}$$

means that every element $c_{ij} = a_{ij} + b_{ij}$. Such addition obeys the commutative and associative laws, i.e., $\mathbf{a} + \mathbf{b} = \mathbf{b} + \mathbf{a}$, and $\mathbf{a} + (\mathbf{b} + \mathbf{c}) = (\mathbf{a} + \mathbf{b}) + \mathbf{c}$.

Multiplication by a number. We should naturally interpret the multiplication of a matrix by an integer k to mean the addition of k

identical matrices. By extension

$$k\mathbf{a} = \mathbf{b}$$

means that $b_{ij} = ka_{ij}$ for every element. Such multiplication obeys the normal laws of algebra.

Multiplication of two matrices. The product **ab** can only be found if the number of columns of **a** is equal to the number of rows of **b**. The product

$$\mathbf{ab} = \mathbf{c}$$

is formed using a rule exemplified by the following diagram

$$\rightarrow \begin{pmatrix} a_{11} & a_{12} \\ a_{21} & a_{22} \end{pmatrix} \begin{pmatrix} \downarrow \\ b_{11} & b_{12} \\ b_{21} & b_{22} \end{pmatrix}$$

$$= \rightarrow \begin{pmatrix} a_{11}b_{11} \overset{\downarrow}{+} a_{12}b_{21} & a_{11}b_{12} + a_{12}b_{22} \\ a_{21}b_{11} + a_{22}b_{21} & a_{21}b_{12} + a_{22}b_{22} \end{pmatrix} \quad \text{(B.1)}$$

in which each element of **c** is the sum of products of the elements in the appropriate *row* of **a** (the first-named) and *column* of **b**. A few examples will soon make the rule clear: the reader should examine a numerical example such as

$$\begin{pmatrix} 1 & 2 \\ 2 & 3 \end{pmatrix} \begin{pmatrix} 2 & 1 \\ 0 & 4 \end{pmatrix} = \begin{pmatrix} 2 & 9 \\ 4 & 14 \end{pmatrix}$$

or an algebraic one such as the matrix form of (1.28):

$$\begin{pmatrix} J_x \\ J_y \\ J_z \end{pmatrix} = \begin{pmatrix} \gamma_{xx} & \gamma_{xy} & \gamma_{xz} \\ \gamma_{yx} & \gamma_{yy} & \gamma_{yz} \\ \gamma_{zx} & \gamma_{zy} & \gamma_{zz} \end{pmatrix} \begin{pmatrix} E_x \\ E_y \\ E_z \end{pmatrix}. \quad \text{(B.2)}$$

Other examples occur in chapters 2, 9, and 11. In (B.2), the J's and E's form *column matrices* and since $\gamma_{xy} = \gamma_{yx}$, etc., the conductivity matrix is *symmetric*.

Multiplication of matrices obeys the associative and distributive laws:

$$(\mathbf{ab})\mathbf{c} = \mathbf{a}(\mathbf{bc}) \quad \text{(B.3)}$$

$$(\mathbf{a} + \mathbf{b})\mathbf{c} = \mathbf{ab} + \mathbf{ac} \quad \text{(B.4)}$$

but the product does not necessarily commute, i.e., $\mathbf{ab} \neq \mathbf{ba}$ in general.

Types of matrix. The *leading diagonal* of a square matrix is that containing the elements a_{ii}. If all elements but those in the leading diagonal are zero, we have a *diagonal matrix*. A diagonal matrix with all non-zero elements equal to 1 is a *unit matrix* denoted by $\mathbf{I}$. Multiplication by $\mathbf{I}$ leaves any matrix unchanged.

The *transpose* of a matrix $\mathbf{a}$, denoted by $\tilde{\mathbf{a}}$ or $\mathbf{a}'$, is obtained by interchanging rows and columns, $a_{ij} \to a_{ji}$. In particular, the transpose of a column matrix like those of (B.2) is a *row matrix* such as $(J_x\, J_y\, J_z)$.

The *inverse* of a matrix $\mathbf{a}$, denoted by $\mathbf{a}^{-1}$, is such that

$$\mathbf{aa}^{-1} = \mathbf{I} \tag{B.5}$$

although $\mathbf{a}^{-1}$ may not exist. To find an inverse can be a lengthy piece of computation and we refer the reader to references for details. It is of course a simple matter to check whether a given matrix is the inverse of another by using (B.5).

A *singular* matrix is a square matrix whose determinant is zero and it has no inverse. An *orthogonal* matrix is a square matrix $\mathbf{a}$ with real elements such that

$$\tilde{\mathbf{a}} = \mathbf{a}^{-1}$$

from which it follows that it also satisfies

$$\mathbf{a}\tilde{\mathbf{a}} = \tilde{\mathbf{a}}\mathbf{a} = \mathbf{I}.$$

Uses of matrices and a note on cartesian tensors. The matrix *representation* of a set of numbers does not imply anything about its physical significance. Matrices may be merely sets of coefficients or variables in a collection of linear equations; some matrices, as in chapter 11, represent operators; others, however, *are* representative of physical quantities capable in principle of measurement.

Thus, a vector (in 3-space or 4-space) is a quantity specified by three or four components referred to a specific set of co-ordinate axes. These components transform as follows if the vector is referred to another set of axes x', y', z':

$$\begin{pmatrix} A_{x'} \\ A_{y'} \\ A_{z'} \end{pmatrix} = \begin{pmatrix} \lambda_{x'x} & \lambda_{x'y} & \lambda_{x'z} \\ \lambda_{y'x} & \lambda_{y'y} & \lambda_{y'z} \\ \lambda_{z'x} & \lambda_{z'y} & \lambda_{z'z} \end{pmatrix} \begin{pmatrix} A_x \\ A_y \\ A_z \end{pmatrix} \tag{B.6}$$

where $\lambda_{i'j}$ are the direction cosines of x', y', z' with respect to x, y, z, i.e., $\lambda_{x'y} = \cos(x', y)$. The extension to a 4-vector is obvious. (B.6) could be concisely written as $\mathbf{A}' = \boldsymbol{\lambda}\mathbf{A}$, where $\mathbf{A}$ and $\mathbf{A}'$ are column matrices. The scalar product of two vectors $\mathbf{A}$ and $\mathbf{B}$ in matrix notation would be written as $\mathbf{A} \cdot \tilde{\mathbf{B}}$ since only by transposing $\mathbf{B}$ can the product be formed.

In a similar way, there are quantities specified by 3×3 or 4×4 elements in 3- or 4-space, each element transforming in a characteristic way when changing from x-, y-, z-axes to x'-, y'-, z'-axes. The transformation for a quantity such as γ in (B.2) can be written as

$$\gamma' = \lambda\gamma\tilde{\lambda} \tag{B.7}$$

where $\boldsymbol{\lambda}$ is the matrix of direction cosines in (B.6). When multiplied out, this means, for example, that

$$\gamma_{x'y'} = \sum_{i,j} \lambda_{x'i}\lambda_{jy'}\gamma_{ij}$$

where i, j both range over x, y, z. Such a quantity is known as a *tensor* in 3-space—strictly as a tensor *of second rank*, since a vector may be regarded as a tensor of the first rank and a scalar as one of zero rank (i.e., invariant).

Tensors may be represented by matrices and when multiplied by a vector written as a column matrix they yield another vector. Thus, when a simple relation occurs between two vectors not in the same direction:

$$\mathbf{A} = \mathbf{kB} \tag{B.8}$$

then $\mathbf{k}$ is invariably a tensor.

By a suitable choice of axes, any symmetric tensor may be diagonalized. The set of axes so found are known as *principal axes* and their use reduces the complexity of the equations represented by (B.8). Thus (1.28), when referred to principal axes, will reduce to

$$J_x = \gamma_{xx}E_x; \qquad J_y = \gamma_{yy}E_y; \qquad J_z = \gamma_{zz}E_z.$$

References

Introductions to matrix methods are given in Heading (1958) and Stephenson (1965). Elementary literature on tensors is very scattered but the introductory chapters of Brillouin (1964) are recommended for their exceptional clarity.

Appendix C

Derivation of E and B fields due to an accelerated charge

In this appendix, all quantities are retarded except for time when denoted by t, thus dispensing with the need for square brackets. The retarded time $(t - r/c)$ is denoted by T.

The problem is the calculation of **E** and **B** from **A** and V, where

$$V = Q/4\pi\varepsilon_0 s; \qquad \mathbf{A} = \mu_0 Q\mathbf{v}/4\pi s; \qquad s = r - \mathbf{v} \cdot \mathbf{r}/c \quad \text{(C.1)}$$

and

$$\mathbf{E} = -\partial\mathbf{A}/\partial t - \mathbf{grad}\ V; \qquad \mathbf{B} = \mathbf{curl}\ \mathbf{A}. \quad \text{(C.2)}$$

(Note that with the convention of Fig. 4.5, $\mathbf{v} = -\dot{\mathbf{r}}$ and $\partial r/\partial T = -(\mathbf{v} \cdot \mathbf{r})/r$.) We first note that the derivative $\partial/\partial t$ must be converted to $\partial/\partial T$ since we are given the values of $\mathbf{v}$, $\dot{\mathbf{v}}$, etc., at retarded times. Moreover, the differential operators **grad** and **curl** are derivatives at constant t (denoted by $\mathbf{grad}_t$ and $\mathbf{curl}_t$) whereas we need them at constant T ($\mathbf{grad}_T$, $\mathbf{curl}_T$).

The relation $T = t - r/c$ does not yield $\partial T/\partial t$ directly, but since from it $r = c(t - T)$ we have that

$$\begin{aligned} \partial r/\partial t = c(1 - \partial T/\partial t) \text{ and also } &= \partial r/\partial T \times \partial T/\partial t \\ &= -(\mathbf{v} \cdot \mathbf{r})(\partial T/\partial t)/r. \end{aligned}$$

Hence $\partial T/\partial t = 1/(1 - \mathbf{v} \cdot \mathbf{r}/c) = r/s$ so that

$$\boxed{\frac{\partial}{\partial t} \to \frac{r}{s}\frac{\partial}{\partial T}} \quad \text{(C.3)}$$

For the gradient of any retarded function, we have that

$$\mathbf{grad}_t = \mathbf{grad}_T + \mathbf{grad}_t\, T \frac{\partial}{\partial T} \tag{C.4}$$

since **grad** is an ordinary partial differential coefficient. To evaluate $\mathbf{grad}_t\, T$, apply (C.4) to r, when

$$\mathbf{grad}_t\, r = \mathbf{grad}_T\, r + \mathbf{grad}_t\, T\, \partial r/\partial T. \tag{C.5}$$

In addition,

$$\mathbf{grad}_t\, r = \mathbf{grad}_t\, c(t - T) = -c\, \mathbf{grad}_t\, T. \tag{C.6}$$

Equating (C.5) and (C.6):

$$\begin{aligned}\mathbf{grad}_t\, T = (\mathbf{grad}_T\, r)/(c + \partial r/\partial T) &= -\mathbf{r}/c(r - \mathbf{v}\,.\,\mathbf{r}/c) \\ &= -\mathbf{r}/cs.\end{aligned}$$

Hence from (C.4)

$$\boxed{\mathbf{grad}_t \to \mathbf{grad}_T - (\mathbf{r}/cs)\, \partial/\partial T}. \tag{C.7}$$

This implies that the vector operator ∇_t becomes $\nabla_T - (\mathbf{r}/cs)\, \partial/\partial T$ so that we have, in a similar way,

$$\boxed{\mathbf{curl}_t \to \mathbf{curl}_T - \frac{\mathbf{r}}{cs} \times \frac{\partial}{\partial T}}. \tag{C.8}$$

Thus

$$\begin{aligned}\mathbf{E} &= -\frac{\mu_0 Q}{4\pi} \frac{r}{s} \frac{\partial}{\partial T}\left(\frac{\mathbf{v}}{s}\right) - \frac{Q}{4\pi\varepsilon_0} \mathbf{grad}_T \left(\frac{1}{s}\right) + \frac{Q}{4\pi\varepsilon_0} \frac{\mathbf{r}}{cs} \frac{\partial}{\partial T}\left(\frac{1}{s}\right) \\ &= \frac{Q}{4\pi\varepsilon_0}\left[-\frac{r}{c^2 s}\left(\frac{\dot{\mathbf{v}}}{s} - \frac{\mathbf{v}}{s^2}\frac{\partial s}{\partial T}\right) + \frac{1}{s^2}\mathbf{grad}_T\, s - \frac{\mathbf{r}}{cs^3}\frac{\partial s}{\partial T}\right].\end{aligned} \tag{C.9}$$

This expression will be found to yield (4.86) if the substitution $s = r - \mathbf{v}\,.\,\mathbf{r}/c$ is made in the $\partial s/\partial T$ and $\mathbf{grad}_T\, s$ terms and the factor $Q/4\pi\varepsilon_0 s^3$ is taken outside the bracket. The identity $\mathbf{grad}\,(\mathbf{v}\,.\,\mathbf{r}) = \mathbf{v}$ can easily be established by using cartesians and this is needed at one stage. The $\dot{\mathbf{v}}$ terms can be written as the triple product of (4.86) but this is best checked by expanding it using (A.2) and seeing that the $\dot{\mathbf{v}}$ terms of (C.9) are obtained.

The **B** field is obtained similarly by using (C.8), and if the factor $(\mathbf{r}/rc)\,\times$ is taken out at an early stage, the rest of the expression will be found to be the sum of those terms in **E** of (4.86) which do not have the direction **r**. Thus (4.87) is justified since $\mathbf{r} \times \mathbf{r} = 0$.

Appendix D

Units and physical constants

Sommerfeld rationalized MKSA units are used throughout this book since they now form part of the S.I. units accepted and agreed by international commissions. Table 1 gives the units in this system together with the number of CGS units in 1 S.I. unit. Gaussian units are starred. The quantity c may be replaced for most work by 3×10^{10}.

To convert equations and formulae in this book to the commonest CGS system, the Gaussian system, the substitutions given in table 2 should be made. Note, however, that some authors prefer to use e.m.u. for current and in that case the additional substitutions $I \to cI$ and $\mathbf{J} \to c\mathbf{J}$ must be made. For further details about unit systems, see *Electricity and Magnetism*, section 16.7.

Table 3 gives some values of important physical constants.

Table 1 Units

Quantity	*S.I. Unit*	*CGS e.m.u.*	*CGS e.s.u.*
Mass, m	kilogram, kg	10^3 g	
Length, l	metre, m	10^2 cm	
Time, t	second, s	1 s	
Frequency, ν	s^{-1} = hertz, Hz	1 Hz	
Velocity, $\mathbf{v}$	m/s	10^2 cm/s	
Linear momentum, $\mathbf{p}$	kg-m/s	10^5 g-cm/s	
Density, ρ_m	kg/m^3	10^{-3} g/cm^3	
Force, $\mathbf{F}$	newton, N	10^5 dyne	
Work, energy, W	joule, J	10^7 erg	
Power, P	watt, W	10^7 erg/s	
Angular momentum, $\mathbf{L}$	kg-m^2/s	10^7 g-cm^2/s	
Torque, $\mathbf{T}$	N-m	10^7 dyne-cm	
Charge, Q	coulomb, C	10^{-1}	*c/10
Current, I	ampere, A	10^{-1}	*c/10
Electric dipole moment, $\mathbf{p}$	C-m	10	*10c
Electric potential difference, V	volt, V	10^8	*10^8/c
Electric field strength, $\mathbf{E}$	V/m	10^6	*10^6/c
Capacitance, C	farad, F	10^{-9}	*10^{-9}/c^2
Resistance, R	ohm, Ω	10^9	*10^9/c^2
Resistivity, ρ	Ω-m	10^{11}	*10^{11}/c^2
Conductance, G	mho, ℧	10^{-9}	*10^{-9}/c^2
Conductivity, γ	mho/m	10^{-11}	*10^{-11}/c^2
Polarization, $\mathbf{P}$	C/m^2	10^{-5}	*10^{-5} c
Displacement, $\mathbf{D}$	C/m^2	$4\pi \times 10^{-5}$	*$4\pi \times 10^{-5}$ c
Magnetic dipole moment, $\mathbf{m}$	A-m^2	*10^3	10^3 c
Pole strength, P	A-m	*10	10 c
Magnetic flux, Φ	weber, Wb	*10^8 maxwell	10^8/c
Magnetic flux density, $\mathbf{B}$	tesla, T (Wb/m^2)	*10^4 gauss	10^4/c
Magnetic field strength, $\mathbf{H}$	A/m	*$4\pi \times 10^{-3}$ oersted	10^8/c
Inductance, L, M	henry, H	10^9	*10^9/c^2
Magnetization, $\mathbf{M}$	A/m	*10^{-3}	10^{-3} c

Table 2 Conversion to gaussian units

Replace	*By*
ε_0	$1/4\pi$
μ_0	$4\pi/c^2$
$\mathbf{D}$	$\mathbf{D}/4\pi$
χ_e	$4\pi\chi_e$
$\mathbf{B}$	$\mathbf{B}/c$
$\mathbf{A}$	$\mathbf{A}/c$
Φ	Φ/c
$\mathbf{H}$	$c\mathbf{H}/4\pi$
V_m	$cV_m/4\pi$
$\mathbf{m}$	$c\mathbf{m}$
$\mathbf{M}$	$c\mathbf{M}$
χ_m	$4\pi\chi_m$
Pole strength P	cP

Table 3 Physical constants

Electronic charge, $e = 1{\cdot}60206 \times 10^{-19}$ C
Electron rest mass, $m = 9{\cdot}1083 \times 10^{-31}$ kg (= 0·511 MeV)
Proton rest mass, $M = 1{\cdot}6724 \times 10^{-27}$ kg (= 938 MeV)
$e/m = 1{\cdot}7589 \times 10^{11}$ C/kg; $M/m = 1836{\cdot}1$
Velocity of light, $c = 2{\cdot}99793 \times 10^{8}$ m/s
Avogadro's number, $N_A = 6{\cdot}0249 \times 10^{26}$/kg
Planck's constant, $h = 6{\cdot}6252 \times 10^{-34}$ J-s
Boltzmann's constant, $k = 1{\cdot}3804 \times 10^{-23}$ J/°K
Electric constant, $\varepsilon_0 = 8{\cdot}854 \times 10^{-12}$ F/m
Classical electron radius, $e^2/4\pi\varepsilon_0 mc^2 = 2{\cdot}8178 \times 10^{-15}$ m
Bohr radius, $(4\pi\varepsilon_0)h^2/4\pi^2 me^2 = 5{\cdot}2917 \times 10^{-11}$ m
Thomson cross-section, $8\pi e^4/3(4\pi\varepsilon_0)^2 m^2 c^4 = 0{\cdot}6652 \times 10^{-28}$ m^2

References

Alfvén, H. and Fälthammer, C-G., *Cosmical Electrodynamics*, 2nd ed., Oxford Univ. Press, 1963.

Anderson, J. C., *Dielectrics*, Chapman and Hall, London, 1964.

Arzeliès, H., *Relativistic Kinematics*, Pergamon Press, London, 1966.

Birss, R. R., *Contemp. Phys.*, **2**, 286, 1961.

Blatt, J. M. and Weisskopf, V. F., *Theoretical Nuclear Physics*, John Wiley and Sons, New York, 1952.

Born, M. and Wolf, E., *Principles of Optics*, 3rd ed., Pergamon Press, London, 1965.

Braddick, H. J. J., *Vibrations, Waves, and Diffraction*, McGraw-Hill Publishing Co., London, 1965.

Brillouin, L., *Tensors in Mechanics and Elasticity*, Academic Press, New York, 1964.

Compton, A. H., *Phys. Rev.*, **20**, 84, 1922.

Cowling, T. G., *Magnetohydrodynamics*, Interscience Publishers, New York, 1957.

Cullwick, E. G., *Electromagnetism and Relativity*, 2nd ed., Longmans, Green and Co., London, 1959.

Cusack, N., *The Electrical and Magnetic Properties of Solids*, Longmans, Green and Co., London, 1958.

Davis, H. F., *An Introduction to Vector Analysis*, 2nd ed., Allyn and Bacon, Boston, 1967.

Dean, K. J., *Transistors, Theory and Circuits*, McGraw-Hill Publishing Co., London, 1964.

De Barr, A. E., *Automatic Control*, Chapman and Hall, London, and Reinhold Publishing Corp., New York, 1962.

Dicke, R. H. and Wittke, J. P., *Introduction to Quantum Mechanics*, Addison-Wesley Publishing Co., Reading, Mass., 1960.

Ditchburn, R. W., *Light*, 2nd ed., Blackie and Son, London, 1962.

Duffin, W. J., *Electricity and Magnetism*, McGraw-Hill Publishing Co., London, 1965.

Earnshaw, J. B., *An Introduction to A.C. Circuit Theory*, Macmillan, London, 1960.

Farley, F. J. M., *Progr. Nucl. Phys.*, **9**, 257, 1964.

Faulkner, E. A., *Principles of Linear Circuits*, Chapman and Hall, London, 1966.

Ferraro, V. C. A. and Plumpton, C., *An Introduction to Magneto-Fluid Mechanics*, 2nd ed., Oxford Univ. Press, 1966.

Fröhlich, H., *Theory of Dielectrics*, 2nd ed., Oxford Univ. Press, 1958.

Garbuny, M., *Optical Physics*, Academic Press, New York, 1965.

Ginzton, E. L., *Microwave Measurements*, McGraw-Hill Book Co., New York, 1957.

Glazier, E. V. D. and Lamont, H. R. L., *Transmission and Propagation*, H.M.S.O., London, 1958.

Goldstein, H., *Classical Mechanics*, Addison-Wesley Publishing Co., Reading, Mass., 1951.

Hamilton, J., *Progr. Nucl. Phys.*, **8**, 143, 1960.

Heading, J., *Matrix Theory for Physicists*, Longmans, Green and Co., London, 1958.

Heitler, W., *Quantum Theory of Radiation*, 3rd ed., Oxford Univ. Press, 1954.

Hemenway, C. L., Henry, R. W. and Caulton, M., *Physical Electronics*, John Wiley and Sons, New York, 1962.

Jackson, J. D., *Classical Electrodynamics*, John Wiley and Sons, New York, 1962.

Jelley, J. V., *Čerenkov Radiation and its Applications*, Pergamon Press, London, 1958.

Kibble, T. W. B., *Classical Mechanics*, McGraw-Hill Publishing Co., London, 1966.

Kittel, C., *Introduction to Solid State Physics*, 3rd ed., John Wiley and Sons, New York, 1966.

Landau, L. D. and Lifshitz, E. M., *The Classical Theory of Fields*, Pergamon Press, London, 1962.

Mallett, L., *C. R. Acad. Sci.*, Paris, **183**, 274, 1926 and **187**, 222, 1928.

Mariner, P. F., *Introduction to Microwave Practice*, Heywood and Co., London, 1961.

Maxwell, J. C., *A Treatise on Electricity and Magnetism*, 3rd ed., Dover Publications, New York, 1904.

Morse, P. M. and Feshbach, H., *Methods of Theoretical Physics*, McGraw-Hill Book Co., New York, 1953.

Panofsky, W. K. H. and Phillips, M., *Classical Electricity and Magnetism*, 2nd ed., Addison-Wesley Publishing Co., Reading, Mass., 1962.

Paskusz, G. F. and Bussell, B., *Linear Circuit Analysis*, Prentice-Hall, Englewood Cliffs, N.J., 1963.

Pauli, W., *Theory of Relativity*, Pergamon Press, London, 1958.

Peierls, R. E., *Rep. Progr. Phys.*, **18**, 424, 1965.

Power, E. A., *Introductory Quantum Electrodynamics*, Longmans, Green and Co., London, 1964.

Rohrlich, F., *Classical Charged Particles*, Addison-Wesley Publishing Co., Reading, Mass., 1965.

Röntgen, W. C., *Ann. Phys. Lpz.*, **35**, 264, 1888, and **40**, 93, 1890.

Rosser, W. G. V., *An Introduction to the Theory of Relativity*, Butterworth, London, 1964.

Rossi, B., *Optics*, Addison-Wesley Publishing Co., Reading, Mass., 1957.

Seitz, W., *The Modern Theory of Solids*, McGraw-Hill Book Co., New York, 1940.

Shaw, D. F., *An Introduction to Electronics*, Longmans, Green and Co., London, 1962.

Shurcliff, W. A., *Polarized Light*, Harvard Univ. Press, 1962.

Smythe, W. R., *Static and Dynamic Electricity*, 2nd ed., McGraw-Hill Book Co., New York, 1950.

Spitzer, L., *Physics of Fully Ionized Gases*, 2nd ed., Interscience Publishers, New York, 1962.

Stephenson, G., *An Introduction to Matrices, Sets and Groups for Science Students*, Longmans, Green and Co., London, 1965.

Tonks, L., *Phys. Rev.*, **54**, 863, 1938.

Tuttle, D. F., *Electrical Networks*, McGraw-Hill Book Co., New York, 1965.

Weisskopf, V. F., *Rev. Mod. Phys.*, **21**, 305, 1949.

Whittaker, E. T., *A History of the Theories of the Aether and Electricity*, 2 vols., Thomas Nelson and Sons, London, 1951.

Answers to problems

Chapter 1

1.1 Additional factor required whose value is ≈ 1 for a normal r's. Thus if a is a constant $\ll 10^{-13}$ cm, we require $f(a/r) \to 1$ as $a/r \to 0$, e.g., $\exp(a^2/r^2)$. A law of the form $\{\exp(-a^2/r^2)\}/r^2$ has the useful property that it tends to zero as $r \to 0$. No evidence exists on either small or large scale that any such modification is necessary. The $g - 2$ experiment described by Farley (1964) shows that the laws of quantum electrodynamics are valid down to distances $\approx 10^{-14}$ cm.

1.2 $\lambda a/2\pi\varepsilon_0(r^2 + a^2)^{1/2}r$. Charge concentrates at ends of finite rod so that λ is never in practice constant, except approximately so near centre of long rod. Here $r/a \to 0$, and $E \to \lambda/2\pi\varepsilon_0 r$ as for infinite rod, λ being charge density *at the centre.*

1.3 Using notation of Fig. 1.1b, $(\sin^2\theta)/r$ = constant.

1.4 Using Fig. A.3a, $V = (\lambda/2\pi\varepsilon_0)\log_e r/r_1$ and hence equipotentials are given by r_1/r = constant, say m. Since $r_1{}^2 = r^2 - 2rd\cos\theta + d^2$, equation becomes $r^2(1 - m^2) - 2rd\cos\theta + d^2 = 0$. Transform to x, y co-ordinates with origin at left-hand line charge giving $[x + d/(m^2 - 1)]^2 + y^2 = m^2d^2/(m^2 - 1)^2$. These are a set of coaxial circles, centres $(-d/(m^2 - 1), 0)$, radii $md/(m^2 - 1)$ as in Fig. A.3b.

1.5 Poisson's equation and (A.17) give $E_r = -\partial V/\partial r = \rho r/3\varepsilon_0 + C/r^2$ where C is a constant. Result follows by substituting for ρ. The next integration to obtain V involves the choice of a zero. Obtain energy by integrating $\frac{1}{2}QV$ over the sphere or $\varepsilon_0E^2/2$ over all space. Proton has radius $\approx 10^{-13}$ cm giving electrostatic energy of ≈ 1 MeV.

1.6 Let **E** be in x-direction. First part: $E_y = 0 = E_z$ everywhere in τ, and hence **curl E** and div **E** being zero mean that derivatives of E_x with respect to x, y, and z are all zero. E_x is therefore constant in magnitude as well as direction. Second part: $\partial E_x/\partial x \neq 0$ along the axis so, because div **E** = 0,

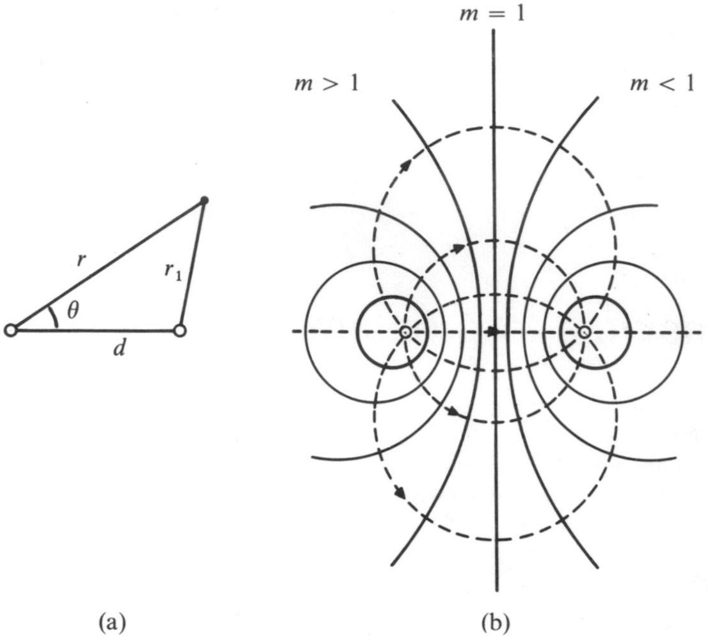

Fig. A.3 (a) Geometry for problem 1.4; (b) equipotentials (full lines) and lines of **E** (broken lines) for two line charges

$\partial E_y/\partial y$ and $\partial E_z/\partial z$ cannot both be zero, but because of symmetry must both be $-\frac{1}{2}\,\partial E_x/\partial x$. This means that a line of **E** immediately adjacent to the axis, in the xy-plane say, has an ever-increasing E_y which must curve the line away from the axis as the distance from the charge increases.

1.7 External field is electrostatic, therefore due to a collection of charges, typical one Q. Force *on* Q due to any spherical shell passes through centre; hence force *on shell* by Newton's law also passes through centre. Applies to whole sphere by superposition.

1.8 $\partial \bar{V}/\partial r = \int (\partial V/\partial r) \sin\theta \, d\theta \, d\phi/4\pi = \int E_n \, dS/4\pi r^2 = 0$ by Gauss's theorem. Thus $\bar{V}$ does not change with r and is same as V at centre ($r = 0$), but if V is a minimum at a point then a small sphere round it must have $\bar{V} > V$ at centre which is impossible. Result does not apply if point is already occupied by charge. Theorem means that no system of charges can be in stable equilibrium under action of electrostatic forces alone.

1.9 Potential due to a 2^L-pole can be written as

$$\mathbf{ds}_L \cdot \mathbf{grad}\,(\mathbf{ds}_{L-1} \cdot \mathbf{grad}\,(\cdots \mathbf{ds}_2 \cdot \mathbf{grad}\,(\mathbf{ds}_1 \cdot \mathbf{grad}\, V_Q)\ldots))$$

where $ds_1, \ldots, ds_L$ are the successive displacements needed to produce the next higher multipole. For the linear quadrupole, V is $-\mathbf{a} \cdot \mathbf{grad}\,(Qa \cos\theta/4\pi\varepsilon_0 r^2)$ using (1.16). To evaluate, use cartesians and (A.3), put $\cos\theta = x/r$ and realize that $\mathbf{a}$ has only an x-component. Then $V = (-Qa^2/4\pi\varepsilon_0)\,\partial(x/r^3)/\partial x$ and the result follows. E_r is given by $3q(3\cos^2\theta - 1)/4\pi\varepsilon_0 r^4$ and E_θ by $3q \sin 2\theta/4\pi\varepsilon_0 r^4$.

1.10 Use $J = nQv$ and a current of 1 A/mm^2 in a copper wire: drift velocity $\approx 0{\cdot}01$ cm/s. In a CRO of anode potential 400 V, electrons have velocity $\approx 10^9$ cm/s and are already approaching relativistic speeds.

1.11 In LIH dielectric, $\operatorname{div}\mathbf{E} = \rho/\varepsilon_r\varepsilon_0$ and hence $\operatorname{div}\mathbf{J} = \gamma \operatorname{div}\mathbf{E} = \gamma\rho/\varepsilon_r\varepsilon_0$. Equating this to $-\partial\rho/\partial t$ and solving yields $\rho = \rho_0 \exp(-t/\tau)$. For ethyl alcohol, $\varepsilon_r = 26$, $\gamma = 3 \times 10^{-4}$ mho/m and so $\tau \approx 10^{-6}$ s. For copper, $\gamma = 5{\cdot}8 \times 10^7$ mho/m and $\tau \approx 1{\cdot}5 \times 10^{-19}$ s.

1.12 Charge does not have to move from one end of the rod to the other. Electrostatic induction and its disappearance can be achieved by movement of charge over atomic distances: in metals, the electrons as a whole move relative to the metallic lattice. For a process taking about 10^{-18} sec the mean drift velocity of problem 1.10 is not appropriate since the electron is virtually free. The second answer might be more appropriate and would give a velocity sufficient for the right magnitude of charge to accumulate.

1.13 If $\gamma_1 \gg \gamma_2$, then $\tan\theta_1 \gg \tan\theta_2$ and for ratios of 10^{-6}, θ_2 is effectively zero. Thus, at whatever angle the current meets the boundary on the metal side it enters the electrolyte normally. The lines of $\mathbf{E}$ are therefore also normal and the boundary is an equipotential.

1.14 $\int \mathbf{J} \cdot \mathbf{E}_Q \, d\tau = \int -\mathbf{J} \cdot \mathbf{grad}\, V \, d\tau = \int V \operatorname{div}\mathbf{J}\, d\tau - \int \operatorname{div}(\mathbf{J}V)\, d\tau$ by (A.24). Second term transforms to surface integral of $V\mathbf{J}$ over a surface at infinity so that since $\mathbf{J} = 0$ there (finite system) it is zero. First term is zero because $\operatorname{div}\mathbf{J} = 0$.

1.16 Flux of particles across an area is nv_x in the x-direction and this is equal to $-D\,\partial n/\partial x$ (Fick's law). D is constant for small gradients. Hence $J = nev_x = -De\,\partial n/\partial x$. In cases with only one type of carrier as in a metal, any concentration gradients are unlikely to be set up because of the opposing electric field produced which would immediately stop the process (problem 1.11 is relevant). Where two types of carrier of opposite sign occur as in semiconductors, electrolytes, or ionized gases, concentration gradients can occur in both without setting up an opposing field. In field-free regions diffusion processes will then predominate.

1.17 $\nabla^2 V - (\mathbf{grad}\, V) \cdot (\mathbf{grad}\, \varepsilon_r)/\varepsilon_r = -\rho/\varepsilon_r\varepsilon_0$.

1.18 $V = \rho[(r^2 - a^2)/2\varepsilon_r + a^2]/3\varepsilon_0$; $P = (\varepsilon_r - 1)r\rho/3\varepsilon_r$.

1.19 $\mathbf{E}_P = -\mathbf{P}/\varepsilon_0$ in the material since it behaves as two surface charges of density $\sigma_P = P$. Thus $\mathbf{D} = \varepsilon_0\mathbf{E} + \mathbf{P} = 0$. Outside, $\mathbf{E} = 0$, $\mathbf{P} = 0$ and hence $\mathbf{D} = 0$. In practice, charges from surroundings neutralize electret charges unlike the analogous case of magnets.

1.20 $\text{Log}_e\, 2$. For many ionic crystals, α_M is between about 1 and 2 and the Coulomb energy is the principal contribution to the energy of the lattice. For the NaCl calculation see Seitz (1940).

1.21 $W' - W = \frac{1}{2}\varepsilon_0 \int (E'^2 + 2\mathbf{E} \cdot \mathbf{E}')\, d\tau$. The last term is the volume integral of $-\mathbf{E}' \cdot \textbf{grad}\, V$ or, by (A.24), of $\text{div}\,(V\mathbf{E}') - V\,\text{div}\,\mathbf{E}'$. This is zero because $\text{div}\,\mathbf{E}' = 0$, V is constant over each surface and $\int \mathbf{E}' \cdot d\mathbf{S} = 0$. Hence $W' - W = \int \frac{1}{2}\varepsilon_0 E'^2\, d\tau$, an essentially positive quantity so that $W' > W$.

1.22 Energy is not a linear function of $\mathbf{E}$ and does not superpose. In a real situation, the superposition of $\mathbf{E}_1$ and $\mathbf{E}_2$ means that two charge systems are brought close to each other. Then $\frac{1}{2}\varepsilon_0 E_1{}^2$ is the energy density of one system when isolated, $\frac{1}{2}\varepsilon_0 E_2{}^2$ of the other and the cross term $\varepsilon_0 \mathbf{E}_1 \cdot \mathbf{E}_2$ is the energy of interaction. Thus $\frac{1}{2}\varepsilon_0(\mathbf{E}_1 + \mathbf{E}_2)^2$ is correct.

1.23 For coplanar dipoles, $U = p_1 p_2 (\sin\theta_1 \sin\theta_2 - 2\cos\theta_1 \cos\theta_2)/4\pi\varepsilon_0 r^3$. Forces and torques are given by appropriate gradients, $F_r = -\partial U/\partial r$, $F_{\theta_1} = -(1/r)\,\partial U/\partial\theta_1$, $T_{\theta_1} = -\partial U/\partial\theta_1$, etc.

1.24 $U = -\mathbf{p} \cdot \mathbf{E}_0/2 = -\alpha\mathbf{E} \cdot \mathbf{E}_0/2$. Since $\mathbf{E}$ and $\mathbf{E}_0$ are never at an angle greater than 90°, U is always negative and is minimized by increases in $\mathbf{E}$ or $\mathbf{E}_0$.

1.26 $\int \mathbf{E} \cdot (\mathbf{D} - \mathbf{D}_0)\, d\tau = -\int (\mathbf{D} - \mathbf{D}_0) \cdot \textbf{grad}\, V\, d\tau = \int \text{div}\,\{V(\mathbf{D} - \mathbf{D}_0)\}\, d\tau - \int V\,\text{div}\,(\mathbf{D} - \mathbf{D}_0)\, d\tau$. First term can be transformed to surface integral over surface at infinity whose value is zero and second term is zero because $\text{div}\,(\mathbf{D} - \mathbf{D}_0) = 0$. Similarly for $\int \mathbf{E}_0 \cdot (\mathbf{D} - \mathbf{D}_0)\, d\tau$. Hence ∂U_E in the form given. Substitution $\mathbf{D}_0 = \varepsilon_0 \mathbf{E}_0$, $\mathbf{D} = \varepsilon_r \varepsilon_0 \mathbf{E}$ and $\mathbf{P} = \varepsilon_0(\varepsilon_r - 1)\mathbf{E}$ gives result.

1.30 Rises.

Chapter 2

2.2 Loop is small, so $\mathbf{B}$ can be taken as uniform over it. Resolve $\mathbf{B}$ into B_n along axis of loop and B_t in plane of loop. $F = I\, dl\, B_n$ on each element is perpendicular to element and proportional to its length: the $\mathbf{F}$'s form a closed chain of vectors and hence have zero resultant. Divide loop into strips with lengths along B_t and show $\mathbf{F} = I\, d\mathbf{l} \times \mathbf{B}_t$ applied to the two elements at the ends of one strip produce a couple given by IB_t multiplied by the area of the strip. Result follows.

2.3 $\mathbf{A} \times (\mathbf{B} \times \mathbf{C}) - \mathbf{B} \times (\mathbf{A} \times \mathbf{C}) = (\mathbf{A} \times \mathbf{B}) \times \mathbf{C}$ which is zero when $\mathbf{A}$ and $\mathbf{B}$ are parallel or when $\mathbf{C}$ is perpendicular to the $\mathbf{AB}$ plane. Hence forces are only equal and opposite between current elements if $d\mathbf{l}_1$ is parallel to $d\mathbf{l}_2$ or if $\mathbf{r}$ is perpendicular to the plane defined by $d\mathbf{l}_1$ and $d\mathbf{l}_2$. Now $d\mathbf{l}_1 \times (d\mathbf{l}_2 \times \mathbf{r})/r^3 = d\mathbf{l}_2(d\mathbf{l}_1 \cdot \mathbf{r})/r^3 - \mathbf{r}(d\mathbf{l}_1 \cdot d\mathbf{l}_2)/r^3$ by (A.2). The first term is $\mathbf{dl}_2(\mathbf{dl}_1 \cdot \mathbf{grad}\,(1/r))$ and the bracketed factor is a perfect differential by (A.19), so that when integrated round a closed path gives zero. The force is thus given by $\oint_1 \oint_2 (\mathbf{dl}_1 \cdot \mathbf{dl}_2)\mathbf{r}/r^3$ and is symmetrical in 1 and 2. There are many discussions in the literature about the correct form for the current element formula, centring round the difference between the Grassmann formula (integrand of (2.6)) and a formula of Ampère's, which did obey Newton's law (see Whittaker (1951)).

2.4 $A_x = -B_0 y/2$, $A_y = B_0 x/2$, $A_z = 0$. $\mathbf{A} = \mathbf{B}_0 \times \mathbf{r}/2$. Circles about the z-axis.

2.5 Use Fig. 10.6, in which J_s = total current I/length b. Hence current element $I\,\mathrm{d}l = J_s b\,\mathrm{d}l = J_s\,\mathrm{d}S$ where $\mathrm{d}S$ is the area A *not* the cross-section.

2.6 Divide into strips of infinite length and use $B = \mu_0 I/2\pi r$ for B due to an infinite current-carrying filament. Result is $\mu_0 J_s/2$, parallel to sheet but in opposite directions on each side of sheet and perpendicular to J_s itself.

2.8 $A_z = (\mu_0 I/2\pi)\log_e(r_2/r_1)$ where r_1 and r_2 are the distances of the field point from the currents. Hence constant $\mathbf{A}$ surfaces are the same as those of V in problem 1.4.

2.9 Define div $\mathbf{H} = \rho_m = -\mathrm{div}\,\mathbf{M}$ by analogy with div $\mathbf{E} = \rho/\varepsilon_0$. Then any sinks of $\mathbf{M}$ are sources of $\mathbf{H}$ and these are the *poles* of elementary magnetism which give rise to fields identical in form to those of charges. In particular, **curl** $\mathbf{H} = 0$ for poles only and hence $\mathbf{H} = -\mathbf{grad}\,V_m$. Clearly we can define a vector field $\mathbf{B} = \mu_0(\mathbf{H} + \mathbf{M})$ which has no sources, unlike **D**. Currents, however, give rise to **H** fields for which **curl** $\mathbf{H} = \mathbf{J}_c$ and hence for which **curl** $\mathbf{B} = \mu_0 \mathbf{J}_c + \mu_0$ **curl** $\mathbf{M}$ so that the effect of magnetization is to add to the vortices of **B** but not to the sources of **B**. The use of **H** is thus more natural if poles are regarded as a satisfactory model, **B** is more natural if Amperian currents are adopted.

2.10 Assume sphere consists of two hypothetical spheres of + and − poles separated by **d** so that $\mathbf{M} = \rho_m \mathbf{d}$, where ρ_m is the density of poles. Use Gauss's theorem (cf. problem 1.5) to show that **H** outside is as if all poles were at the centre (i.e., sphere acts as a dipole at the centre of moment $4\pi a^3\mathbf{M}/3$); and that **H** inside is $\pm \mathbf{r}\rho_m/3$ for *each* sphere. The two spheres give a resultant at any point of $-\rho_m\mathbf{d}/3 = -\mathbf{M}/3$. This is often called the demagnetizing field and the 1/3 a demagnetizing factor, because if the magnetization is induced by an external field $\mathbf{H}_0$, the resultant internal field is $\mathbf{H}_0 - \mathbf{M}/3$. Two other methods are available: to use the equivalent surface density of poles (cf. problem 8.6) or to use equivalent surface currents.

2.11 Note particularly in the sketches how **H** has surface poles as sources where the discontinuity in **M** occurs, while **B** has surface currents as vortices.

2.13 See *Electricity and Magnetism*, chapter 14.

2.14 Because div $\mathbf{B} = 0$, the total flux over any closed surface is zero.

2.16 A variation of B_x with x must be accompanied by a variation of B_y with y or B_z with z or both (see problem 1.6). These latter variations are responsible for the force on a small current loop.

2.17 Inside: $E = ner/2\varepsilon_0$ away from centre, $B = \mu_0 nevr/2$ transversely. Resultant force away from axis is $ne^2r(1 - \varepsilon_0\mu_0 v^2)/2\varepsilon_0$. Since $\varepsilon_0\mu_0 = 1/c^2$ and $v < c$, the force is always positive and defocusing. In a neutral current, the electric force disappears to a first order and only the focusing magnetic force is left. This is the origin of the *pinch effect*.

2.18 Radius of orbit $= mv_\perp/eB$. Magnetic dipole moment $=$ current $\times$ area $= ev_\perp r/2$ or $K_\perp/B$. Direction opposes **B** and this is the origin of a diamagnetic contribution to the susceptibility of metals from the motion of free electrons.

2.19 In cylindrical co-ordinates, div **B** $= 0$ means that $B_r = -r(\partial B_z/\partial z)/2$, assuming that $B_r = 0$ when $r = 0$. $F_z = ev_\perp B_r = -\frac{1}{2}ev_\perp r\,\partial B_z/\partial z = -m_z\,\partial B/\partial z$ using problem 2.18, where m_z is magnetic moment, i.e., F_z is towards weaker **B**. Also by problem 2.18, $K_\perp = m_z B_z$ so that $\partial K_\perp/\partial z = m_z\,\partial B_z/\partial z + B_z\,\partial m_z/\partial_z$. By this problem, $\partial K_\perp/\partial z = -\partial K_\parallel/\partial z$ since $K_\parallel + K_\perp$ is a constant of the motion. $-\partial K_\parallel/\partial z = -F_z = m_z\,\partial B_z/\partial z$ and hence $B_z\,\partial m_z/\partial z = 0$ or m_z is a constant of the motion. Can also show flux $= \pi a^2 B_z$ is proportional to $K_\perp/B_z$ and hence to m_z and must also be constant.

2.20 In $\mathbf{F} = Q(\mathbf{E} + \mathbf{v} \times \mathbf{B})$ write $\mathbf{v}$ as $\mathbf{v}' + (\mathbf{E} \times \mathbf{B})/B^2$ and show that in a classical frame of reference moving with velocity $-(\mathbf{E} \times \mathbf{B})/B^2$ the electric field disappears.

2.21 See *Electricity and Magnetism*, section 11.5.

2.22 If **curl H** $= \mathbf{J}_c = 0$, **H** can be expressed as $-$**grad** V_m and hence $\mathbf{H} \cdot \mathbf{B} = \mathbf{B} \cdot$ **grad** $V_m = V_m$ div **B** $-$ div $(V_m\mathbf{B})$. The first term is zero since div **B** $= 0$, and the second, when integrated over space, transforms to a surface integral at infinity which is zero for a finite system as in (1.57).

2.23 Use argument following (1.72) and $\mathbf{M} = \mathbf{B}/\mu_0 - \mathbf{H}$.

Chapter 3

3.1 Approximately (a) 1 cm, 70 μm, (b) 0·7 μm, (c) 30 Å, (d) 0·7 Å.

3.6 If initial fields are $\mathbf{B}_0$, $\mathbf{H}_0$ and final ones **B**, **H**, then $\delta U_M = \int (\frac{1}{2}\mathbf{B} \cdot \mathbf{H} - \frac{1}{2}\mathbf{B}_0 \cdot \mathbf{H}_0)\,d\tau$. Show that the volume integrals of $(\mathbf{H} - \mathbf{H}_0) \cdot \mathbf{B}$ and $(\mathbf{H} - \mathbf{H}_0) \cdot \mathbf{B}_0$ over space are zero and turn δU_M into the form $\frac{1}{2}\mathbf{H}_0 \cdot \mathbf{B} - \frac{1}{2}\mathbf{H} \cdot \mathbf{B}_0$. Since $\mathbf{B}_0 = \mu_0\mathbf{H}_0$ and $\mathbf{B} = \mu_r\mu_0\mathbf{H}$, the result follows. In air, the χ_m factor is replaced by $(\chi_m - \chi_m')$ since hydrostatic pressures develop of just such magnitude as to support the displaced air.

3.7 $\mathbf{F} = \int (\mathbf{M} \cdot \mathbf{grad})\,\mathbf{B}_0\,d\tau$ and since $\mathbf{B}_0 = \mu_0\mathbf{H}_0 \approx \mu_0\mathbf{H}$ and $\mathbf{M} = \chi_m\mathbf{H}$, we have the integrand equal to $\mu_0\chi_m(\mathbf{H} \cdot \mathbf{grad})\,\mathbf{H}$ or $\frac{1}{2}\mu_0\chi_m$ **grad** (H^2), since inside the material **curl H** $= 0$ and the integrand only extends over the material.

3.9 Induced current density at r from centre is $J = \gamma vB = \gamma r\omega B$. Body force per unit volume is $\mathbf{J} \times \mathbf{B}$ or $\gamma r\omega B^2$ opposing motion. Couple is $\gamma r^2\omega B^2$ about centre and an elementary ring sustaining this has volume $2\pi rx\, dr$. The total couple by integration is thus $(2\pi x\gamma B^2 a^3/3)\dot{\theta}$ and this adds to the damping factor already present.

3.10 $\tau \approx \mu_r\mu_0\gamma L^2$ where L is a characteristic dimension of the conductor. This is about 1 second for copper with $L = 10$ cm.

Chapter 4

4.1 Power radiated over sphere radius $R = 4\pi R^2 N$ and $N = EH$. In nearly plane wave, $N = E^2/120\pi$ by (4.35) and so $P = R^2E^2/30$ and hence $E = (30P/R^2)^{1/2}$. Thus $E = 10$ V/m for the lamp and 1/800 V/m for the transmitter.

4.2 E at surface $= V/l$ where V is p.d. between points l apart. H is $I/2\pi R$ where R is radius of wire. Directions are such that $\mathbf{E} \times \mathbf{H}$ points towards wire. Consider inward flow of energy across coaxial cylindrical surface of length l radius r: curved surface has area $2\pi rl$ and $N = VI/2\pi rl$ and so total power flowing in $= VI$ or RI^2 where R is resistance of length l. Around a battery the direction of $\mathbf{H}$ would be the same but the resultant $\mathbf{E}$ would be opposite giving an outward flow of energy. This picture of the process of energy exchanges in a steady state does not add anything to our understanding and its only value is to show the consistency of the calculation using $\mathbf{N}$.

4.3 Using (4.40) and Maxwell: $\mathbf{k} \cdot \mathbf{E} = 0$, $\mathbf{k} \cdot \mathbf{B} = 0$, and $\mathbf{k} \times \mathbf{E} = \omega\mathbf{B}$. From the last, $\mathbf{E} \cdot \mathbf{B} = \mathbf{E} \cdot (\mathbf{k} \times \mathbf{E})/\omega$ which is zero.

4.4 Elimination of $(kz - \omega t)$ yields the equation $x^2/E_1{}^2 + y^2/E_2{}^2 - (2xy \cos \delta)/E_1E_2 = \sin^2 \delta$. Transform to x', y' co-ordinates rotated through angle ϕ using $x = x' \cos \phi - y' \sin \phi$, $y = x' \sin \phi + y' \cos \phi$. An ellipse referred to its principal axes as co-ordinate axes has no cross terms and this condition yields $\tan 2\phi = (2E_1E_2 \cos \delta)/(E_1{}^2 - E_2{}^2)$. For further information about the specification of polarized waves, see Shurcliff (1962).

4.5 $\mathbf{E}_-$ is right polarized; negative.

4.6 Given any elliptically polarized beam of the form of (4.44) with complex amplitude $\hat{\mathbf{x}}E_1 + \hat{\mathbf{y}}E_2\, e^{i\delta}$ and two opposite circularly polarized beams $E_1'(\hat{\mathbf{x}} + i\hat{\mathbf{y}})$ and $E_2'(\hat{\mathbf{x}} - i\hat{\mathbf{y}})$ of combined amplitude $\hat{\mathbf{x}}(E_1' + E_2') + i\hat{\mathbf{y}}(E_1' - E_2')$, it is always possible to find E's such that the two are equivalent, provided $\delta = \pi/2$, i.e., the initial phases of the circularly polarized beams lie along one of the axes of the ellipse.

4.7 One representation would be $E_x = 0$, $E_y = -2 \cos \{(200\pi/3)(x - ct)\}$, $E_z = 2 \sin \{(200\pi/3)(x - ct)\}$ V/m; $B_x = 0$, $B_y = (2/c) \sin \{(200\pi/3)(x - ct)\}$, $B_z = -(2/c) \cos \{(200\pi/3)(x - ct)\}$ T.

4.8 $1/120\pi$ W/m^2.

4.10 $\mathbf{E} = \mathbf{grad}\,\mathrm{div}\,\boldsymbol{\Pi}_e - (1/c^2)\,\partial^2\boldsymbol{\Pi}_e/\partial t^2 = \mathbf{curl}\,\mathbf{curl}\,\boldsymbol{\Pi}_e + \Box^2\boldsymbol{\Pi}_e$; $\mathbf{B} = (1/c^2)\,\partial/\partial t\,(\mathbf{curl}\,\boldsymbol{\Pi}_e)$. Condition is $\Box^2\boldsymbol{\Pi}_e = 0$.

4.11 From (4.72); or note that since $\mathbf{p}$ is not a function of space coordinates (1.16) can be written $V = -\mathrm{div}\,(\mathbf{p}/4\pi\varepsilon_0 r)$.

4.12 $\mathbf{E} = -\mathbf{curl}\,(\partial\boldsymbol{\Pi}_m/\partial t)$; $\mathbf{B} = \mathbf{curl}\,\mathbf{curl}\,\boldsymbol{\Pi}_m$. Radiated power $P = 2[\ddot{m}]^2/3(4\pi\varepsilon_0)c^5$ or $(\mu_0/4\pi)2[\ddot{m}]^2/3c^3$.

4.15 Retarded time is $t - r/c$ and so QQ′ is vr/c. Hence s is NP and $s^2 = r_0{}^2 - \mathrm{QN}^2 = r_0{}^2 - (v^2r^2\sin^2\theta)/c^2$. $\mathrm{OP} = r\sin\theta = r_0\sin\theta_0$ and the given result follows. $\mathbf{E} = Q\mathbf{r}_0(1-\beta^2)/4\pi\varepsilon_0 r_0{}^3(1-\beta^2\sin^2\theta_0)^{3/2}$ where $\beta = v/c$. $\mathbf{B} = \mathbf{r}\times\mathbf{E}/rc = (1/c)E\sin \mathrm{QPQ}'$. Using sine rule in triangle Q′PQ, $\sin\mathrm{QPQ}' = (v\sin\theta_0)/c$ and so $\mathbf{B} = (v/c^2)E\sin\theta_0$ or $(\mathbf{v}\times\mathbf{E})/c^2$.

4.17 Force due to $\mathbf{E}$ is repulsive $Q^2(1-\beta^2)^{-1/2}/4\pi\varepsilon_0 r_0{}^2$. Force due to $\mathbf{B}$ is attractive $\beta^2 \times$ force due to $\mathbf{E}$. Thus resultant is repulsive $Q^2(1-\beta^2)^{1/2}/4\pi\varepsilon_0 r_0{}^2$ where $\beta = v/c$. Compare problems 2.17 and 11.9.

4.19 Normal pressure $u_{\mathrm{EM}}\cos^2\theta$, tangential pressure $u_{\mathrm{EM}}\sin\theta\cos\theta$. Over a hemisphere, $\overline{\cos^2\theta} = 1/3$ and $\overline{\sin\theta\cos\theta} = 0$.

4.20 Normal pressure $u_{\mathrm{EM}}(1+f)\cos^2\theta$, tangential pressure $u_{\mathrm{EM}}(1-f)\sin\theta\cos\theta$. Use (4.100) or argue from change of momentum.

4.21 Namely, that $E = pc$. The momentum of a photon $p = h/\lambda$ can be written vectorially as $\mathbf{p} = \hbar\mathbf{k}$ where $\hbar = h/2\pi$ and $\mathbf{k}$ is the wave vector.

Chapter 5

5.1 The expansion is

$$\frac{1}{|\mathbf{r}-\mathbf{r}_i|} = \frac{1}{r} + \left(x_i\frac{\partial}{\partial x} + y_i\frac{\partial}{\partial y} + z_i\frac{\partial}{\partial z}\right)\left(\frac{1}{r}\right) + \frac{1}{2}\left(x_i{}^2\frac{\partial^2}{\partial x^2} + \cdots\right)\left(\frac{1}{r}\right) + \cdots.$$

Differentiation at the field point P gives negative signs in the second, fourth terms, etc., but differentiation at the origin gives positive signs everywhere. Evaluation of successive differentiations of $(1/r)$ gives the terms of (5.5) using, for instance, $\partial r/\partial x = x/r$.

5.4 (a) $p_x = Qa$, $q_{xx} = 2Qa^2$. All other components zero.
(b) $q_{xx} = 4Qa^2$. All other components zero.
(c) $\mathbf{p} = 0$; $q_{xx} = q_{yy} = q_{zz} = 4Qa^2$; $q_{xy} = q_{yz} = q_{zx} = 0$.

5.5 Take an elementary circular slice of ellipsoid somewhere along the z-axis and divide it into annular rings. For each ring evaluate $\rho(3z^2 - r^2)\,\mathrm{d}\tau$ and integrate to obtain q_{zz} of slice. Then integrate from $z = -a$ to $+a$. Note that a prolate ellipsoid $(a > b)$ has a positive q_{zz}.

5.7 $\mathbf{dr}$ is an element of the path C and $\frac{1}{2}\mathbf{r}\times\mathbf{dr}$ is the vector area of the triangle obtained by joining the ends of $\mathbf{dr}$ to the origin O. Draw a cone with O as vertex and C as base when the integral is the vector area of the curved conical surface. If C bounds a plane area $\mathbf{dS}$ (direction along the normal), the elementary vectors areas of the cone surface can be resolved into components along $\mathbf{dS}$ (perpendicular to the plane of C) and the perpendicular to $\mathbf{dS}$. The latter form a closed set of vectors of zero resultant. The former give a resultant which is simply the projection of the curved surface on to the base and is therefore $\mathbf{dS}$ itself. This is independent of the position of O relative to C.

5.8 $\mathbf{m} = \frac{1}{2}\int \mathbf{r} \times \mathbf{J}\,d\tau$. Take a new origin O′ at $\mathbf{a}$ so that $\mathbf{r} = \mathbf{r}' + \mathbf{a}$ and $\mathbf{m}' = \frac{1}{2}\int \mathbf{r} \times \mathbf{J}\,d\tau - \frac{1}{2}\int \mathbf{a} \times \mathbf{J}\,d\tau$. Second term is $\frac{1}{2}\oint I\mathbf{a} \times \mathbf{dr}'$ or $\frac{1}{2}I\mathbf{a} \times \oint \mathbf{dr}' = 0$.

Chapter 6

6.1 Let $\mathbf{A}_0 = \mathbf{A}_1 - \mathbf{A}_2$, when div $\mathbf{A}_0 = 0$, **curl** $\mathbf{A}_0 = 0$. $\mathbf{A}_0$ may therefore be written as the gradient of a scalar field V_0 satisfying $\nabla^2 V_0 = 0$ and tending to a constant value over a surface at infinity. By the uniqueness theorem of section 6.1, V_0 = constant everywhere and hence $\mathbf{A}_0 = 0$.

6.2 $p_{ij}Q_j$ = potential of ith conductor due to Q_j on jth. Hence potential energy of Q_i due to $Q_j = p_{ij}Q_iQ_j$. Same energy can be shown to be $p_{ji}Q_jQ_i$. Sphere is raised to a potential $Q/4\pi\varepsilon_0 r$ by the point charge treated as a very small charged conductor.

6.3 $p_{ac} = p_{bc} = p_{cc} = 1/4\pi\varepsilon_0 c$, $p_{ab} = p_{bb} = 1/4\pi\varepsilon_0 b$, $p_{aa} = 1/4\pi\varepsilon_0 a$. $c_{bb} = 4\pi\varepsilon_0 b^2(c - a)/(b - a)(c - b)$ and is the required capacitance.

6.4 $(c_{11}c_{22} - c_{12}{}^2)/(c_{11} + c_{22} + 2c_{12})$.

6.5 $(\log_e (d/a))/\gamma\pi$.

6.6 $2\pi\gamma/\log_e (b/a)$.

6.7 $(d + a)^3/(d - a)^3$.

6.8 $\pi\varepsilon_0/\log_e (2h/a)$.

6.9 $\pi\varepsilon_0/\log_e \{(h + (h^2 - 4a^2)^{1/2})/2a\}$ or $\pi\varepsilon_0/\cosh^{-1} (h/2a)$.

6.10 Attraction of $3p^2/32\pi\varepsilon_0 r^4$.

6.11 $V = -E_0 r \cos\theta$ as $r \to \infty$, so only the A_1 term of all the first set in (6.45) can exist. Moreover, V = constant for all θ at $r = a$ so that all terms must depend on θ in the same way and hence only the B_1 term of the second set in (6.45) can exist. Thus $V = Ar\cos\theta + (B\cos\theta)/r^2$ and it is easy to show that $A = -E_0$, $B = a^3E_0$. Thus sphere behaves as if it added a dipole field due to $\mathbf{p} = 4\pi\varepsilon_0 a^3\mathbf{E}_0$ to the pre-existing field (cf. (6.21)).

6.12 Assume $V_0 = -E_0 r\cos\theta + (p'\cos\theta)/4\pi\varepsilon_0 r^2$: this satisfies condition that field tends to uniform $\mathbf{E}_0$ at infinity and effect of sphere is that of dipole $\mathbf{p}'$ outside. Inside, assume $V_i = E'r\cos\theta$, a uniform field. Continuity of V and $\varepsilon_r\,\partial V/\partial r$ at surface (from continuity of E_{tan} and D_n) give (6.23).

6.13 Scalar potential applicable and obeys Laplace's equation. Hence solution of type (6.45). Along z-axis ($\theta = 0$), V_m is given by $I\Omega/4\pi$, where Ω is the solid angle as in (2.20). Here $V_m = \frac{1}{2}I\{1 - (1 + a^2/z^2)^{-1/2}\}$. Expanding this using the binomial theorem, we get the coefficients A_l and B_l as in (6.46). We find $B_1 = a^2/2$, $B_2 = 0$, $B_3 = -3a^4/8$, etc. All A_l are zero. Hence to terms in $1/r^5$:

$$B_r = \mu_0 I a^2 (\cos\theta)/2r^3 - 3\mu_0 I a^4(5\cos^3\theta - 3\cos\theta)/8r^5$$

$$B_\theta = \mu_0 I a^2 (\sin\theta)/4r^3 - 9\mu_0 I a^4 \sin\theta(5\cos^2\theta - 1)/32r^5.$$

6.15 For two media, $B_{n1} = B_{n2}$ means that $\oint \mathbf{A}_{t1} \cdot d\mathbf{l} = \oint \mathbf{A}_{t2} \cdot d\mathbf{l}$, where the paths are taken in media 1 and 2 respectively and are parallel and close to the boundary. Since this must be true for any path, $\mathbf{A}_{t1} = \mathbf{A}_{t2}$ or $\mathbf{A}_{tan}$ is continuous. The discontinuity in H_{tan} means that there must be an equal discontinuity in the tangential component of $(\mathbf{curl\ A})/\mu_r$.

6.16 Inside, $A = C - \mu_r\mu_0 I r^2/4\pi a^2$, $B = \mu_r\mu_0 I r/4\pi a^2$, $H = Ir/4\pi a^2$. Outside, $A = C - (\mu_0 I/4\pi)(\mu_r + 2\log_e(r/a))$, $B = \mu_0 I/2\pi r$, $H = I/2\pi r$.

6.17 (6.31) is appropriate and gives $V = Cx + V_0$ where C is a constant.

6.18 Boundary conditions at $x = 0$, $y = 0$, $x = a$ give

$$V = \sum_1^\infty A_n \sin(n\pi x/a)\sinh(n\pi y/a).$$

Boundary condition at $y = a$ gives $V_0 = \sum A_n \sin(n\pi x/a)\sinh(n\pi)$. Multiplying both sides by $\sin(m\pi x/a)$ and integrating from 0 to a leaves only one non-zero term equal to $a/2$ on the right, for $n = m$. On the left the integral is 2 for odd m, zero for even m. Thus for m odd, $A_m = 4V_0/a \sinh(m\pi)$.

Chapter 7

7.1 Note that all multipole moments are zero.

7.2 First part follows from $\mathbf{k} \cdot \mathbf{E} \neq 0$ and equation (7.12). The vectors $\hat{\mathbf{s}}$, $\mathbf{H}$, $\mathbf{D}$ form a right-handed triad, as do $\hat{\mathbf{t}}$, $\mathbf{H}$, and $\mathbf{E}$, while $\mathbf{B}$ and $\mathbf{H}$ lie in the same direction.

7.3 $\mathbf{D}' \cdot \mathbf{D}'' = D_x'D_x'' + D_y'D_y'' + D_z'D_z''$. By substituting $E_x' = D_x'/\varepsilon_x\varepsilon_0 = v_x^2 D_x'/c^2\varepsilon_0$, etc., it can be shown that the scalar product can be expressed as the sum of two terms like the left-hand side of (7.16) multiplied by $c^4(\hat{\mathbf{s}} \cdot \mathbf{E}')(\hat{\mathbf{s}} \cdot \mathbf{E}'')/(v_p''^2 - v_p'^2)$. By (7.16), $\mathbf{D}' \cdot \mathbf{D}'' = 0$.

7.6 Use the Poynting vectors. Thus for the case of Fig. 7.4, $N_i = n_1^2 E_i^2/\mu_0 c$. For energy balance, show that $N_r \cos\theta_r + N_t \cos\theta_t = N_i \cos\theta_i$ using (7.37) and (7.38).

7.8 $R_\parallel = \tan^2(\theta_i - \theta_t)/\tan^2(\theta_i + \theta_t)$; $R_\perp = \sin^2(\theta_i - \theta_t)/\sin^2(\theta_i + \theta_t)$;
$T_\parallel = (\sin 2\theta_i \sin 2\theta_t)/\sin^2(\theta_i + \theta_t)\cos^2(\theta_i + \theta_t)$;
$T_\perp = (\sin 2\theta_i \sin 2\theta_t)/\sin^2(\theta_i + \theta_t)$.

Chapter 8

8.2 Use equation (4.48) for the mean energy flux.

8.3 $4\pi\varepsilon_0 a_0{}^3$.

8.4 $e^2/m(\omega_0{}^2 - \omega^2)$.

8.5 Use potential energy U to show that when all positive ions are displaced by x, U = constant + a term proportional to $x^2/r_0{}^2$. Hence find the force on one ion and equate to eE. Polarizability is $4\pi\varepsilon_0 r_0{}^3/Y$ where $Y = \sum_0^\infty (1/(2n+1)^3)$.

8.6 $\mathbf{P}/3\varepsilon_0$.

8.9 $v_g = c/\{n + \omega\,(\mathrm{d}n/\mathrm{d}\omega)\}$.

8.12 Lorentz gives $\varepsilon_r = (1 + 2K\alpha)/(1 - K\alpha)$ where $K = n_v/3\varepsilon_0$ and ε_r is infinite when $\alpha = 1/K$. This allows possibility of finite **P** for zero **E** as in electrets or ferroelectrics: Onsager's formula does not.

Chapter 9

9.1 $(1/LC)^{1/2}$, $(3/LC)^{1/2}$.

9.4 Using partial fractions. $\mathscr{L}(I) = V_0/s(sL + R) = V_0/sR - V_0L/R(sL + R)$. Hence $I = V_0(1 - \mathrm{e}^{-Rt/L})/R$.

9.5 $\mathrm{e}^{-Rt/L}/L$.

9.6 $\mathrm{e}^{-t/CR}/R - H(t - \tau)\,\mathrm{e}^{-(t-\tau)/CR}/R$.

9.8 1/80 A.

9.9 $\begin{pmatrix}1 & Z_1\\ 0 & 1\end{pmatrix}\begin{pmatrix}1 & 0\\ 1/Z_2 & 1\end{pmatrix}\begin{pmatrix}1 & Z_1\\ 0 & 1\end{pmatrix} = \begin{pmatrix}1 + Z_1/Z_2 & Z_1 + Z_2 + Z_1{}^2/Z_2\\ 1/Z_2 & 1 + Z_1/Z_2\end{pmatrix}$.

9.11 $Z_1 = (z_{11}z_{22} - z_{12}{}^2)/(z_{22} - z_{12})$; $Z_2 = (z_{11}z_{22} - z_{12}{}^2)/(z_{11} - z_{12})$; $Z_3 = (z_{11}z_{22} - z_{12}{}^2)/z_{12}$.

9.12 $z_{11} = j\omega L_1$, $z_{22} = j\omega L_2$, $z_{12} = \pm j\omega M$. Hence T-section has series elements $L_1 \pm M$, $L_2 \pm M$ and a parallel element M.

9.13 From the definition of Z_k, a load of Z_k must give an input impedance of Z_k for any length of line. Thus, if the ratio V/I equals Z_k at $x = 0$ it must equal Z_k at any other x. In that case, Z_k must $=(L/C)^{1/2}$ and a wave in one direction only is present. The propagation constant is $\log_e(V_{in}/V_{out})$ and since $V = V_{max}\exp(\pm jkx)$ we have $\gamma = \pm jk$ or $\pm j\omega(LC)^{1/2}$.

9.14 See *Electricity and Magnetism*, section 10.10.

Chapter 10

10.1 Assume that the x-direction is so chosen that $E_y = 0$ at some point. Use Maxwell's equations to show that the B_x field at the same point does not vary with z or t, i.e., it is zero as far as wave propagation is concerned.

10.2 $\mathbf{E} = \hat{\mathbf{r}}(E_0/r)\cos(kz - \omega t)$; $\mathbf{B} = \hat{\boldsymbol{\theta}}(E_0/cr)\cos(kz - \omega t)$.

10.3 $\mathbf{E}_r = -\hat{\mathbf{x}}E_0 \exp\{i(k_0 y \sin\theta + k_0 z \cos\theta - \omega t)\}$; resultant is $\mathbf{E} = \hat{\mathbf{x}}E_0 \exp\{i(k_0 z \cos\theta - \omega t)\} \sin(k_0 y \sin\theta)$. When $\nu = \nu_c = nc/2a$, $\lambda_g = \infty$ and $\theta = 90°$, i.e., no propagation occurs. Energy in plane wave propagates at c along k_0 so that component along z is $v_e = c\cos\theta$. This is also the group velocity so that $v_p v_g = c^2$.

10.5 $B_z = B_0 \cos(\pi y/b) \exp\{i(k_g z - \omega t)\}$; $k_g{}^2 - k_0{}^2 = \pi^2/b^2$;
$E_x = -i(k_0 cbB_0/\pi) \sin(\pi y/b) \exp\{i(k_g z - \omega t)\}$; $E_y = 0$;
$B_x = 0$; $B_y = -i(k_g bB_0/\pi) \sin(\pi y/b) \exp\{i(k_g z - \omega t)\}$.

10.6 $\overline{\mathbf{N}} = \frac{1}{2}\,\mathrm{Re}\,(-\hat{\mathbf{y}}E_x H_z{}^* + \hat{\mathbf{z}}E_x H_y{}^*)$. Since $E_x H_z{}^*$ is imaginary, $\overline{\mathbf{N}} = \frac{1}{2}\hat{\mathbf{z}}\,\mathrm{Re}\,(E_x H_y{}^*) = \hat{\mathbf{z}}(k_g k_0 cb^2 B_0{}^2/2\pi^2\mu_0) \sin^2(\pi y/b)$. Total power over cross-section $= k_g k_0 cb^3 aB_0{}^2/4\pi^2\mu_0$.

10.7 Crucial term is $\sin^2(N\alpha/2)/\sin^2(\alpha/2)$ where $\alpha = (\omega a \cos\theta)/c$. Principal maxima are as in a linear diffraction grating and occur at $\alpha = 0$ and α approximately $= (2n + 1)\pi/N$.

Chapter 11

11.4 Scalars: ρ, V, Φ. Pseudo-scalars: poles, electric flux, div **B**. Vectors: ∇, **D**, **E**, **r**, **J**, **P**, **A**. Pseudo-vectors: **B**, **H**, **curl E**.

11.11 Since $P = \mathrm{d}E/\mathrm{d}t$ where E is the total energy, $P = P'$ because E and t are both 4th components of a 4-vector and transform between S and S' in the same way. Thus P for the accelerating charge which is momentarily stationary in S (given by (4.91)) transforms to P' in S' given by

$$P' = \frac{Q^2}{6\pi\varepsilon_0 c^3} \frac{\{a'^2 - \beta^2(a_y{}'^2 + a_z{}'^2)\}}{(1 - \beta^2)^3}.$$

The velocity of the particle in S' is $-\mathbf{v}$ along the x-axis. In the linear accelerator, **a** and **v** are parallel, $a_y{}' = 0$ and $a_z{}' = 0$. In circular accelerators, **a** and **v** are perpendicular and so at an instant $a_x{}' = 0$, $a_z{}' = 0$, and $a_y{}' = a$. The v^2/r acceleration inherent in betatron and synchrotron orbits leads to large radiation losses for fast particles ($\beta \to 1$) which are a serious limitation on the attainable energy.

Index

THIS BOOK HAS BEEN SET IN MONOPHOTO TIMES NEW ROMAN 10 ON 12 POINT
AND PRINTED AND BOUND IN GREAT BRITAIN BY
WILLIAM CLOWES AND SONS, LIMITED, LONDON AND BECCLES